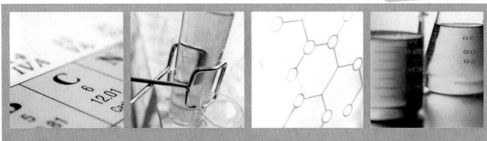

CH 227/228/229

Experiments in General Chemistry

Laboratory Manual

FOURTH EDITION

Deborah Berkshire Exton

Department of Chemistry and Biochemistry

University of Oregon

macmillan learning
curriculum solutions

Printed in the United States of America

10 9 8 7 6 5 4 3 2 1

ISBN 978-1-5339-1243-5

Macmillan Learning Curriculum Solutions
14903 Pilot Drive
Plymouth, MI 48170
www.macmillanlearning.com

Exton 1243-5 F19

Sustainability
Hayden-McNeil/Macmillan Learning Curriculum Solutions is proud to be a part of the larger sustainability initiative of Macmillan, our parent company. Macmillan has a goal to reduce its carbon emissions by 65% by 2020 from our 2010 baseline. Additionally, paper purchased must adhere to the Macmillan USA Paper Sourcing and Use Policy.

Hayden-McNeil partners with printers that use paper that is consistent with the environmental goals and values of Macmillan USA. This includes using paper certified by the Forest Stewardship Council (FSC), Sustainable Forestry Initiative (SFI), and/or the Programme for the Endorsement of Forest Certification (PEFC). We also offer paper with varying percentages of post-consumer waste as well as a 100% recycled stock. Additionally, Hayden-McNeil Custom Digital provides authors with the opportunity to convert print products to a digital format to use no paper at all. Visit http://sustainability.macmillan.com to learn more.

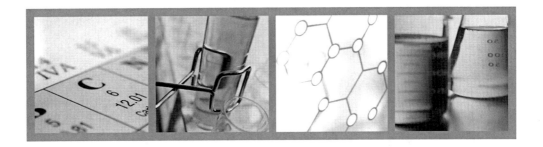

Table of Contents

CHEMICAL AND LABORATORY SAFETY POLICIES & PROCEDURES

GENERAL LABORATORY INFORMATION & PROCEDURES

EXPERIMENTS

APPENDICES

ACKNOWLEDGMENTS

This lab manual could not have been written without the contributions of many people at the University of Oregon. In particular, I would like to acknowledge Roger Leonard and the UO teaching laboratories' preparative staff for their work in developing and troubleshooting experimental procedures. I would also like to thank the Graduate Teaching Fellows who have worked closely with the students and offered many valuable suggestions to improve the experiments. And finally, a thank you to the thousands of students who have piloted the laboratory experiments throughout the years.

PREFACE

> "The future will be green, or not at all. This truth lies at the heart of human-kind's most pressing challenge: to learn to live in harmony with the Earth on a genuinely sustainable basis."

> **—Sir Jonathon Porritt**

Green Chemistry is our discipline's unique contribution to the overall movement leading toward a better, more sustainable world. The term refers to the design of chemical products and processes that will ensure a safe and clean environment for future generations. Often called chemistry that is benign by design, the goal of green chemistry is to prevent pollution in the first place, rather than dealing with pollutants after they are formed. Green chemistry relies on the set of twelve principles that follow on the next page. These principles can be used to design or re-design molecules, materials and chemical transformations to be safer for human health and the environment. Through the study of green chemistry you will be able to see that chemistry can be used to prevent, rather than cause, environmental problems and learn about the role of chemistry and chemists in a sustainable world.

This laboratory manual incorporates green chemistry in two different ways. The experiments have been designed to be procedurally green though this does not mean that there are no chemical risks or hazardous waste products associated with the experiments. What it does mean is that every experiment has been designed or modified to reflect green chemistry principles while at the same time maintaining the learning goals of the General Chemistry laboratory course.

The experiments have also been designed to deliver a green chemistry message, highlighted in a special section in each experiment entitled Chemistry in a Sustainable World. As you read through these segments, you will learn why the procedures that you are performing are greener than the procedures traditionally employed in the General Chemistry laboratory. You will also gain knowledge of how the techniques and concepts that you are studying apply to real-world sustainability issues. Finally, you will be challenged to think more deeply about these concepts and incorporate green chemistry concepts in your laboratory reports.

THE TWELVE PRINCIPLES OF GREEN CHEMISTRY

Originally published by Paul Anastas, Ph.D. and John Warner, Ph.D. in *Green Chemistry: Theory and Practice* (Oxford University Press: New York, 1998).

1. **Prevention**
   It's better to prevent waste than to treat or clean up waste afterwards.

2. **Atom Economy**
   Design synthetic methods to maximize the incorporation of all materials used in the process into the final product.

3. **Less Hazardous Chemical Syntheses**
   Design synthetic methods to use and generate substances that minimize toxicity to human health and the environment.

4. **Designing Safer Chemicals**
   Design chemical products to effect their desired function while minimizing their toxicity.

5. **Safer Solvents and Auxiliaries**
   Minimize the use of auxiliary substances wherever possible to make them innocuous when used.

6. **Design for Energy Efficiency**
   Minimize the energy requirements of chemical processes and conduct synthetic methods at ambient temperature and pressure if possible.

7. **Use of Renewable Feedstocks**
   Use renewable raw material or feedstock whenever practicable.

8. **Reduce Derivatives**
   Minimize or avoid unnecessary derivatization if possible, which requires additional reagents and generates waste.

9. **Catalysis**
   Catalytic reagents are superior to stoichiometric reagents.

10. **Design for Degradation**
    Design chemical products so they break down into innocuous products that do not persist in the environment.

11. **Real-time Analysis for Pollution Prevention**
    Develop analytical methodologies needed to allow for real-time, in-process monitoring and control prior to the formation of hazardous substances.

12. **Inherently Safer Chemistry for Accident Prevention**
    Choose substances and the form of a substance used in a chemical process to minimize the potential for chemical accidents, including releases, explosions, and fires.

CHEMISTRY DEPARTMENT POLICY ON SAFETY GOGGLES

Approved eye protection is required for all people in all locations where a chemical hazard has been identified.*

The chemistry laboratory can be a hazardous place; consequently the University of Oregon makes safety our highest priority. Federal and state laws mandate that persons working in potentially hazardous environments wear personal protective equipment (PPE).[1] While little that you will be asked to do is intrinsically dangerous, a majority of the materials that you handle are in some way potentially hazardous if they are handled carelessly.

One of the most vulnerable parts of your body is your eyes and they must be protected from chemical splashes. Oregon law requires the use of personal protective equipment.

> Eye protection is required for all personnel and any visitors whose eyes may be exposed to liquid chemical or physical hazards. Any personal protective equipment (PPE) designated for eye and face protection should meet the requirements listed in ANSI Z87.1 and OR-OSHA 1910.133 regulations.

General eye and face protective guidelines include the following:

- Safety goggles are recommended in chemical operations where there is potential for chemical splashes or flying particles.
- Safety glasses with side shields are required in any operation where there is potential for eye exposure to projectiles.
- Face shields are necessary where there is potential exposure to projectiles or chemical splashes from harmful liquids. Face shields provide maximum protection to the face and throat. Face shields should not be used as a substitute for eye protection.

Therefore, we **require** that approved safety goggles be worn at all times (covering the eyes) when you are working with chemicals, in the vicinity of others using chemicals, or in rooms where chemicals are available for use. There are no exceptions to this rule. Your laboratory instructor will remind you to wear safety goggles, and you will not be permitted to work in the laboratory if you do not wear them.

If you have a problem with goggles fogging, we recommend that you leave the laboratory to remove the goggles for a short period of time; be sure to put them back on before returning

---

* No chemical hazard exists when all chemicals are appropriately stored in closed, designated cabinets, and chemicals are not in use. Chemicals located on bench tops, carts, or open shelving are readily available for use and, as such, pose a chemical hazard.

1 National Research Council (U.S.). Committee on Prudent Practices for Handling Storage and Disposal of Chemicals in Laboratories.; National Research Council (U.S.). Board on Chemical Sciences and Technology. Prudent practices in the laboratory: handling and disposal of chemicals; National Academy Press: Washington, D.C., 1995. This document is available on the web. Search for the National Academies Press and the title of the document.

to the lab. Goggles may not be removed in the laboratory unless your instructor has told you to do so and announced that no chemical hazard exists.

The chemistry department will provide goggles for all students and visitors that provide both splash and high impact protection and conform to the current manufacturing standard, ANSI/ISEA Z87.1-2015. Individuals who desire to bring their own goggles must have prior approval before use. The goggle lens and frame must be marked with both "Z87+" and "D3" or a copy of the manufacturer's Z87.1-2015 compliance certificate for the exact style/model must be presented. Goggles manufactured and tested under prior ANSI standards are not acceptable for use.

Contact Lenses

In the past, the chemical profession and others have been concerned about the use of contact lenses in potentially hazardous environments. However, the American Chemical Society and the American Optometric Association, among others, have issued new statements regarding contact lens use. OSHA's preamble for the final rule on personal protective equipment in 1994 states: "OSHA believes that contact lenses do not pose additional hazards to the wearer and additional regulation is unnecessary." The ACS states, "Recent studies and experience have suggested that, in fact, contact lenses do not increase risks but can actually minimize or prevent injury in many situations. Because of the ever-increasing use of contact lenses and the benefits they provide, the American Chemical Society Committee on Chemical Safety, having studied and reviewed the issue, is of the consensus that contact lenses can be worn in most work environments provided the same approved eye protection is worn as required of other workers in the area."[2] If you are involved in a chemical exposure such as a splash or fume affecting the eye area while wearing contact lenses, please alert the emergency responders to this situation. The contact lenses will need to be removed to facilitate eye rinsing; these should not be re-inserted before consulting with qualified medical personnel.

Approved eye protection is required for faculty, staff, students and visitors in locations where a chemical hazard has been identified, regardless of whether or not the person wears contact lenses.

---

2 Committee on Chemical Safety, A. C. S. Safety in the Academic Chemistry Laboratories, *7th ed., Vol. 2;* *American Chemical Society: Washington, D.C., 2003, p. 5.*

LABORATORY SAFETY GUIDELINES[3]

Submission of a *Safety Policies and Procedures* Signature Sheet, signed by both the student and the laboratory teaching assistant, is required before any student may work in a laboratory.

In order to have an enjoyable learning experience that facilitates scientific discovery and skill development in the laboratory, it is essential to have a safe environment for you and those working around you. The use of laboratory chemicals and laboratory equipment has some inherent risk, but this may be minimized by following proven protocols developed by industry, State and Federal government entities, and professional organizations. To achieve this end, you are required to read and adhere to the following safety precautions and laboratory protocols. If you do not understand a rule, seek an explanation from your teaching assistant or Instructor.

1. **Notify the instructor or lab assistant immediately if you have an accident, observe another student who has had an accident or needs assistance, or observe behavior or procedures which you feel may be hazardous. Minor first aid is available in the laboratory and at the Student Health Center (for Health Fee paid students during clinic hours). In the event of a more serious injury, we will contact the University of Oregon Police Department at 6-6666 or Eugene Fire & EMS at 911 for emergency assistance. To protect your health and financial stability, the University of Oregon recommends that all students have health insurance to help cover unexpected medical expenses that may arise.**

Emergency Procedures

2. General Safety
   - Learn the locations of the safety equipment in your laboratory. This includes safety showers and eyewashes, fire blankets, fire extinguishers, and first aid kits.
   - Review the evacuation route and note the assembly point; this is posted in the lab. If an alarm or other situation requires evacuation, shut off heating equipment and leave immediately.

3. If chemicals are spilled:
   - If chemicals are spilled on you or if you see chemicals spilled on another student, call for help from your instructor and wash immediately with water. If splashed in the eye or face, shout "I need help—I have splashed a chemical in my eye (face)." Please indicate if you are wearing contact lenses. If your neighbor experiences this situation, assist them to the eyewash-shower station while seeking help from the Instructor. Don't wait for symptoms of injury or pain to develop; rinse the affected area with water immediately, and continue rinsing for 15 minutes or until medical help arrives.

---

3 *Some of the information contained in this document is modified from "Chemical and Laboratory Safety Policies and Practices" prepared by the Department of Chemistry at St. Olaf College (revised August 15, 2005).*

- Work with your teaching lab assistant to clean up minor spills on the bench or floor. Notify nearby students of the presence of broken glassware and/or chemicals, and keep people from walking through the area until cleanup is complete. Don't try to pick up broken glass yourself. Always notify the teaching lab assistant of major spills.

4. In case of fire:
   - If clothing is burning, slowly walk to the safety shower and pull the cord (or ask someone nearby to pull the cord). If a shower is not readily available do one of the following: (1) drop and roll on the floor to extinguish the flames; or (2) have another person loosely cover you with a fire blanket after you have dropped to the floor to extinguish the flames.
   - If a fire develops on the bench top or floor, seek assistance (TA/Instructor) and warn people to clear the area.

Safety Goggles and Clothing

5. Eye protection must be worn in the laboratory at all times, **even when performing non-chemical operations**. Please see the *Department Policy on Safety Goggles* for more information. Protective eyewear, especially common-use gear, should be cleaned regularly before use.

6. Clothing worn in the laboratory offers a first line of protection. Clothing must completely cover the body with no skin exposed from the shoulders to the feet, and have a neckline at or above armpit level. Clothing with loose portions, such as open sweaters, baggy cuffs, and hanging scarves should be avoided since they may catch on glassware and equipment, may drag through spills, and in some cases may be a fire hazard. The responsibility for wearing appropriate attire to the laboratory rests with the student. Students observed wearing inappropriate attire will be asked to change clothes before entering the laboratory.

7. Loose, long hair should be tied back so that it does not catch on fire, become entangled in equipment, exposed to chemicals, or provide an impediment to vision. Similarly, some jewelry can also pose problems in the laboratory environment. Please consult your lab instructor if you have concerns or questions. Rubber bands are available in the stockroom.

8. Shoes with solid soles and fully closed tops, insteps, and heels must be worn in chemical laboratories regardless of the work that is occurring. Open-toe shoes, slippers, sandals, and traditional open heel clogs do not provide protection from chemical splashes, spills, falling objects, and materials hidden in the toe space along bench areas. Students observed wearing inappropriate footwear will be asked to change them before entering the laboratory.

9. The lab instructor may recommend or require you to wear protective gloves and/or a lab coat, and appropriate items will be provided. Typically gloves will be a disposable type. Check to ensure the absence of cracks or small holes in the gloves before each use. Gloves should be removed when hand protection is no longer needed for

the operation that poses a hazard. To prevent the transfer of chemical residue, never touch your skin or clothing with a gloved hand. Always remove gloves before handling such things such as doorknobs, instruments, computer keyboards, writing implements, and laboratory notebooks. This will avoid transfer contamination to other common use areas. If a contact hazard arises later in the lab, get a fresh pair. If you are unsure how to properly remove a glove without making contact with the outer surface, see your teaching assistant. Remember to wash your hands with soap and water after removing your gloves. Lab coats need to stay buttoned at all times. Your TA will describe the protocol for lab coat storage, routine replacement, and handling in the event that it becomes contaminated.

Handling Chemicals

10. Be aware of the hazards of the laboratory chemicals you are using. Become familiar with the special hazards associated with compressed gasses, biological hazards, vacuum systems, radioactive isotopes, and cryogenics before using or transporting these items. Learn how to interpret labels and observe all indicated precautions. Consult with Environmental Health and Safety for specific UO recommendations.

11. Double check the container before using any laboratory chemical.

12. Do not taste laboratory chemicals.

13. Avoid skin contact with all laboratory chemicals. Pay particular attention to corrosives as these reagents can destroy tissue.

14. Work in fume hoods when so instructed. This equipment is designed to minimize exposure to hazardous or noxious vapors and gasses. Become familiar with the proper placement of equipment and sash opening to ensure correct operation. If you need to smell a vapor, do not put your nose directly above a flask, beaker, or other vessel containing laboratory chemicals. Holding the vessel at least one foot away, use your hand to gently and very cautiously fan the vapors toward your nose.

15. Never use your mouth to pipet. Use rubber bulbs or other suction devices for pipet filling and please do not pipet directly from reagent bottles.

16. Always add acids to water; never add water to acids. Combining acid and water frequently generates heat and may result in spattering. Adding the acid to the water reduces the amount of heat generated at the point of mixing and provides more water to disperse the heat. In general, make all dilutions by adding the laboratory chemical or reagent to the water; make additions slowly and use cooling if necessary.

Label all flasks, beakers, test tubes, and other vessels according to their chemical contents; ideally labels should be placed on vessels prior to adding the chemical(s). This facilitates both identifying chemicals during an experiment and following proper waste disposal procedures.

17. Hold reagent bottles and other vessels containing liquids so that any drips will be opposite the label, and hold them so any previous drips on that same side do not get on your hand. Clean off any drips or spills. If necessary, ask for help from your instructor or lab assistant.

18. When transferring laboratory chemicals from one container to another, remember to make these transfers away from your face and below eye level.

19. Dispose of laboratory chemicals, wastes, and residues in designated containers and record the waste on the log sheet as directed by your instructor. Do not put waste into the sink drains unless directed to do so by the Instructor. Do not return unused laboratory chemicals to reagent bottles as contamination may result; treat this as waste. Put used needles, razor blades, and the like into the "Sharps Waste" container.

20. Do not remove laboratory chemicals or equipment from the laboratory.

21. Do not bring laboratory chemicals from another laboratory into the teaching labs.

22. Be aware of the activities of others working in the same area. Do not use flammable chemicals in close proximity to open flames. Be aware that many organic vapors are heavier than air and may travel along a solid surface to an ignition source and flash back to an open container.

Laboratory Supervision

23. Do not perform any unauthorized experiments or procedures in the chemistry teaching labs. Students may try new experiments and procedures only if they have been discussed with and approved by your instructor. Familiarize yourself with the experiment before reporting to the laboratory.

24. Students may not work alone in the chemistry teaching labs. All laboratory work must be under the supervision of a Chemistry Department faculty member or laboratory teaching assistant.

Behavior in the Laboratory

25. Food and beverages are not permitted in the teaching labs; this prohibition includes both consumption and storage. The use of all tobacco products, including smokeless and e-cigarettes, is not permitted. Due to possible contamination, the application of cosmetics or the insertion of contact lenses is not permitted in the teaching labs.

26. The use of cell phones, radios, iPods, MP3 players, and other devices for playing music or videos have the potential for distracting attention from experimental work or emergency announcements and their use, therefore, is not permitted in the teaching labs.

27. Use caution when moving through the laboratory; avoid sudden movements and be cautious when changing direction. Any "horseplay" or behavior that is harassing, disruptive, and aggressive or in any way presents a hazard to those working in the laboratory is forbidden. Any student or group of students engaging in such behavior may be dismissed by faculty or staff and may receive no credit for the experiment.

28. Keep aisles and bench tops free of packs, garments, and other extraneous items. Large items that do not fit in the designated storage space, such as skateboards or luggage, cannot be brought into the lab. Bikes may not be stored in the hallways.

Other Procedures

Glassware

29. If you need to insert glass tubing into a rubber stopper, consult your instructor before proceeding. This procedure presents a potential for injury from broken glass and proper precautions are essential. Use soapy water or glycerin as a lubricant and a towel to protect your hand; always grasp tubing close to stopper and use a twisting motion to insert. Do not attempt to salvage old rubber stoppers. Please bring them to your TA for proper disposal.

30. Put broken glassware in the specially marked glass waste containers. Use a brush and dust pan to collect the broken pieces.

31. Use caution when attempting to remedy stuck ground glass joints. Seek knowledgeable assistance for the correct procedure.

Heating Operations

32. Never leave burners or hot plates unattended. Turn gas and power off when you leave the workstation.

33. Exercise caution for heating operations; use tongs or thermal gloves for moving vessels, support rings, and hot plates. Remember, there is no visual indication that these items (metal and glass) may be hot.

34. Exercise caution when heating liquids in test tubes; keep test tube pointed away from people. Bumping can violently eject solution.

35. Use caution for distillations, especially with flammable solvents. Follow your laboratory manual for setup and operations. Do not take organics to dryness.

Liquid Extractions

36. Exercise caution when making liquid extractions. When using a separatory funnel, keep one hand on the stopper to prevent it from ejecting from the funnel and vent the separatory funnel often as pressure can build-up causing ejection of solution.

Special Conditions

37. The use of specialized equipment, non-atmospheric conditions, cryogenics, ionizing radiation, unattended operations, pyrophoric, or other potentially hazardous reagents and reactions will be covered by additional safety protocols put in place by the Instructor and the Teaching Labs Coordinator and will follow ACS guidelines. Please follow these special protocols explicitly.

Concluding the Laboratory Session

- Clean your work area, glassware, and return equipment to its designated location.
- Make sure the gas and power are off, and computer work is closed out.
- Wash your hands before leaving the lab.

Registered students, teaching assistants, faculty, and department staff are permitted in the teaching laboratories. All visitors must obtain prior approval and be accompanied by an authorized staff member.

If you have any sensitivities or conditions which you believe may impair your ability to handle laboratory chemicals, please discuss these concerns with your instructor. If you are or think you may be pregnant, please consult your physician for advice.

THE LABORATORY NOTEBOOK AND LAB REP(WRITING

Maintenance of an acceptable laboratory notebook will be emphasized ın ...
Chemistry Laboratory course. Record keeping and data interpretation are skills that you
will use throughout your scientific career. The ability to prepare an adequate and reliable
record of results is a fundamental requirement for all successful experimental work.

The most important criterion for an acceptable lab notebook is that the record be complete
enough for a second person, who has studied chemistry, to be able to follow your experimental work, thus being able to repeat the experiment and to obtain the same results. The
record must be written *while you do your work*. Your records should reflect your work so
well that any odd results can be interpreted later, even if you don't notice them at the time.
Later, you can do calculations, etc.

All entries in the laboratory notebook are to be made in ink. If errors are made, simply cross
them out with a single line. *Never obliterate entries*; at a later time you may find that this
information is useful. All data and observations are to be entered *directly* into the notebook,
not on scraps of paper. While you may want to wait to record data until after the lab is over
in order to have a neat notebook, it is more important to have a complete, accurate record
of all original data and observations, complete with smudges, spills, and cross-outs. Your
laboratory notebook should provide a complete record of the work that you have done
throughout the year in the lab. If it is necessary to omit information on a page in your lab
notebook, place a large X over the information but do not remove the page from the notebook. (Pages should *never* be removed from a lab notebook.)

For each experiment, organize your notebook into sections beginning with appropriate
headings (Title, Procedure, Data, etc.). Carbon copies of your lab book pages are to be
submitted weekly as part of your lab report. In addition, include on **every** page:

> Your name
>
> TA name
>
> Date
>
> Experiment Title

Lab Reports

Lab reports are submitted in two parts: the pre-lab, which is turned in on the day the experiment is performed, and the final report, to be turned in **at the beginning** of the following
lab section. In general, the following three questions will be asked when evaluating each
section of material that you submit:

1. Does the section contain essential, accurate information?

2. Does the section contain extraneous or misleading information?

3. Is the section written in a fluent, cohesive, and concise manner, and is it written according to the following guidelines?

Guidelines for Writing the Pre-lab

To be *completed before going to lab*, in your laboratory notebook:

Title

Beginning Questions

Beginning questions are research questions you can answer by doing a series of experiments and collecting data and observations. Often there are two or three "little questions" worth exploring that will lead to the answer of a big question. Usually, students will write their beginning questions on the board before the start of lab.

Beginning questions are often in the form of "How does one variable depend on another variable?"

Beginning questions that are not acceptable include:

1. "Why" questions

2. Factoid questions

3. Questions that can be answered with "yes" or "no"

4. Questions that can be answered without doing the experiment: "Do strong acids have a lower pH compared to weak acids?"

Experimental Purpose

Brief statement of why you are doing the lab. What is the experimental goal? This may be different than the beginning question(s). For example "This experiment is being done to determine the identity of an unknown metal carbonate.

Include any relevant balanced equations.

Procedure

Propose your plan for how the beginning questions can be answered by doing an experiment. This should be a step-by-step version written in your words. Your writing should be detailed enough to enable a chemist to replicate the experiment exactly as it is written in your laboratory notebook. Complete sentences are not necessary and diagrams can and should be used where appropriate.

Example of an outline of a procedure for heating a substance in a crucible:

clean crucible

dry to constant wt. w/heating

add about 5g unknown

heat gently 1st, then strongly for 10–15 min

cool-weigh-reheat-cool-weigh-repeat to constant wt.

Safety

List the specific safety concerns associated with the lab experiment you are about to conduct.

Do not list safety concerns that are general to all experiments, such as wearing goggles and appropriate clothing.

Data Tables

Anticipate the data that you will be collecting and prepare appropriate data tables. These may be changed once you begin the experiment but this is a good start.

Lab work, to be *completed in lab*:

As part of the pre-lab lecture or your TA's pre-lab instructions, you will be told about any procedural modifications and experimental design changes. Be sure to include these changes and modifications in your lab notebook.

All relevant data and observations should be recorded.

Before leaving lab, all relevant measurements and observations must be recorded. Data should be compiled in tables when appropriate. Include anything noteworthy that you observe such as color and temperature changes, formation of a precipitate, etc. All numerical entries must have appropriate units. It is not necessary for this section to be extremely neat, but it should be legible and in some sort of order. If you make a mistake recording data cross it out with ONE line. If you have to cross out an entire trial use a large X, and include a brief note as to why you did it. Don't forget to record the numbers of any unknowns.

Include any class data and statistics when relevant.

Claims: Before leaving lab, your claims statements should be written in your lab notebook. The claim statements are written in response to your beginning questions and should be able to be supported by the evidence (data) that you and your classmates collected in lab.

Turn in carbon copies of the above before leaving lab. Data used in calculations in your report must agree with these notebook pages.

Guidelines for Writing the Post-laboratory Report

Unless instructed otherwise, all reports should follow these formal report guidelines. Writing should be done in the first person, in essay form. Reports must be word processed. In general, the following three questions will be asked when evaluating each section of material that you submit:

1. Does the section contain essential, accurate information?

2. Does the section contain extraneous or misleading information?

3. Is the section written in a fluent, cohesive, and concise manner, and is it written according to the following guidelines? We will not want to grade a 10-page report.

At the top of the first page, include

- Your name
- Partner name when appropriate
- TA name
- Date
- Experiment title

Introduction

The introduction section serves as a brief "opening statement" of your report:

Explain the goals or desired results. What was the experimental purpose?

Summarize the procedure used to address the goals in 4–5 sentences.

State the safety concerns unique to this experiment.

Wrap up this section by stating the beginning questions answered by performing the experiment. **A common mistake** is to state all the BQs you had *before* you performed the experiment. In a post-laboratory report, you have the opportunity to examine your data and results carefully and *selectively answer only those BQs that were actually answered by the experiment* and calculations or graphs. Including BQs that were not answered is meaningless here.

Experimental

Data and Observations

All relevant raw data as measured from a device (i.e., analytical balance) reported to all of the decimal places displayed by the device. For example, when using an analytical balance record in your notebook the exact display of the mass from the balance using all four decimal places, reporting the error and the unit of measurement; example 23.6789 ± 0.0001 g. Record all physical observations. Raw data or experimental results should be presented in a table. Measurements must include appropriate units.

When relevant, report the raw data collected by your lab table or class.

It is generally best to use data tables to record your data. A good data table might look like this:

TABLE 1. Raw data for observed spectra for fireworks

Trial #	Heading 1 (units) *Precision: if applicable*	Heading 2 (units) *Precision: if applicable*	Heading 3 (units) *Precision: if applicable*
1			
2			
3			

Observations: 1. fireworks completed burning in 45 seconds for all trials

2. the red color is fainter than expected

Calculations, Graphs, and Chemical Equations

- If the same calculation is applicable to each data point collected, show a sample calculation with all work, including unit conversions. If multiple calculation steps were required, show worked-out sample calculations for one dataset.

- Then include a tabulated form for all the results calculated using these steps. See Table 2.

- Show calculation for average, standard deviation and % error where applicable. Remember to round to the appropriate number of sigfigs.

TABLE 2. Calculated results

Trial #	Heading 1 (units) *Precision: if applicable*	Heading 2 (units) *Precision: if applicable*	Heading 3 (units) *Precision: if applicable*
1			
2			
3			

Average: report to appropriate # of sigfigs

SD: report to appropriate # of sigfigs

Number of datasets/points: $n =$

- Provide balanced chemical equations when appropriate.

Graphs

- Give each graph a caption which summarizes the information conveyed using the graph.

Preferably, insert graphs as "images" in word document where required.

Claims and Evidence

(Claim) Answer the beginning question(s) in the format of assertive statements/claims in one paragraph.

(Evidence) Provide evidence and a written argument to support your claim(s) in the next paragraph. Your data and class data are one-half of the evidence. The other half is your interpretation of the data. A graph of your data provides an insight into the relationship of variables.

Discussion/Conclusion, Error Analysis, and Reflection

- Summarize your results here if you have not covered it in the Claims and Evidence section.

- Include comments about the accuracy of your results (you may need to look up literature values sometimes). Use the standard deviation as a source of commenting about the overall agreement of class data.

- **Answer *all* the questions posed in the lab manual text in this section**. These answers can be in different paragraphs if it makes your report organized + easier to read and understand. Writing should be in essay form and answers should not be bullet-pointed.

- Since this is at the very end of your lab report, you can easily refer *back* to data tables, graphs and calculated results to support your answers/conclusions here.

Reflection

- The goal of writing a reflection section is to connect the experiment/findings to big-picture ideas/critical understanding. How does one experiment help you connect multiple ideas, applications, and real-world scenarios?

Including connecting concepts and relevant thoughts/comments/sources with similar results confirming your findings here demonstrates your understanding of the experiment well.

Reflection topics to be included in every formal report:

Do not provide a list of bullet points when responding to these questions.

a. **EXTEND:** Propose an idea(s) for further experimentation. How could the procedure be modified to extend the investigation? Note: This extension is not simply a repeat of the experiment to collect more data. An extension of the experiment is one that would require a new beginning question.

b. **CH 221/2/3 LECTURE TOPICS:** Which lecture topics from CH 221/2/3 can be connected to this experiment? Explain briefly.

c. **APPLICATIONS:** How can a concept or technique from this experiment connect to a real-world application? Explain briefly.

    d. **RELATED READING:** Confirm, dispute, or explain your findings using appropriate literature sources. Include appropriate citations for these sources.

    e. **GREEN CHEMISTRY:** Identify relevant principles of green chemistry and briefly explain how they were implemented or addressed in this experiment. (Note: This should not be limited to comments about waste disposal.)

References

- Always insert references as superscript numbers at the end of the phrase/sentence when you insert something from another source.

- Next, add a citation in appropriate format under the References section. To do this, go to the References tab, and insert a "References" or "Works Cited" section. This section appears (by default) at the very end of the document.

- Insert the references as a numbered list in appropriate format.

- See the examples that follow.

Citing a Scientific Journal Article

- In-text with parentheses: (Last Name et al. Year)

- References/Works Cited: Last Name, Initials; Last Name, Initials; Last Name, Initials. Article Title. *Journal* **Year**, *Volume(Issue)*, page numbers.

Citing an Online Source

- In-text with parentheses: (Last Name), ("Page/Article Title"), or (Website Title)

- References/Works Cited: Last Name, First Name. "Page/Article Title." *Website Title.* Publisher, Date Published, Website URL. Accessed [date].

Citing a Book or Print Source

- In-text with parentheses: (Last Name Page)

- References/Works Cited: Last Name, First Name, First & Last Name, and First & Last Name. *Book Title*, Edition. Location: Publishing Company, Date.

General Information Regarding Grammar and Style: The post-laboratory report should be regarded as a formal scientific report. This differs from expository writing in that the writing should be clear and succinct and not contain humor or emotion. In addition to adhering to the normal rules of grammar, your report should comply with the following guidelines compiled from **The ACS Style Guide**.[4]

- Be brief. Wordiness generally adds nothing but confusion and detracts from your report.

- *Tense:* Report experimental observations and results using the past tense. The properties of substances are reported in the present tense. Never use the future tense.

---

4 The ACS Style Guide, A Manual for Authors and Editors, *Dodd, J., Ed; American Chemical Society, Washington, DC, 1986.*

Incorrect: A plot of volume versus temperature **will yield** an x-intercept of absolute zero.

Correct: A plot of volume versus temperature **yielded** an x-intercept of absolute zero.

- *Voice*: Use the first person active voice where appropriate.

  Poor: It was determined from the data that…

  Better: I determined from the data that…

- Phrases such as "I believe…" or "We concluded…" are unnecessary, as are personal opinions.

- Units of measurement are treated as collective nouns and take singular subject.

  Incorrect: Five grams of NaCl **were** added to the solution.

  Correct: Five grams of NaCl **was** added to the solution.

- Every table must have a brief title that describes its contents. Every column must have a heading that describes the material below it.

- Graphs should fill a full page and be drawn according to the guidelines in the laboratory text.

- All tables and graphs should be keyed into the text and sufficiently discussed.

In addition:

- Always use complete sentences.

- Proofread.

- Remember, you must spell all words correctly; spelling counts. Use a dictionary or the spell checker on your word processing program and don't forget to proofread.

- Never report measurements without units.

Format: Report margins should be 1-inch throughout (top, bottom, right, and left). Use a font that is easy to read (for example, Times, Palatino, etc.) and a 12-point font size. The overall length of the text portion of the report, excluding tables and calculations, should be no longer than two pages.

UNCERTAINTY, ERROR, AND PRECISION IN QUANTITATIVE MEASUREMENTS

Much of the work in any chemistry laboratory involves the measurement of numerical quantities. A quantitative measurement tells us three things:

- numerical quantity

- appropriate units

- uncertainty of the measurement

The first two of these are fairly easy to understand but the last one, uncertainty, needs some explanation. There is always an uncertainty associated with physical measurements, due not only to the care with which you take the measurement, but also to the care with which the measuring device is calibrated. If you have done all that you can to minimize error in taking the measurement, your recorded values should then reflect the uncertainty (precision) of the measuring tool. This is usually the smallest numerical value that can be estimated with the measuring device. For example, imagine trying to measure the length of the following line segment using a cheap metric ruler:

©Hayden-McNeil, LLC

Is the length of the line between 4 and 5 cm: Yes, definitely.

Is the length between 4.0 and 4.5 cm? Yes, it looks that way.

But is the length 4.3 cm? Is it 4.4 *cm*?

Given the precision of the ruler, and our ability to estimate where between a set of marked graduations (the tick marks on the ruler) a measurement falls, we are somewhat uncertain about what number to record after the decimal. So, what we can say is that the actual length is around 4.4 cm, but it might be closer to 4.3 cm, or it might be closer to 4.5 cm. In other words, we think the length is 4.4 cm but we might be off by 0.1 cm in either direction. We would record this measurement in this way:

$$4.4 \pm 0.1 \ cm$$

Keeping track of the uncertainty would be cumbersome if the uncertainty had to be reported this way each time the measurement itself were reported or used in a calculation. Therefore, we use *significant figures* to imply the precision of a measurement without having to state the uncertainty explicitly. In this course, we will assume an uncertainty of ±1 in the last recorded digit unless stated otherwise. The measurement recorded above could then be recorded just as

$$4.4 \ cm$$

and the uncertainty of ±0.1 cm would be implied (but you still, *always*, have to include the units). Note that when using this method, it is very important that you record all significant digits. If you measured a mass and found it to be 2.0000 ± 0.0001 g, it would be wrong to record the mass as

$$2 \ g \ (\text{wrong!})$$

Instead you must include all significant figures, even if they happen to be trailing zeroes:

$$2.0000 \ g \ (right!)$$

The uncertainty which we have been discussing so far is always associated with *individual* physical measurements. The value that you are trying to find, when you make such a measurement, has a true value which is unknown and is fundamentally unknowable. Because there is (unavoidable) uncertainty in your measurements, the values you get when taking a *series* of measurements will tend to scatter around the true value. For example, if the above line was measured with several different rulers, a series of measurements would be obtained, each of which might be slightly different.

The difference between the true value and any given measured value is called the **error** in the measurement.

Experimental error, when used in this context, has a very specific meaning and does not necessarily imply a mistake or blunder. If you know about a mistake or blunder, you can, at least in principle, fix the problem and eliminate the mistake. Some experimental error is intrinsic. While it can be minimized, it cannot he eliminated. A perfectly executed experiment, with no mistakes or blunders, still has experimental error. Experimental error falls into two categories: determinate and indeterminate.

Determinate errors have a definite direction and magnitude and have an assignable cause (their cause can be *determined*). Determinate error is also called systematic error. Determinate error can (theoretically) be eliminated.

Indeterminate errors arise from uncertainties in a measurement, as discussed above. Indeterminate error is also called random error, or noise. Indeterminate error can be minimized but cannot be eliminated.

Let's imagine that you weigh a calibration weight several times. The calibration weight is supposed to weigh 10.0 g, but each time you weigh it, you get a value that is about 2.0 g too large (error has both magnitude and direction). You look more closely at the weight and discover that there is a piece of tape stuck on the weight. That's a determinate error. (You were able to determine the cause of the error.) Now, you repeat your weighings of the calibration weight (after removing the tape) and collect a series of values. All of the values fall near 10.0 g, but some are a bit higher, some are a bit lower, some differ from 10.0 by 0.1 g, others differ by 0.2 g. This random fluctuation is the result of indeterminate error.

If the only errors affecting a measurement are random (i.e., you have managed to eliminate all sources of determinate error), then taking a large number of measurements will yield values that are symmetrically distributed to either side of the true value. The data are said to be distributed according to a Gaussian, or normal distribution. (You may know this as a bell-curve.) If you have many measurements, then for every individual measurement that is a bit too small, there will be another one that is a bit too large. If you take the **mean**, or **average**, of many such measurements, the random errors will tend to cancel out. Individual measurements can have fairly large errors, but the mean of many such measurements will

tend to fall close to the true value of the quantity under investigation. The more measurements you take, the closer the mean will be to the true value.

It is important to note that although taking the mean of many measurements will give a good *estimate* of the true value, the true value remains fundamentally unknowable. There are two reasons for this. As the number of measurements increases the mean approaches the true value asymptotically, but for the mean to *equal* the true value, you would have to take an infinite number of measurements. The second reason is that the mean approaches the true value if and only if the only sources of error are random. We can never be 100% certain that all sources of determinate error have been eliminated. Therefore, we can never be 100% certain that the value toward which the mean is converging really represents the true value or whether it represents the true value modified by some small determinate error. In practice, we just assume that the mean equals the true value, and for most work, that's just fine.

The mean of a set of measurements indicates the center of the normal distribution. The width of the normal distribution is given by the standard deviation. Taking again the example involving the 10.0 g calibration weight, a series of measurements that ranges from 9.9 to 10.1 g is obviously "better" in some sense than a series of measurements that ranges between 7.0 and 13.0 g. Standard deviation is a measure of how widely a series of measurements is spread around the mean. Measurements that are closely clustered together (and around the mean) have a small standard deviation. Measurements that are widely spread apart have a large standard deviation. It might make intuitive sense to you that measurements that are clustered closely together are "better," but here is a statistical reason: the smaller the standard deviation, the faster the mean converges toward the true value. That is, if the standard deviation is very small, it might take only a handful of measurements before the mean gives a very good estimate of the true value. When the standard deviation is large, many more measurements must be taken before the mean gives as good an estimate of the true value.

Two related concepts, defined below, are precision and accuracy. In the figures which follow, imagine that the center of the target represents the true value of some observable that interests us, and the crosses are individual measurements of that observable.

Precision refers to how closely multiple measurements of the same quantity cluster to one another.

Accuracy refers to how closely multiple measurements of the same quantity cluster around the *true* value.

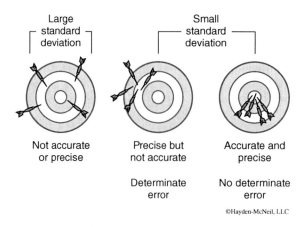

Large standard deviation

Small standard deviation

Not accurate or precise

Precise but not accurate

Accurate and precise

Determinate error

No determinate error

©Hayden-McNeil, LLC

Sometimes measurements that are not precise will distribute around the expected value in such a way that the mean of the measurements closely matches the expected value. In such a case, it is tempting to say that the data are accurate but not precise. However, by definition, data that are not precise cannot be accurate.

As discussed previously, all individual measurements are subject to uncertainty and the uncertainty should be reported (although it may be reported implicitly with significant figures). The uncertainty tells what you think the magnitude of the error in your individual measurements *should be*. Standard deviation, on the other hand, tells what the magnitude of the error in a series of measurements *actually is*. Whenever you make three or more quantitative measurements of some observable, you should report a standard deviation. When deciding how to report your value, follow these guidelines:

Step	Mean	Std. Dev.
1. Calculate the standard deviation.	10.145	0.467
2. Round standard deviation to one significant digit.	10.145	0.5
3. Round mean so it has same number of digits after the decimal point as the standard deviation.	10.1	0.5
4. Report mean and standard deviation as mean ± one standard deviation.		10.1 ± 0.5

These four steps work for most experiments. However, it is possible that in following this procedure you could end up with more significant figures than the data allow. For example, if you started with three significant figures (5.00 mL), you cannot report a mean with four significant figures. In this case, you must:

5. Round the original unrounded mean so that it has the same number of significant figures as the value that limited the number of significant figures in the experiment. (For example, 5.00 mL provides 3 significant figures.)

6. Round the original unrounded standard deviation so that its last digit is in the same place as the place of the last digit of the newly rounded mean.

In some instances this procedure may yield a standard deviation of zero (i.e., density = 1.02 ±0.00 g/mL). This does not mean that error does not exist in the experiment, but rather, to the ability that you are able to detect, you cannot calculate an error. This error is said to be "below the experimental detection limit."

Both mean and standard deviation have the same units as the individual measurements.

Standard deviation can be used to compare two values or to compare an experimentally determined value with a literature value. A property of the normal distribution is that 95.5% of the values in a series of measurements fall within two standard deviations of the mean. If you take another measurement, you can expect with 95.5% certainty that it will fall within two standard deviations of the mean. If, instead, it falls (say) seven standard deviations away, then the probability is very low that you were still measuring the same thing. Similarly, if you collect a series of data, compute the mean, compute the standard deviation, compare your mean value with a literature value, and discover that your mean value is within two standard deviations of the literature value, then you can say with some confidence that your results agree with the literature value. If, on the other hand, your mean is (say) seven standard deviations away from the literature value, then you cannot claim to have reproduced the expected value, and you better start searching for determinate errors (either that or you have just discovered something wonderful and new—but search for the determinate errors first, okay?). Note that this last described situation is analogous to the middle target.

Calculation of the Mean and Standard Deviation

Calculation of the mean and standard deviation is a small part of the very large field of statistics. The mean ($\bar{x}$) of a series of measurements is equal to the sum of the individual measurements ($\sum x_i$) divided by the total number of measurements (N):

$$\bar{x} = \frac{\sum x_i}{N}$$

Once the mean has been calculated, the standard deviation (s) is determined using the following equation:

$$s = \sqrt{\frac{\sum (\bar{x} - x_i)^2}{(N-1)}}$$

When in the statistics mode, modern calculators can quickly calculate the average and standard deviation. Because you will frequently need to report these values, it is important that you learn to do the calculations using your calculator rather than going through these tedious calculations "by hand."

Calculation of Percent Error

The percent error allows you to report the error in your measurement relative to a literature value, or other known value.

$$\% \text{ error} = \frac{|\text{literature value} - \text{measured value}|}{\text{literature value}} \times 100$$

Reading Graduated Measuring Devices

Many laboratory measurement devices are *graduated*—that is, they are marked with equally spaced lines corresponding to incremental values of the quantity measured. For example, a 100-mL graduated cylinder is marked with large lines every 10 mL and smaller lines every mL. It is graduated in mL. Similarly, burets are graduated in 0.1 mL, 10-mL measuring pipets to 0.1 mL, and standard laboratory thermometers in degrees.

The standard procedure for reading a value from a graduated device is summarized as follows:

Estimate the value to **one decimal place** more than the level of graduation.

This means that you should record the volume measured with a 100-mL graduated cylinder to the nearest 0.1 mL. Record a buret reading to the nearest hundredth of a mL (if the liquid level falls exactly on a major graduation, say at 14.00 mL, write 14.00, not 14).

You will be expected in this course to adhere to this procedure. Failure to do so will introduce more uncertainty than actually exists.

Acknowledgment

The assistance of Dr. Christopher Grant in the writing of this chapter is acknowledged.

GRAPHING

Often the goal of an experiment is to find the relationship between two variables (pressure and volume, time, and temperature, etc.). As one variable changes, so does the other. Graphing is a useful way to visualize and describe these relationships. Because the use of graphs is so common in the sciences, it is important that you know how to construct and interpret graphs. For this class, all graphs must be drawn using a computer graphing program unless otherwise instructed. Refer to Appendices C and D for graphing instructions using *MS Excel*. When preparing a graph, adhere to the following general guidelines:

1. Tabulate all data to be graphed before beginning.

2. Use the x-axis for the independent variable (that which is experimentally varied) and the y-axis for the dependent variable (that which is a function of the independent variable).

3. Decide on the limits of the graph (maximum and minimum values). The lower left corner of the graph does not have to represent zero on either axis unless you have data in this region. For greatest accuracy, select scales so that the graph nearly fills the page.

4. Select divisions on the axes which are easy to read. For example, one square may equal 1, 2, 5, 10, or 10, 20, 50, 100, but rarely 3.75 or some other "odd" number. Be aware that the default values determined by a computer may not seem "logical" and it may be necessary to manually set these values.

5. Grid lines should be shown on the graph. (If drawn by hand, all graphs are to be on graph paper with at least 10 squares per inch.)

6. Label both axes with both quantity and units. For example: "Pressure (torr)."

7. Draw the best straight line or smooth curve through the points, rather than linking them in a "connect the dots" fashion. If the data appear to be linear, the best straight line should be determined by performing a linear regression analysis (see the following section). Not all points fall exactly on the straight line or smooth curve, since each point has experimental error. The deviation of a point from the best straight line or curve gives a measure of the error. If the line is extrapolated past the range of the measured values, this extension should be indicated by a dashed rather than a solid line.

8. Title the graph in a descriptive manner.

This is an example of a poor graph created with Microsoft Excel:

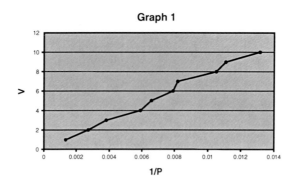

COMMENTS:

1. The graph is too small.

2. The title does not convey any useful information.

3. The axes are not labeled with words and the labels do not include units.

4. There are no vertical gridlines and the horizontal gridlines are too widely spaced.

5. Data points are connected in a "connect the dots" style, rather than with a smooth curve.

6. The gray background is distracting and is not standard scientific style.

This is a much better graphical representation of the same data:

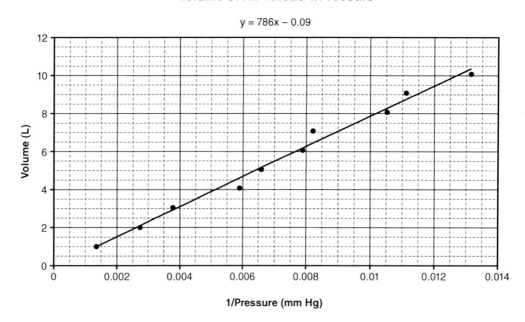

Linear Relationships

While recognizing a pattern (linear, exponential, etc.) in data is helpful, it is even more useful to develop a mathematical equation that fits the data. This equation can then be used to calculate the value of the dependent variable at any value of the independent variable. In chemistry, we frequently encounter situations in which there is a linear relationship between the experimental variables.

If the plot of y vs. x gives a straight line, it is said that the dependent variable (plotted on the y-axis) is *directly proportional* to the independent variable (plotted on the x-axis). In that case, we can then fit the data to the equation for a straight line, $y = mx+b$, where m is the slope of the line and b is the y-intercept. In some instances, a straight line arises when the data is fit to the equation $y = m(1/x) + b$. The variables are then said to be *inversely proportional*. It can be seen that when there is a linear relationship between the two variables, the slope is the constant factor which relates the variables and the y-intercept is simply the value of the dependent variable when the independent variable is zero. (This may not necessarily be the point where the curve intercepts the y-axis on your particular graph.) Once these two parameters have been determined, the equation for a straight line can be used to find the value of y for any value of x.

The values of the slope and y-intercept are generally difficult to obtain directly from the graph. This is due in part to the difficulty in "eyeballing" the best straight line through the points, and also because the slope and intercept should represent the same level of precision as the data. (It is frequently impossible to assign the appropriate number of significant figures to a best fit line which has been drawn by hand.) A better approach is to apply statistics to define the most probable straight line fit of the data. For all linear plots prepared for the General Chemistry laboratory course, you will be expected to determine the slope and y-intercept using the method of **linear regression analysis** (or method of **least squares**). **See the image of a good graph for an example of a best fit line through the data.**

A linear regression analysis determines the best fit straight line through the points by minimizing the sum of the squares of the deviations of the points from the line. Or, in simpler terms, it determines the line which minimizes the distances of the points from the line. This analysis of the data can be quickly done using a computer spreadsheet program or graphing calculator. Remember that your eyes are smarter than your calculator and you must always include a graph in your lab report. This graphical representation of the data allows you to visualize the relationship between the variables, see the "scatter" in the data, and consider whether "bad" or questionable data exists.

Reading the Graph

Remember that the precision of the information obtained from the graph should match the precision of the data that went into the graph. It is not desirable to lose significant digits when reading the graph, nor is it possible to generate more. Therefore, if the data used to generate the graph had N significant figures, numbers read from the graph should also have N significant figures. This rule holds true as well for values of the slope and y-intercept obtained by linear regression analysis. It will generally be necessary to round the values obtained from your calculator or computer program to the correct number of significant figures.

MASS MEASUREMENTS[5]

The choice of balance used to determine the mass of chemicals in lab depends on the precision (or number of significant figures) required. The maximum mass that the balance can accommodate must also be considered. In this course you will use two balances—the top-loader and the analytical balance. Of the two, the top-loader is much sturdier and can accommodate larger masses but does so with some loss of precision.

General Guidelines for Balance Use

1. Balances should not be moved. Please check with your instructor if you have reason to change the location of a balance.

2. Keep balances *clean*. Any chemicals left on or near the balances will eventually damage them and may also harm you or your fellow students. Whenever you walk away from a balance, be sure that you have left it clean, even if someone else made the mess.

3. Be *gentle*, please. The balances used in this course are sensitive instruments and will be damaged or destroyed by rough use.

4. Always use the same balance for repeat measurements and weigh by difference to minimize errors.

5. Never place chemicals directly on the pan. This protects the balance from corrosion and allows you to recover all of the chemical being weighed.

6. Always remove the weighing container from the balance before any transfer of liquids and solids.

7. Close all doors before you record the mass of a substance. If doors are not closed, drafts may cause inaccurate measurements.

8. Never weigh hot objects or substances.

9. Fingerprints have weight. Have clean hands before using the balance or touching containers that will be weighed and touch as little as possible.

Guidelines for Finding the Mass of a Solid or Liquid

The usual procedure consists of first determining the mass of a sheet of weighing paper or a receiving vessel on the balance pan. Then the substance of interest is added and a second reading is taken. The difference between the two masses corresponds to the mass of the added substance. The mass of the receiving vessel is called the *tare*. Many balances have an automatic taring control. That is, with receiver on the pan, the scale can be set to read zero. Then the substance to be weighed is added and its mass is read directly.

---

5 *Adapted from J. W. Long,* Experiments in General Chemistry, *third edition, Kendall/Hunt Publishing, Dubuque, Iowa, 1992.*

Alternatively, weighing "by difference" is sometimes convenient. First a small vessel containing a reagent is weighed. Then some of the reagent is delivered to a receiver and the vessel is weighed again. The difference equals the mass of the reagent delivered.

The Top-Loading Balance

The top-loading balances are much sturdier than the analytical balances, but they are not nearly as precise or sensitive. They are, however, sensitive enough to show quite a bit of drift when someone walks by, stirring the air. They also show considerable drift from air currents set up by the ventilation system. You should take note of this and not use the top-loaders for weighings that require high precision. They are primarily designed for ease of use (speed).

Actual use of the top-loading balance is simple: first place an empty container or piece of weighing paper on the balance pan and zero the mass reading by pressing down on the black bar marked "tare" on the front of the balance. Wait at least 5 seconds—until 0.00 appears in the window. Then put the material to be weighed in the container or on the paper and read the mass.

The Ohaus Analytical Balance

Care of the Balance

1. This balance is an expensive, precision instrument. Please treat it carefully.

2. Do not place any object weighing over 100 g on the pan. Check the rough mass on a top-loading balance if in doubt.

3. Be sure that your container is clean before placing it in the pan compartment.

4. Never transfer chemicals inside the pan compartment.

5. When you are finished weighing, clean out the pan compartment with the brush provided and wipe off the balance bench with a towel if necessary.

6. The care, cleanliness, and general condition of the balances, the balance benches, and the balance room are the joint responsibility of the class as a whole. If your TA finds the balances left dirty, you will be asked to clean them up. In extreme cases, points will be deducted from your report.

Operation of the Balance

1. Make sure that the pan and the pan compartment are clean.

2. Zero the balance by pressing the zero button, wait until zeroes appear in the readout window.

3. Open the door and very carefully place your container on the pan.

4. Close the door and record the digital values shown in the readout window.

VOLUME MEASUREMENTS[6]

Chemists measure volumes of liquids with one of several different types of volumetric glassware. The one chosen in a particular situation depends on the precision required and the purpose of the experiment. These devices are:

- graduated cylinder: used when high precision is not necessary;
- volumetric flask (TC): used to prepare solutions of precisely known concentration;
- buret (TD): used to deliver a variable but precise volume of liquid;
- transfer pipet (TD): used to transfer a specific precise volume;
- measuring pipet (TD): used to transfer a range of specific precise volumes.

The designations "TC" and "TD" indicate that the devices are calibrated to *contain* a certain amount of liquid (TC), or to *deliver* a precise volume (TD). These designations are usually marked on the devices themselves. The temperature "20°C" is also marked on them, indicating that they deliver the volumes promised at 20 degrees Celsius only. Specific information about the precision and accuracy of different glassware is included in a table at the end of this section.

Cleanliness

Make sure that the device is clean. To check cleanliness, fill with water and let it drain out. Examine the inner walls for water drops. No drops means the glassware is clean and you can proceed to rinse with reagent. If it isn't clean, use soap and water to clean it or soak for a few minutes in cleaning solution. After cleaning, the glassware must be thoroughly rinsed with tap water followed by three or four portions of deionized water. Finally, rinse three more times with reagent solution. It is generally unnecessary to dry volumetric glassware.

The Meniscus

The surface of most liquids forms a marked curvature, or *meniscus*. It is common practice to use the bottom of the meniscus as the point of reference in calibrating and using volumetric glassware. This can be seen more easily by holding a piece of white paper with a black rectangle on it behind the graduations.

When you read the level of liquid in any glassware, it is important that your eye be at the same level as the top of the liquid. This minimizes what is known as *parallax* error. Parallax will cause the volume to appear smaller than it actually is if the meniscus is observed from above, and larger if viewed from below.

---

6 *Adapted from J. W. Long,* Experiments in General Chemistry, *third edition, Kendall/Hunt Publishing, Dubuque, Iowa, 1992.*

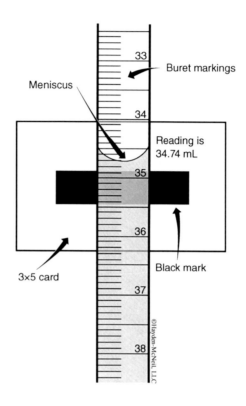

Meniscus

33

Buret markings

34

Reading is
34.74 mL

35

36

Black mark

3×5 card

37

38

©Hayden-McNeil, LLC

Reading the Calibrations

It is important that you read every device with the liquid column *absolutely vertical*—devices at angles don't give proper volume readings.

Some of the volumetric glassware, notably the buret, are calibrated "upside-down." This means that the top of the buret reads "0.00 mL" and the bottom reads "25.00 mL" (or whatever total volume the buret you have delivers). Keep this in mind when you read any volumetric device so that you will first check to see whether the device you are using is "right-side-up" or "upside-down." Remember that for the "upside-down" devices, for example, if the meniscus is one-tenth of a major division below 4.00 mL it should be read 4.10 mL, while for a "right-side-up" device the same position would be read at 3.90 mL.

Volumetric Flask

With the volumetric flask, most beginners have trouble with overfilling. Once the volumetric flask is overfilled, you cannot save anything and can only discard the contents and start over. To avoid overfilling, always make the addition of the last one-half inch to one inch of water in the neck of the flask using a dropper or a pipet. Never add this last portion of water from a plastic squeeze bottle!

Buret

With the buret, filling is critical. In particular, be sure that the tip of the buret (below the stopcock) is filled with the liquid in the buret. Fill the tip by overfilling the buret, then opening the stopcock completely to sweep out the air. If the tip is left empty and then the buret is used, it will fill sometime during use and the volume used to fill the empty tip will be read as volume delivered from the buret—which it clearly isn't! Another common error in using a buret is caused by the presence of a bubble of air in the buret tip, directly below the stopcock. If an air bubble is present at the start of titration, it may fill in during the titration, causing an error in the volume of liquid delivered from the buret. Usually the bubble can be dislodged by draining the buret for a second or two with the stopcock wide open. If this fails, the bubble may be expelled by *carefully* shaking the buret while draining liquid into a sink. Also, be sure to wipe the tip of the buret free of any drops of liquid before use.

Pipet

Following are some drawings to help you master the proper use of the pipet. Referring to the drawings:

1. Use a rubber bulb which is clean and dry to draw liquid up into the pipet.

2. Draw the liquid up until it is above the line near the top of the pipet.

3. Then move the bulb quickly out of the way and put your index finger—not your thumb!—over the top of the pipet.

4. Wipe the tip of the pipet.

5. Place the pipet tip on a dry surface of the container from which you have just drawn the liquid and, holding the pipet exactly vertical and the container at a slight angle, allow (by rocking your index finger just a bit) the liquid to drain out until the bottom of the meniscus just touches the line.

6. Then, without any sudden jerking, move the pipet to the container you want to add liquid to. If this involves much movement, you should minimize the possibility of accidental spillage from the pipet by holding the pipet horizontally during the movement.

7. Finally, allow the liquid to drain into the container, holding the pipet vertical and the container at a slight angle. Watch the liquid drain out. "TD" pipets are made so that they keep a small amount of liquid in the tip yet deliver the correct volume of liquid. You should simply watch, count to ten when the meniscus stops moving down, and withdraw the tip from the container's surface.

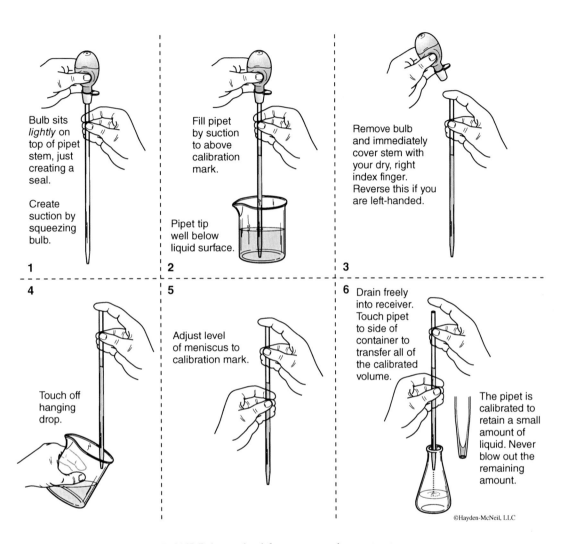

1 Bulb sits *lightly* on top of pipet stem, just creating a seal.

Create suction by squeezing bulb.

2 Fill pipet by suction to above calibration mark.

Pipet tip well below liquid surface.

3 Remove bulb and immediately cover stem with your dry, right index finger. Reverse this if you are left-handed.

4 Touch off hanging drop.

5 Adjust level of meniscus to calibration mark.

6 Drain freely into receiver. Touch pipet to side of container to transfer all of the calibrated volume.

The pipet is calibrated to retain a small amount of liquid. Never blow out the remaining amount.

©Hayden-McNeil, LLC

FIGURE 1. Method for using a volumetric pipet

TABLE 3. Volume Measurements and Tolerances in Common Laboratory Glassware

Glassware	Volume (mL)	±Uncertainty
Volumetric pipets	1.000	0.006
	2.000	0.006
	5.00	0.01
	10.00	0.02
	25.00	0.03
	50.00	0.05
Volumetric flasks	10.00	0.02
	25.00	0.03
	50.00	0.05
	100.00	0.03
	250.00	0.12
	500.00	0.20
Buret	0.00–50.00	0.01
Erlenmeyer flasks	100	5
	250	10
Beaker	50	5
Graduated cylinder	10.0	0.1
	100.0	0.5

VOLUMETRIC ANALYSIS: TITRATION

Volumetric analysis by **titration** is one of the most useful and accurate techniques available to the analytical chemist. This procedure allows the experimenter to determine the concentration of a substance of interest. The reaction that is monitored during a titration can be represented by

$$aA + tT \rightarrow products$$

where A is the analyte (the substance we are interested in) and T is referred to as the titrant. The titrant is a solution of known concentration that is added incrementally, normally from a buret, to the analyte. Solutions, such as the titrant, which have accurately determined concentrations, are referred to as standard solutions and their concentrations are determined by a process known as **standardization**.

The addition of the titrant is continued until an amount of titrant chemically equivalent to that of the analyte has been added. It is then said that the equivalence point of the titration has been reached. In order to know when to stop the addition of titrant, the chemist may use a chemical substance, called an indicator, which responds to the appearance of excess titrant by changing color. The point when the color change occurs, which may or may not be exactly at the equivalence point, is known as the endpoint of the titration.

The concentration of the analyte is calculated from the volume of titrant required to reach the equivalence point, the concentration of the titrant, and the stoichiometry of the reaction.

There are four major types of reactions which are used for titrimetric analysis:

1. Acid–base: There are a large number of acids and bases which can be determined by titration. The titrants are generally standard solutions of strong acids or bases, such as HCl or NaOH.

2. Oxidation–reduction: Chemical reactions involving redox processes are widely used for titrations. The equivalence point is frequently determined by monitoring a species which undergoes a color change as it is oxidized or reduced.

3. Precipitation: The precipitation of silver cation with the halogen anions is a widely used titrimetric procedure. The reaction is

$$Ag^+ + X^- \rightarrow AgX(s)$$

    where X^- can be chloride, bromide, iodide, or thiocyanate (SCN^-) ion.

4. Complex formation: Many organic reagents, such as ethylenediaminetetraacetic acid (EDTA), form stable complexes with a number of metal ions and are widely used for the titrimetric determination of these metals.

The Titration Procedure

Titrations are generally performed using a buret. A buret is a precisely bored glass tube with graduations that allow the volume of liquid delivered, to be measured. This is done by reading the level before and after draining liquid from the buret. Common laboratory burets have total capacities of 25 or 50 mL, and are graduated to 0.1 mL. A buret reading can therefore be estimated to the nearest 0.01 mL. Because a delivered volume is the difference between two buret readings, the uncertainty in the delivered volume is 0.02 mL.

1. Set up the buret: Place the buret in a buret clamp with the stopcock handle to the right. Be sure the buret is properly positioned in the clamps so it is completely vertical and not at an angle. You will deliver solution to the titration flask by turning the stopcock.

2. Check for cleanliness: Fill the buret with deionized water to above the 0.00 mL mark, then let the water run out the tip into a spare beaker. With the buret, filling is critical. In particular, be sure that the tip of the buret (below the stopcock) is filled with the liquid in the buret. Fill the tip by overfilling the buret, then opening the stopcock completely to sweep out the air. If the tip is left empty and then the buret is used, it will fill sometime during use and the volume used to fill the empty tip will be read as

volume delivered from the buret—which it clearly isn't! Another common error in using a buret is caused by the presence of a bubble of air in the buret tip, directly below the stopcock. If an air bubble is present at the start of titration, it may fill in during the titration, causing an error in the volume of liquid delivered from the buret. Usually the bubble can be dislodged by draining the buret for a second or two with the stopcock wide open. If this fails, the bubble may be expelled by carefully shaking the buret while draining liquid into a sink. Also, be sure to wipe the tip of the buret free of any drops of liquid before use.

Examine the inner wall of the buret for water drops. No droplets indicate the buret is clean. If not, clean according to the standard procedure for cleaning volumetric glassware.

3. Rinsing and conditioning: Place approx. 30 mL reagent solution in a small beaker. Empty the buret and close the stopcock. Pour about 5 mL reagent solution into the buret and run 2 mL out of the tip into a spare beaker or your waste container. Take the buret out of the clamp and rotate it slowly while pouring the rest of the reagent out the top. Repeat two more times. The walls of the buret should now be coated with reagent solution.

4. Titrating Samples:

   a. Fill the buret according to the above procedure, being sure that the tip is filled with reagent solution.

   b. Once the buret tip is filled and free of bubbles, drain until the liquid level is just below the 0.00 mL mark. (It is unnecessary to have the liquid level at exactly the 0.00 mL mark.) Touch the inside of a spare beaker to the buret tip to remove any drops of liquid before use. Read and record the volume level in the buret to the nearest 0.01 mL. This is the initial reading.

   c. Place an Erlenmeyer flask containing the analyte under the buret tip and lower the buret so the tip is just above the lip of the flask. Open the stopcock and, while swirling the flask, run reagent solution into the flask. (Time-saving tip: Before beginning, perform a quick calculation to estimate the approximate volume of titrant which will be required.) Titrant can be added quickly until approximately 80% of the estimated volume has been delivered. At this point, begin adding reagent "dropwise" as you swirl the flask. The endpoint color will persist longer and longer as you near the endpoint. As you approach the endpoint, it is desirable to deliver less than one drop at a time from the buret. (The volume of one drop delivered from a 50-mL buret is approx. 0.05 mL.) To deliver a fraction of a drop, carefully open the stopcock until part of a drop is hanging from the buret tip. Alternatively, you can allow just a fraction of a drop to emerge from the buret by very rapidly turning the stopcock 180° through the open position (from closed to closed). Then touch the inside glass wall of the receiving flask to the buret tip to transfer the liquid to the wall of the flask. Rinse down the sides of the flask with deionized water. Stop the addition of titrant at the first persistent color of the indicator. If a drop of titrant remains on the buret tip, transfer it to the flask by touching the side of the flask to the buret tip. Rinse down the sides of the flask with deionized water. Read the liquid level in the buret. This is the final reading.

exp1

Pipet and Analytical Balance Techniques

INTRODUCTION

This activity is designed to provide you with an introductory experience using a pipet and an analytical balance. Before you go to lab, please read the section in your lab manual on the proper way to use a mass balance (page xxxv) and the proper way to measure volume using a transfer pipet (pages xxxviii–xxxix). Refer to the diagrams on those pages to guide you as you learn how to pipet. While you are in lab, you have the option of watching a short video that can be found on the laboratory computers illustrating proper pipet techniques. You will be using a pipet and an analytical balance in next week's experiment so it is useful to begin to learn proper lab techniques the first week of your laboratory course. Before doing the activity, it is wise to practice pipetting deionized water until you are certain you can deliver exactly 10.00 mL of water to a clean beaker or Erlenmeyer flask.

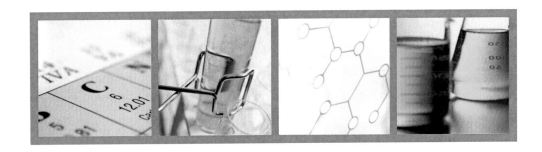

NOTES
▼

BEGINNING ACTIVITY

Before doing this activity, it is wise to practice pipetting deionized water until you are certain you can deliver exactly 10.00 mL of water to a clean beaker or Erlenmeyer flask. Your TA will demonstrate this technique. For more detailed instructions, you should refer to the diagrams on page xxxix, which show you how to use a pipet.

In the middle of the lab are two different solutions, each stored in a stock bottle. What obvious physical differences do you observe about these solutions? Record these observations in the space on page 5.

BEGINNING QUESTION

How do the masses of equal volumes of the two solutions compare to one another? What does this suggest about the identities of the solutions?

ACTIVITY

In order to save time and to save on the quantities of solutions needed, two students at your table will analyze solution A (colorless solution) and two students will analyze solution B (blue solution).

- Collect about 50 mL of solution A or solution B in a clean dry beaker. Label this beaker with a piece of label tape (stock solution A or B). Do not weigh this beaker.

- Using the analytical balance, determine the exact mass of a second clean dry beaker. Record this mass in the appropriate space in the data table on the next page.

- At your work station, "condition" the pipet by rinsing it three times with your solution.

- Pipet 10.00 mL of the solution into the clean dry beaker that you previously weighed.

- Determine the mass of the second beaker plus the pipetted liquid. Record this mass in the appropriate space in the data table on page 5.

- Dispose of the weighed liquid in the sink.

- Repeat this process one more time with a second 10.00 mL pipetted sample.

- All remaining liquids should be disposed of in the sink. *Do not return any liquids to their stock bottle.*

- Return your used pipet to the collection bin in the laboratory. Remove all labeling tape from beakers.

- Record data from your table group partners in the table on the following page.

PIPET AND ANALYTICAL BALANCE TECHNIQUES

Leah Dorsey
Name

_____
TA

_____
Lab Section

OBSERVATIONS:

	Soln A	Soln A	Soln B	Soln B
Mass of beaker				
Mass of beaker + solution				
Mass of the solution				
Mass of beaker				
Mass of beaker + solution				
Mass of the solution				
Average mass of solution				

CLAIM:

exp2

Density Exploration

Welcome to the General Chemistry laboratory! Depending on your background, this may be a very recognizable place or it may feel like a foray into an unfamiliar environment. Whichever it is, you should be more comfortable with the laboratory and procedures by the end of this week's experiment. It has been designed to introduce, or re-introduce, you to some of the basic procedures that you will be using in the laboratory throughout the year. BEFORE ATTENDING LAB, read the chapters in this text on the proper use of laboratory balances and volumetric pipets and maintaining a proper laboratory notebook.

As important as experimental technique is, it is nothing without appropriate data analysis. One of the primary data analysis tools that you will use in this course is a spreadsheet. Therefore, this introductory lab also includes an introduction to basic spreadsheet analysis.

You will be practicing basic laboratory procedures while investigating the concept of density. Before coming to lab, be sure to look up a definition of density and the formula to calculate it. Record your definition and the formula in your laboratory notebook as part of your pre-lab preparation.

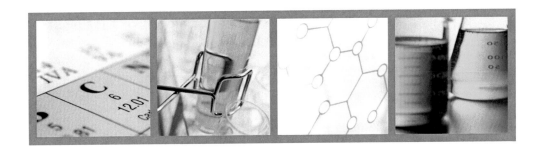

DENSITY OF COPPER

This analysis should be done with the other members of your laboratory group. Your task is to devise and carry out two independent methods for the determination of the density of various copper samples. As you are writing your pre-lab before the lab, indicate two possible methods you feel will allow you to determine the density. When you get to lab, you will work with your classmates to determine the two specific methods to be used.

Procedure

Discuss the two different methods for determining the density of a solid with the other students at your lab table. Divide up the work so two members of your group (working individually) will use one experimental method and two members will use the other method. Record the method that you will be using in your lab notebook. You will notice that there are different sizes and shapes of copper in the lab. Mix it up so that the members of your table group are investigating different sizes and shapes of copper samples. Record the shape of the piece of copper that you are investigating in your lab notebook and then make the appropriate measurements to determine its density.

After determining the density of your sample, exchange it with a group member who is performing the other method of determination and repeat your analysis with the new sample of copper. In this way, the density of each sample of copper will be determined twice, using each of the different methods. You and the members of your group will individually determine the density of two different pieces of copper, using the same method each time.

Lab Notebook

Be sure to record the actual procedures that you are using. Remember, laboratory notebooks should contain enough detail to enable a scientist to replicate your experiment. Set up data tables and record all data and observations. Be sure all measured values are reported with units and the appropriate number of significant figures. If you are not certain of the appropriate number of significant figures to report in your notebook for your measurements, please check with your instructor.

Calculate the density of the two samples you analyzed.

Compare your results with the other members of your group. Based on analysis of your group's data, determine the answers to these questions and record them in your laboratory notebook.

- Do the same pieces of copper have the same densities using both methods?
- Do you have more confidence in one method over another? Explain.
- What is the relationship between the size and shape of the copper pieces and the density?

- Is it appropriate to calculate an average value for the density? Explain.
- What conclusions can you reach regarding the density of the copper samples?

After ensuring your results are consistent with others' in your group, enter your data in the class database.

DENSITY OF SOFT DRINKS[1]

According to a 2012 Gallup poll,[2] nearly half of all Americans drink at least one soft drink (soda) every day. The primary ingredient in most soft drinks is water, along with colors, flavors, sweeteners, and carbon dioxide gas to provide effervescence. Regular soft drinks are typically sweetened with high fructose corn syrup while diet soft drinks use sugar substitutes known as artificial sweeteners.

You will again be working with your table group of four students. Each table will measure either the regular (non-diet) version of a soft drink or the diet version of the same soft drink. Work with your TA and classmates to determine which table will be working with which drink. Propose a reason why it is important to get rid of any dissolved gas bubbles before doing your density determination.

To perform this analysis, you will obtain a precisely measured volume of the soft drink and measure its mass. Using this information, you will be able to calculate the density.

Procedure

Each student will be determining the density of three samples of a soft drink, *using the same volume each time*. This will give you a set of *duplicate* measurements. Other students will do the same process, some using the same volume as you and others using different volumes. Students who use the same volume as you will be making *replicate* measurements. The volumes to be used should be 6 mL, 11 mL, 15 mL, or 20 mL. Work with your TA and your classmates to ensure that volumes over this entire range are being measured. The choice of which volume you use isn't important but it is important to know exactly what the volume is.

Volumetric pipets will be used to obtain your samples of soft drink. These pipets are more precise than a graduated cylinder and volumes should be recorded to two places after the decimal place. Your lab instructor will demonstrate the technique for filling and draining these pipets.

---

1 Adapted from Burke, K.A.; Greenbowe,T.J.; CHEM 177L Laboratory Experiments, *Hayden-McNeil Publishing, Plymouth, MI, 2012.*

2 http://www.gallup.com/poll/156116/nearly-half-americans-drink-soda-daily.aspx (accessed 6/2019)

NOTES

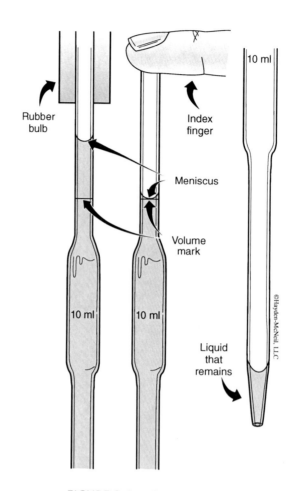

FIGURE 2-1. Volumetric pipet

Before using the pipet to transfer your soft drink samples, practice pipetting deionized (DI) water until you are comfortable using your pipet to precisely and accurately obtain a known volume of water. Then, rinse the pipet two times with the soft drink that you will be analyzing. To do this, draw 2–3 mL portions of the soft drink into the pipet using the red suction bulb. Roll the pipet to wet the interior surfaces. Discard the soft drink into the appropriate waste container.

Using the pipet, transfer your first sample to a 50-mL beaker for mass measurements. Be sure that this beaker is clean and thoroughly dry each time that you are going to use it to determine a mass. To find the mass of the soft drink, the recommended strategy would be to determine the mass of the empty beaker, transfer the sample to it, and then find the mass of the filled beaker. Repeat this process for each of your three samples. After finishing, immediately rinse the pipet as instructed by your TA.

Lab Notebook

Again, record the procedure that you are using and set up data tables to record all data and observations. Check with your TA to ensure you are reporting the appropriate number of significant figures for your measurements.

Waste Disposal

Soft drinks are fairly acidic, primarily because of phosphoric acid, added to give the dinks a sharper flavor. We must always be aware of what we are putting down the drain and even though something like a soft drink seems fairly benign, when the total amount that is used by all students performing this experiment is considered, we have too much acidic volume to pour directly down the drains. Therefore, the acid in the soft drinks will need to be neutralized before disposal according to the instructions that are provided in lab.

Proceed to the next section to analyze your data.

SPREADSHEETS, STATISTICS, AND DATA ANALYSIS

Spreadsheets are a very powerful tool for the analysis of numerical information and will be used regularly in this course. For this lab, you will be using a spreadsheet to determine the density of each of your samples, as well as the average density. In this course, we will be using Microsoft Excel for our spreadsheet program. You can do this analysis on the laboratory computers, or, if there is no more wet chemistry being done in your work area and you have a spreadsheet program, you can use your personal laptop computer. Please note that students assume all responsibility for personal computers when using them in the lab.

1. Appendix C in your laboratory text is a summary of basic spreadsheet operations using Microsoft Excel. Be sure to refer to these instructions as you work your way through the following tasks.

2. Open a new spreadsheet.

3. Enter your data from your density of soft drinks experiment into the spreadsheet:

    *   Start with column headings. These should be "Sample," "Mass (g)," "Volume (mL)," and "Density (g/mL)." Units should always go into the column headings and not into the data cells.

    *   Enter the sample number (1–3) into column A.

    Timesaving tip: When entering a sample number, type the first two numbers into separate cells, above and below each other. Highlight the two cells. Position the cursor over the lower right corner of the lower cell. When it changes from a thick cross to a thin cross, hold the mouse button down and drag the cursor

NOTES
▼

down the column through the cells that you wish to number. Excel will automatically fill in the correct number. This same technique can be used to enter times of day, days of the week, etc. Practice a few to see for yourself. The trick is to use two cells to let Excel know how you want to increment the change, and then it will figure the rest out from there.

- Enter the mass of each sample in column B, without units. Be sure to use the appropriate number of significant digits.

- Enter the volume of each sample in column C, with appropriate significant figures and without units.

Now we come to the real power of Excel, and that is to make complicated calculations painless. We'll start by calculating the density of your samples and the average density.

4. Calculate the density in column D. To do this, click on the first cell in column D below the heading. Type in the calculation for density using the appropriate cell values instead of the words "mass" and "volume." For example, if your first mass measurement is recorded in cell B2 and your first volume measurement is recorded in cell C2, in column D2 you would enter the following formula:

$$=B2/C2$$

(Note that whenever you want Excel to perform a calculation, it is always necessary to start with the = sign.)

Hit return and the density will be displayed.

5. Use the fill down feature to calculate the density for each trial.

6. Calculate the average (or mean) density value:

- Position the cursor in the first empty cell in column D. Highlight the cell by clicking on the mouse. You now need to enter the formula to calculate the average, and tell Excel which cells you are averaging over:

- Type: **=average(**

- Move the cursor to the top cell containing data in the column.

- Hold the mouse button down and drag the cursor down to the last cell containing data, highlighting all the cells. In the formula bar, you will see something like **=AVERAGE(D2:D4**

- Close the parentheses and hit the return key. The average value will be displayed in the cell where you have been working.

NOTES

7. Calculate the standard deviation:

- Position the cursor in the cell beneath the calculated average.
- Type: **=stdev(**
- Repeat the process that you used to calculate the average. The standard deviation will be displayed in the cell where you have been working.

8. You have now created a spreadsheet that displays the data and the calculated values for the density, mean and standard deviation. Customize the spreadsheet with borders, shading, and headings if desired. Title the spreadsheet.

9. Print the spreadsheet by typing ⌘P.

10. Note that Excel does not understand significant figures or know how to round. You will need to take care of this on your own.

11. Enter your average density values into the class database.

Compare your results with the other members of your group. Based on analysis of your group's data, determine the answers to these questions and record them in your laboratory notebook.

- Did you use a sweetened or unsweetened drink? What is the average density that you determined?
- How did your results compare to other students who used the same volume as you?
- Did students using different volumes obtain the same or different results for the same drink? Does the volume that was used make a difference in the density?
- Based on your class' data, would you say that density is an *intensive* or an *extensive* property?
- How does experimental error affect your results if you had to fill the pipet more than once or had to use two different pipets to obtain your desired volume?
- If a student did not properly use the correct technique for pipetting and consistently used 0.10 mL more of volume than what was reported, how would this influence the calculated value of the density?
- Use a resource on the internet to locate the density of the two types of soft drinks as reported by the manufacturer. Indicate the source that you are citing and whether this site provides valid information. Compare your experimental value to the reported value.
- How does the experimental value of the density of a sweetened soft drink compare to the density of an unsweetened drink? Propose a reason for any differences revealed by your observations, class discussions and external sources of information.

DISCUSSION/CONCLUSION

You will not be submitting a formal lab report for this week's lab. Instead, you will be writing a "Slim Report," with a summary and discussion of your laboratory experience. This will be similar to the conclusion section that you will be writing in your formal laboratory reports later in the term. Writing should be done in the first person, in essay form. *Do not provide a list of bullet points or list of answers to the questions.* The overall length should be between one and two pages.

Address these points in your "Slim Report":

Beginning Question(s)

What question(s) did I have? What question(s) did the class group decide to investigate?

Claim, Evidence and Analysis

What results can I report? (Claim) What is my interpretation of my data and class data (graphs, class data, trends, or other analysis) to respond to my beginning question(s)? (Evidence)

Reading and Reflection

1. What are the possible sources of error? How would those errors impact my results?

2. What new ideas have I developed after completing this laboratory experiment, OR, how could this experiment be extended if more time and materials were available?

3. How can I identify and explain a specific topic from the General Chemistry lecture course (CH 221) that is related to this laboratory experiment?

4. How can I make a valid connection between this laboratory work and a real-life application?

5. What related reading have I done to explain, confirm, or dispute what has been learned via this laboratory experience? Report and cite at least one relevant and valid source, other than Wikipedia or the chemistry lecture and laboratory texts and lecture notes.

In addition to this discussion, submit your Excel spreadsheet with your individual data for the soft drink determination.

exp3

Galvanized Nails, Quality Control, and an Introduction to Green Chemistry

CHEMISTRY IN A SUSTAINABLE WORLD

Green Chemistry is the use of chemistry for pollution prevention. More specifically, green chemistry is the design of chemical products and processes that are more environmentally benign than conventional methods. This new approach to pollution prevention is the central focus of the U.S. Environmental Protection Agency's Green Chemistry Program.

> "Chemistry is the creative science that introduces new substances into the world, and in so doing, changes the world. With green chemistry we're able to design those substances so that they also protect human health and preserve the environment."
>
> —Dr. Ronald Breslow,
> past president of the American Chemical Society

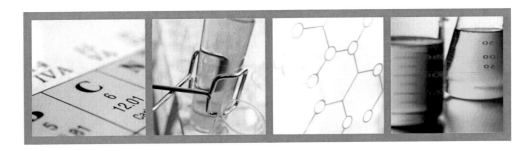

NOTES
▼

[Handwritten notes in margin:]
Mil: 0.0003002 g/mm²
2: .0003096
3: .0002578
4: .0003208
5: .0003020?

Experiments in this lab manual have been designed whenever possible to meet the green chemistry challenge. In addition to incorporation of materials that expose students to lower chemical risks, experiments have also been designed to minimize the amount of waste that is produced by the large number of students taking general chemistry. Whether in the teaching lab, research lab, or an industrial setting, experiments are done for the purpose of answering a question or questions that have been posed about the system being studied. This week in lab, you will also consider what is left over when the experiment is finished and how to process the chemical waste that has been generated.

INTRODUCTION

This experiment addresses the question of uniformity within a given lot of galvanized nails. These are iron nails that have been coated with a layer of zinc, or galvanized, to prevent the iron from rusting. When an iron nail rusts, it undergoes an oxidation reaction with water to form iron oxide, or rust. If a layer of zinc is present, it becomes oxidized instead of the iron, thus protecting the nail. The protectiveness of the zinc coating does not last forever, however. Eventually, a galvanized nail will rust, but the process takes quite a bit longer than rusting of uncoated nails.

The process of coating iron with zinc is known as galvanization. The two most common methods of galvanization are electrolysis and "hot dipping." Hot dipped nails have a thicker zinc coating than electrolyzed nails, though the coating is less uniform. The highest industry standard (ASTM A-153) for galvanized nails is an average of 1 oz of coating per square foot. A slightly lower standard (NER 272) within the industry is 0.28 oz/ft². Poor quality nails may not comply with either of these standards. Because of the lack of uniformity in hot dipped nails, a large number of nails must be analyzed and the average coating determined in order to know whether a particular brand of nails complies with a particular standard.

The task of the general chemistry laboratory students this week is to determine whether the nails from a given factory comply with the industry standard. This will be accomplished by studying the reaction that occurs when a galvanized nail is placed in contact with hydrochloric acid. This layer of zinc will dissolve in an acidic solution:

$$Zn(s) + 2HCl(aq) \rightarrow ZnCl_2(aq) + H_2(g) \tag{1}$$

By measuring the mass of a galvanized nail before and after its reaction with hydrochloric acid, you will be able to determine the mass of zinc coated on the nail. (The process of weighing a sample and the product of its reaction with a known reagent is known as a gravimetric analysis.) The iron in the nails will also react with acid, but only after all of the zinc has reacted. By stopping the reaction at the appropriate time, you will avoid dissolving the iron of the nail.

Replicate measurements with five different nails will probably not result in identical measurements. Recall, the question that you must try to answer is whether a particular brand of nails, on average, complies with one of the industry standards. Calculation of the mean and standard deviation of your results will allow you to begin to address this question. However, interpretation of such a small data set makes it difficult to come up with a definitive answer. To provide a larger, more statistically significant data set, you will enter your values into the class data bank and analyze the results obtained by the entire class.

Every chemistry experiment generates "waste" of some form, and this lab is no exception. An experimenter must always determine if the waste is hazardous and how it should be handled. For example, in this laboratory procedure, you will generate an acidic waste solution containing zinc and chloride ions. The chloride ions don't present a problem, but according to regulations, neither the zinc ions nor the acidic solution are permitted to go down the drain. Without any treatment, the entire volume of waste generated would require disposal at a hazardous waste facility. The second portion of this lab requires that you process the waste in a manner that minimizes the volume and works to meet the green chemistry goals.

NOTE

Unless specifically instructed otherwise, always assume that water is the only substance that can be safely poured down the drain.

PROCEDURE

All data should be neatly recorded in tabular form. As part of your pre-lab assignment, try to anticipate the data that will be collected and prepare data tables in your lab notebook before coming to lab. If you get into the habit of regularly doing this you will shorten the amount of time actually spent in the lab. You will generally be able to determine what data tables will be needed by carefully reading the experimental procedure. Be sure to leave extra space to record information that you may not have anticipated. Always allow space to record observations.

A data table for this laboratory might look like this:

Trial #:	1	2	3	4	5
Length of nail					
Start time					
Stop time					
Initial mass of nails (g)					
Final mass of nails (g)					
Observations					

NOTES
▼

SAFETY NOTE

Hydrochloric acid is corrosive and can cause burns. Use with caution.

GLOVE USE

In this experiment, you will be using a fairly concentrated solution of hydrochloric acid and it is appropriate to wear gloves during the "wet chemistry" portion of the lab. Gloves may hinder your dexterity and should be used for personal protection *only* when handling hazardous chemicals. While a student in this course, you should develop the ability to judge when it is appropriate to wear gloves and when it isn't. Remember chemicals that get on the gloves will contaminate any other surface you touch, so it is important that you always practice appropriate "glove protocol" and remove gloves before touching common surfaces (doorknobs, keyboards, faucet handles, etc.) or your pen and laboratory notebook. Gloves must always be removed when leaving the laboratory.

---

1. Obtain 5 nails from the side laboratory bench. Use a ruler to measure the length of each nail in millimeters. Using calipers, measure the diameter of the nails and record these measurements in your notebook.

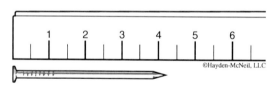

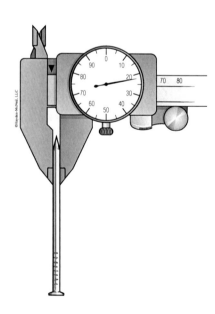

2. Using the analytical balance, determine the mass of one of the nails. Note which balance you used and be sure to use the same balance for all subsequent weighings.

3. Place the nail in the bottom of a small (15×125 mm) test tube and place the test tube in a test tube rack or small beaker.

4. When you are ready to begin, add sufficient 6 M hydrochloric acid (HCl) to cover the nail. Record the time and any observations.

QUESTION TO PONDER

How do you know that the gas bubbles are hydrogen? A characteristic of hydrogen gas is that it reacts explosively with the oxygen in air. None of the other substances that you could imagine being formed in this reaction have this property. Therefore, you can confirm the presence of hydrogen gas by holding a match just above the test tube while gas bubbles are coming out of solution. Do this as soon as possible after adding the acid to the test tube and listen for a pop. Be sure to record observations. Dispose of used matches as instructed.

5. After the nail has been in acid for 5 minutes (or as directed), pour the contents into a "waste beaker." Use forceps to remove the nail from the beaker, rinse the nail with water, wipe dry, and reweigh.

6. In the meantime, repeat steps 2–5 with the other four nails. Use the same waste beaker for all test tubes.

7. Place used nails in the labeled container.

WASTE MANAGEMENT

One of the twelve principles of green chemistry states that it is better to prevent waste than to treat or clean up waste afterwards. By extension, this principle indicates that if waste is produced, the quantity should be minimized whenever possible. The first step in determining whether a procedure complies with this principle is to assess what substances remain after the procedure has been completed. We will assume that the reaction in equation (1) has gone to completion and that the reaction products are hydrogen gas, which bubbled off, and zinc ions. Because an excess of hydrochloric acid was added, the first step is to test the solution's acidity to see if it is still acidic. This can be done using pH test strips. A pH below 7 indicates the presence of an acid, pH of 7 is neutral, and a pH greater than 7 indicates a basic solution.

The standard method for dealing with aqueous acidic waste is to add base to neutralize:

$$H^+(aq) + OH^-(aq) \rightarrow H_2O(l) \qquad (2)$$

NOTES

If the base used is sodium hydroxide (NaOH), the zinc ions will react with hydroxide ions to form insoluble zinc hydroxide:

$$Zn^{2+}(aq) + 2OH^-(aq) \rightarrow Zn(OH)_2(s) \qquad (3)$$

Maximum removal of zinc from solution by this method occurs at pH 8.6. At this pH, the level of dissolved zinc is reduced to approximately 0.3 mg/L,[1] well below the legal limit in discharged wastewater of 1 mg/L. The zinc now exists in a different physical state, as small solid particles of zinc hydroxide. The zinc removal process is not complete until these metal solids are removed from the wastewater. Because these solids are finely divided, removal is generally accomplished by sedimentation over time, followed by filtration. The solids produced are referred to as sludge and must be disposed of as a hazardous waste.

1. Use pH paper to test the pH of your waste solution. If it is acidic, it will need to be neutralized with NaOH, using the following procedure.

2. Obtain approximately 80 mL of 2 M NaOH from a dispensing container. First check the pH of the untreated waste by daubing a small piece of indicating paper with a drop of solution from a stir rod. Then, using the lines on the beaker as a guide, add one ~40 mL portion of 2 M NaOH to your waste beaker, mix, and recheck the pH. If it is below pH 6, add ~10 mL more NaOH and re-measure. If it is still below pH 6, repeat with additional ~5 mL portions. Note: expect the total NaOH addition to be in the range of 55–65 mL from testing five nails. Don't worry if you exceed pH 6 by the color indication in this "rough" neutralization step—it will be corrected in the next step on the combined waste. Record any observations.

3. Combine your waste solution with others' at your table into one 1000-mL poly beaker. Use DI water to rinse your waste beaker into this larger beaker.

4. Following the instructional placard, turn the pH meter on, immerse it in the combined spent product solution, and observe the pH. The meter itself can be used for gentle stirring. If the pH is below 8.6, add NaOH incrementally using a poly transfer pipet. If the pH is above 8.6, add 1 M HCl incrementally with mixing while monitoring the pH. You will notice that when you approach the 8.6 target value, little reagent addition is required to make changes. A pH in the range of 8.3–8.9 is acceptable.

5. Make and record observations of the waste beaker contents.

6. Turn off the pH meter, rinse the probe with DI water, and return the meter to the holding beaker solution. After recording observations, take the solution containing the zinc hydroxide precipitate to one of the "sedimentation stations" for disposal. Put the used nails and excess NaOH solution in the labeled containers in the hood. Finish cleaning the remaining tray equipment.

---

1 *Ayres, David M., Davis, Allen P., Gietka, Paul M.*; Removing Heavy Metals from Wastewater, *University of Maryland Engineering Research Center Report, 1994.*

7. At the end of the week's labs, the aqueous waste will be tested to verify that zinc levels have been reduced to legal disposal levels and the zinc hydroxide sludge will be disposed of according to environmental regulations.

CALCULATIONS

Enter your data into the class database. (This must be done before you leave lab!) Your TA will email the class data to you at the end of lab for later analysis.

Calculations are to be done in lab, using MS Excel. Once you have the data entered into a spreadsheet, you can use the calculation abilities of Excel to do all of the calculations.

- Open a new spreadsheet in Excel. In the first column, enter the length of the nails in mm. (Be sure to enter column headings in the first row.)

- In the second column, enter the radius of the nails in mm. (This is one half the diameter you measured in step one.)

- In the third column, calculate the surface area of the nails in mm^2. For this calculation, assume that the nails are cylindrical. The formula for the surface area of a cylinder is $2\pi r^2 + 2\pi rh$, where h is the length of the nail. Let's assume that your data for the first nail has been entered in row 4, so you are now working in cell C4. To enter this equation, type the formula:

$$=2*PI()*B4\wedge2+2*PI()*B4*A4$$

Note: The A4 and B4 notations refer to the cells where the length and radius of the nails are entered. You should substitute the appropriate values for your spreadsheet.

Once this formula has been entered, "drag and fill" down the column to calculate the surface area of all the nails. (See Appendix C of the lab text for further Excel instructions.)

- In the fourth column, enter the initial mass of the nails. In the fifth column, enter the final mass of the nails.

- In the sixth column, calculate the mass of zinc lost per nail (column 4–column 5). Again, you only need to type the formula once and then use the fill down feature to enter the formula in the remaining cells.

- In the seventh column, calculate the percentage mass lost per nail ((column 6/column 4)*100).

- In the eighth column, calculate the mass lost per mm^2 (column 6/column 3).

- Calculate the average: length, mass loss, percentage mass lost, mass lost per mm^2, and standard deviations.

NOTES
▼

- Title the spreadsheet and put your name on it. Print for inclusion with your lab report.

- Convert the industry standards of 1.0 oz/ft^2 and 0.28 oz/ft^2 to the units used in this experiment, g/mm^2. Be sure to square values as well as units when doing this conversion.

DISCUSSION/CONCLUSION

Refer to the posted guidelines for writing a laboratory report.

exp4

Stoichiometry: Determination of the Identity of a Metal Carbonate

INTRODUCTION

One of the benefits of being trained as a chemist is the ability to answer questions and solve mysteries based on chemical analysis. In this experiment you will be working with a compound known as a carbonate, meaning that it contains the anion CO_3^{2-}. The goal is for you and your classmates to determine the identity of this carbonate. More specifically, you will determine whether it is sodium carbonate, potassium carbonate or rubidium carbonate. These are all white crystalline solids and difficult to distinguish by merely looking at them. Instead, a chemical analysis is necessary to determine the identity. The technique you will be using is referred to as *gravimetric analysis*.

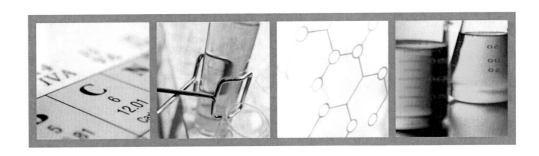

23

There are several different gravimetric methods, the final step of which always involves weighing. Typically, an ion, which is referred to as the *analyte*, is precipitated out of solution by reaction with an appropriate reagent. The resulting precipitate is then separated from the solution by filtration, dried and weighed. Based on the mass of the precipitate and its composition, the concentration of the ion in the original solution can be determined. For example, consider the case of a chloride determination where the goal is to determine the quantity of chloride ions (Cl^-) present in a sample. The chloride in the original sample can be precipitated out of solution by addition of silver ions (in the form of silver nitrate):

$$Ag^+(aq) + Cl^-(aq) \rightarrow AgCl(s) \tag{1}$$

If an excess of Ag^+ is added, it can be assumed that all of the chloride will be present in the precipitate. The $AgCl(s)$ is then collected and weighed and from this, the mass of Cl^- that was originally present can be determined.

HISTORICAL NOTE

Professor Theodore Richards of Harvard University and his graduate students used this method to determine the atomic masses of 25 of the elements. In recognition of this work, Professor Richards became the first American to win the Nobel Prize in Chemistry in 1914.

In this experiment you will determine the percentage by mass of carbonate in an unknown carbonate salt. First you will dissolve a measured mass of the unknown salt in water. (Remember that soluble salts dissociate into cations and anions when dissolved in water.) You will then add an excess of aqueous strontium chloride, another soluble salt, to the aqueous solution of the unknown salt. This will result in the precipitation of the carbonate as strontium carbonate as indicated in the following balanced ionic chemical equation.

$$Sr^{2+}(aq) + CO_3^{2-}(aq) \rightarrow SrCO_3(s) \tag{2}$$

The strontium carbonate precipitate will be collected by filtration, dried and weighed. The amount of carbonate that is present can be determined from the mass of the strontium carbonate. Since strontium chloride is added in excess, and since the precipitation reaction is assumed to go to completion, conservation of mass considerations tell us that the number of grams of carbonate recovered in the precipitate is equal to the number of grams of carbonate in the original sample, allowing for the calculation of the percentage by mass of carbonate in the original sample. Once the percentage by mass is known, it is just one more step to determine the identity of the unknown.

NOTES

PROCEDURE

1. You will react a sample of the unknown carbonate in the mass range of 1.0 g to 3.0 g with an excess of strontium chloride:

    a. Work with other members of your group to determine what mass of the carbonate each of you will use to ensure that the entire mass range is covered.

    b. Record the molarity of the strontium chloride solution in lab. Calculate how much of this solution should be used to ensure that it is the excess reactant. For the purposes of this calculation, assume that your unknown is the carbonate with the smallest molar mass.

    c. Weigh out your sample of unknown carbonate and transfer it to a 400-mL beaker. Add approximately 150 mL deionized water and stir to dissolve the sample.

    d. Add the calculated amount of strontium chloride solution to the beaker and stir. Allow the precipitate to settle for a few minutes.

    e. Use a poly pipet to get 1–2 mL of supernatant (liquid) from the reaction beaker. Transfer this to a well plate and test for precipitation reaction completeness by adding a drop of $SrCl_2$ from center table dropper bottles. Did you observe any further precipitate formation? If so, the precipitation reaction was not complete. Empty well back into the reaction beaker with a rinse from your squirt bottle and add another 10 mL of strontium chloride. Stir and allow it to settle and then repeat the test for precipitation completeness. Continue this process until no further precipitation is observed. This will ensure that the strontium chloride is in excess and no more carbonate remains in solution.

2. Separate the product from the aqueous solution by filtration:

    a. Connect the Büchner funnel apparatus, without the funnel, to the vacuum line and turn on at the wall valve (Figure 4-1). Make sure the vent valves on the flasks are closed (perpendicular to the valve). Check the vacuum by placing your hand across the top of the funnel adapter ring with the funnel off. If you do not feel strong suction there is a leak somewhere in your system that should be eliminated before proceeding. If the vacuum is satisfactory, place the funnel on the adapter ring. Using a pen provided in lab, write your name on a piece of filter paper, **weigh** and place in the Büchner funnel. Wet the paper with deionized water from your wash bottle. You should see the filter paper being sucked down against the holes in the funnel and the water should quickly pass through into the filter flask.

NOTES

▼

FIGURE 4-1.

b. To filter your sample, slowly pour into the center of the filter paper
    (Figure 4-2). Use more deionized water to rinse your beaker so that all
    the solid is collected. Rinse the solid on the filter paper with more water.
    Continue to draw air through your sample until as much water as possible
    has been removed. When you are finished, turn off the vacuum at the wall
    valve.

a   b   c

FIGURE 4-2.

c. Place the filter paper on a watch glass and place in the drying oven (Figure 4-3). Once all samples have been collected, the oven will be closed and samples will be allowed to dry uninterrupted for 1 hour, or as specified by your instructor.

| a | b | c |

FIGURE 4-3.

3. While your sample is drying, work with your laboratory benchmates on these tasks. Record your work in your laboratory notebook.

   a. Calculate the percent mass of carbonate in strontium carbonate, sodium carbonate, potassium carbonate and rubidium carbonate.

   b. Create molecular level drawings that represent the two reactant solutions before the reaction and the contents of the beaker after the reaction. These should be clearly labeled to identify the different species that are represented.

4. After drying, allow the sample to cool and then weigh the $SrCO_3$ precipitate and filter paper. Determine the mass of $SrCO_3$ by subtracting the initial mass of the filter paper.

CALCULATIONS AND ANALYSIS (to be done in lab)

Determine the mass of the $SrCO_3$ precipitate by subtracting the mass of the filter paper from the total mass.

Use the percent mass of CO_3^{2-} in $SrCO_3$ to determine the mass of carbonate present in the precipitate.

The law of conservation of mass tells us that the mass of CO_3^{2-} in $SrCO_3$ is equal to the mass of CO_3^{2-} in the original unknown. Use this mass and the mass of the original unknown sample to determine the percentage mass of CO_3^{2-} in the original unknown sample.

Compare this percentage mass to the different percentage masses that you previously calculated to determine the identity of the unknown.

Record your data and results in the class Excel spreadsheet.

DISCUSSION/CONCLUSION

Make sure to refer to the report writing guidelines for information on what to include in your report. Don't forget to report your results as well as the class results. Everyone in your class had the same unknown. Were their results consistent in terms of the percentage mass of carbonate in the unknown? If not, can you propose reasons why? Did using a different initial mass have any impact on the final analysis? How did the presence of a class data set impact your confidence in the identification of the unknown?

exp5

Observing Chemical Reactions/ Writing Chemical Equations

In the General Chemistry lecture you have learned a method of categorizing chemical reactions that is based on the underlying chemical principles, such as oxidation–reduction, acid–base, etc. An older method breaks reactions down into four major categories based on the number and nature of the reactants and products.

- A *single displacement* reaction occurs when a free element, A (usually a metal), displaces another element, B, from a compound to produce a different compound and a different free element. In these reactions, atoms appear on one side of the equation and as part of a compound on the other side of the equation.

$$A + BY \rightarrow AY + B$$

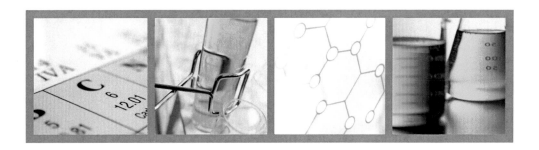

NOTES

- A *double displacement* (*metathesis*) reaction occurs when two compounds exchange ions or elements to form new compounds. In all such reactions, one of the products is either a compound that will separate from the reaction mixture in some way—frequently as a solid or gas—or a stable molecular compound, usually water, that doesn't necessarily separate from the reaction mixture.

$$AX + BY \rightarrow AY + BX$$

A **neutralization** reaction is a double displacement reaction of an acid and a base. Normally, an acid reacts with a base to form a salt and water. Neutralization reactions occur because of the formation of the stable water molecule. If exactly equivalent amounts of acid and base have been combined, a neutral pH of 7 will be observed. (pH is a measurement of acidity.) Neutralization reactions are accompanied by the evolution of heat.

- A direct *combination* or *addition* reaction occurs when two elements combine to form a single compound.

$$X + Y \rightarrow XY$$

It is also possible to combine an element with a compound to form a new compound or combine two compounds to form a new compound.

- A *decomposition* reaction occurs when heat or some other influence causes a compound to dissociate or decompose into the elements from which it was made, an element and a compound, or two simpler compounds.

$$AQ \rightarrow A + Q$$

In this laboratory experiment you will be exploring these different categories of reactions by observing a series of reactions and writing the balanced chemical equations for the processes.

CHEMISTRY IN A SUSTAINABLE WORLD[1]

Chemists are often called upon to evaluate chemical processes to determine which meet their specific needs. Before performing this experiment you will evaluate several different reactions in terms of their compliance with green chemistry goals. Your evaluation will determine which reactions you will run in lab.

---

1 *Adapted from* BeyondBenign Green Chemistry Education. *http://www.beyondbenign.org/K12education/highschool.html (accessed 6/2019).*

PROCEDURE

Part A—Use of a Bunsen Burner

This is the first experiment in which you will be using a Bunsen burner, and it is important to familiarize yourself with it and its operation before proceeding. The Bunsen burner is a convenient source of heat in the laboratory and will be used many times this year. It can be dangerous if you do not use a Bunsen burner properly and, therefore, certain safety measures need to be taken.

• Before using the Bunsen burner, be sure that long hair has been tied back and there are no loose papers near the flame area.

• In case of an emergency, remember that the quickest way to shut off the gas flow is at the valve to the main gas line.

• After the burner has been in use, do not touch the chimney because it may be very hot.

Before using a Bunsen burner, you have to understand its structure. There are many styles of laboratory burners, and the burners used at the University of Oregon may look slightly different from those that you are familiar with but they all function in the same basic way. Much like a gas kitchen stove, the Bunsen burner requires gas and air for proper functioning. The amount of air and gas mixed in the chamber is varied by use of two adjustments. Adjusting the collar controls airflow, and gas flow is controlled by adjusting the knob under the burner. The gas flow can also be adjusted at the main valve to the gas line. View the video on proper use of the Bunsen burner before proceeding.

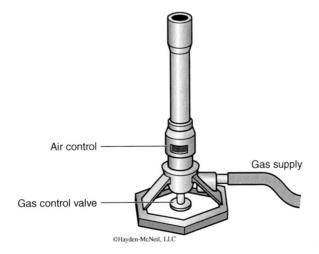

Air control

Gas supply

Gas control valve

©Hayden-McNeil, LLC

FIGURE 5-1. Bunsen burner

NOTES

Examine your burner and locate the gas and airflow adjustments. Make a sketch of the burner in your lab notebook and label these components.

Connect your Bunsen burner to the gas source using rubber tubing and check the operation of the air and gas controls before lighting the burner. Close the air vents all the way and then carefully light the burner. Describe the flame.

With a limited air supply, you probably observed that a cool, yellow, sooty flame was produced. Adjust the airflow until the yellow color is gone to obtain a nonluminous, pale blue, hot flame.

IMPORTANT SAFETY NOTE

This burner is not designed to operate continuously with a yellow flame. Gas combustion inside the barrel transfers heat to the working components and can result in gas leaks, possibly causing a fire at the valve assembly. DO NOT OPERATE the Bunsen burner with a yellow flame.

Group Work

The video that you watched indicates that the optimized blue flame has two distinct parts as seen by observation. Work with members of your group to devise a way in which you can test to see if all parts of this flame are equal in temperature, or if one area is hotter than the rest. Describe and perform your test.

Part B—Reaction Evaluation

Work with members of your lab group for this portion of the experiment.

Analyze each reaction in Table 5-1. Of the two possible reactions within each of the six groups (A, B, C, etc.), decide using the Twelve Principles of Green Chemistry (page vi) which reactions you will complete. In your lab notebook, prepare a table and record the reaction number, the identity of the reactants, and the green chemistry criteria used for selecting each reaction. Wait until the TA discussion before proceeding to Part C.

NOTES

▼

TABLE 5-1. The Reactions

Reaction Number	Reaction
A1	Place a pea-sized amount of baking soda, $NaHCO_3$, in a small test tube. Add 10–20 drops of vinegar (acetic acid) dropwise.
A2	Working in a fume hood, place a pea-sized amount of solid Na_2SO_3 in a small test tube. Add 10–20 drops of 6 M HCl dropwise.
B1	Place approx. 1 mL of 0.1 M sodium oxalate, $Na_2C_2O_4$, in a small test tube. Add an equal volume of 0.1 M $CaCl_2$ dropwise. Mix after each addition.
B2	Place approx. 1 mL of 0.1 M $MgCl_2$ in a small test tube. Add an equal volume of NaOH dropwise. Mix after each addition.
C1	Drop a pea-sized wad of steel wool into approx. 1 mL of 3.0 M HCl. Note: Steel wool is composed primarily of iron and when dissolved in solution, the iron that is present can be assumed to be Fe^{2+}.
C2	Sand a small piece of magnesium metal with steel wool and drop into approx. 1 mL of 1.0 M $CuCl_2$.
D1	Place approx. 10 mL hydrogen peroxide (5–6%) in a test tube. Add a small sample of potato/catalase. Quickly place a rubber stopper LIGHTLY into the test tube. Observe and allow the reaction to continue for about 10 sec. Light a wooden splint using a match. When the splint has burned for a few seconds, blow out the flame. The splint should still be glowing. Remove the stopper and place the glowing splint into the test tube.
D2	Place a pea-sized amount of $CuCO_3$ in a small test tube. Using a test-tube clamp, hold over the hottest part of a Bunsen burner flame and heat for 5 minutes or until a change is observed.
E1	*Quickly*, add up to 2 mL of 2.0 M NaOH to an equal volume of 1.0 M H_2SO_4.
E2	*Quickly*, add up to 2 mL of 2.0 M NaOH to an equal volume of 1.0 M $HClO_4$.
F1	Place a pea-sized quantity of CaO in a small test tube. Add 10 mL water.
F2	Using crucible tongs, hold a small piece of copper wire in the hottest part of the Bunsen burner flame for 30 sec. After the wire is cooled, scrape the surface with the edge of a scoopula.

NOTES

Part C—Experimental Observation

After the TA discussion and working independently, perform the six experiments that you selected from Table 5-1, one from each category. Pay special attention to the items below.

1. Use approximately 1 mL of each solution unless otherwise indicated. One mL fills about ¼ inch (6 mm) in the bottom of the small test tubes on your equipment tray.

2. Don't rush. Give the reactions time to occur. If you don't observe an immediate change, wait for five or ten minutes and observe again.

3. If you are uncertain of a particular result, you may want to repeat an experiment.

4. Keep good notes on how the reagents look before and after you mix them and all changes that you observe during the experiment; feel the test tube to see if any heat is evolved. In general, use all of your senses (except taste!) to get information about the reactions.

5. Use pH paper to test solutions both before and after the additions to determine whether each mixture is acidic or basic: $pH < 7$ = acidic, $pH > 7$ = basic.

After completing all of the experiments, work with the members of your lab group to predict the category of reaction and reaction products. DO NOT leave lab until this has been done.

CALCULATIONS

There are no calculations for this lab. However, you will need to write balanced molecular equations for all of the reactions that you performed. For the reactions in parts A, B, C, and E, include net ionic equations as well.

DISCUSSION

Provide the usual introduction and background information in your discussion. For each experiment that you performed, report the following information in an easy to read tabular format.

1. the reason the experiment was selected, citing green chemistry principles,

2. how you knew a chemical reaction took place,

3. the type of chemical reaction,

4. balanced molecular equation(s),

5. ionic and net ionic equations for the reactions in set A, B, C, and E.

TABLE 5-2. Solubility of Ionic Compounds

Soluble Ionic Compounds	**Insoluble** Ionic Compounds
1. All compounds with Group *IA* ions (Li^+, Na^+, K^+, etc.) and compounds with ammonium ion (NH_4^+).	5. All compounds with hydroxide ion (OH^-), *except* those of Group *IA* and NH_4^+, Ca^{2+}, Sr^{2+}, and Ba^{2+}.
2. All compounds with nitrate ion (NO_3^-), acetate ion ($C_2H_3O_2^-$), and most with perchlorate ion (ClO_4^-).	6. All compounds with carbonate ion (CO_3^{2-}) and phosphate ion (PO_4^{3-}), *except* those of Group *IA* and NH_4^+.
3. All compounds with chloride ion (Cl^-), bromide ion (Br^-), and iodide ion (I^-), *except* those with Ag^+, Pb^{2+}, Cu^+, and Hg_2^{2+}.	7. All compounds with sulfide ion (S^{2-}), *except* those of Group *IA* and NH_4^+, Ca^{2+}, Sr^{2+}, and Ba^{2+}.
4. All compounds with sulfate ion (SO_4^{2-}), *except* those with Ca^{2+}, Sr^{2+}, Ba^{2+}, and Pb^{2+}.	

TABLE 5-3. Gas-Forming Reactions

Metal carbonate *or* bicarbonate + acid → metal salt + $CO_2(g)$ + $H_2O(l)$
$NiCO_3(s) + H_2SO_4(aq) \rightarrow NiSO_4(aq) + CO_2(g) + H_2O(l)$
$NaHCO_3(aq) + HNO_3(aq) \rightarrow NaNO_3(aq) + CO_2(g) + H_2O(l)$
Metal sulfide + acid → metal salt + $H_2S(g)$
$Na_2S(aq) + 2\ HCl(aq) \rightarrow 2NaCl(aq) + H_2S(g)$
Metal sulfite + acid → metal salt + $SO_2(g)$ + $H_2O(l)$
$Na_2SO_3(aq) + 2\ HCl(aq) \rightarrow 2NaCl(aq) + SO_2(g) + H_2O(l)$
Ammonium salt + strong base → metal salt + $NH_3(g)$ + $H_2O(l)$
$NH_4Cl(aq) + NaOH \rightarrow NaCl(aq) + NH_3(g) + H_2O(l)$

exp6

What's That Stuff? Qualitative Analysis of Chemical Unknowns[1]

INTRODUCTION

Imagine that you are a forensic scientist and have been given a white powdery substance to identify. Is it an illegal drug or a poison, or is it harmless baking powder from the kitchen? The task of identifying unknown substances is a regular part of the work of forensic scientists and those who work in the field of analytical chemistry. This can seem like a daunting task when one considers the vast number of known chemical substances. However, by using a systematic approach to determine what chemical category the unknown falls into, the task can be made much easier. In this laboratory exercise you will play the role of analytical chemist by developing a scheme to unambiguously identify each of 40 different common chemical substances. However, unlike the analytical or forensic chemist, you only need to uniquely identify each chemical from the other 39 on the list, not all of the possible chemicals in the world. In contrast to experiments that you are familiar with, you won't be given specific instructions about how to

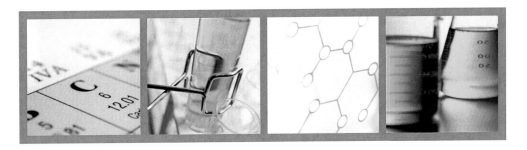

1 *Adapted from* Experiments in General Chemistry, *7/e, by Weis, G.S.; Greco, T.G.; Rickard, L.H.; 1997. pp. 59–66.*

38

EXP 6: What's That Stuff?
Qualitative Analysis of Chemical Unknowns

NOTES

proceed. Instead, you will develop your own analytical procedure using physical and chemical methods of analysis. As part of this process, you will create an identification flowchart that will lead you like a road map to the identity of any of the substances on the list. Many of the concepts and principles that you will use in developing your identification scheme should already be familiar to you from your General Chemistry class and experiments that you have done previously. Later in the term you will have the opportunity to test your analytical scheme when you will be given a subset of the chemicals to identify during a laboratory practical exam. You will only be permitted to use your laboratory notebook and identification flowchart on the exam, so careful record keeping is important.

CHEMISTRY IN A SUSTAINABLE WORLD

You may be wondering about the large number of chemicals used in this procedure and the total amount of waste that will be generated by students in this course. "Going green" is not always a straightforward process, and it is often necessary to reach a compromise between the achievement of experimental goals and the elimination of all chemical risk. This compromise often involves modification of experimental procedures and substitution of more benign reactants. When assessing substances it is important to consider not only their physical and chemical properties but also their toxicity and impact on the environment. For this experiment, chemicals have been selected that are as benign as possible, and a microscale format will be utilized to decrease the amount of chemicals used and the total waste produced.

PRE-LAB

Because you are not following a well-defined procedure, you may be uncertain as to what experimental procedure should be included in your pre-lab write-up. For this experiment, outline the general approach that you will be taking when you get to lab, without necessarily detailing the specific tests and chemicals. This procedure should clearly indicate that you have a clear plan for what you will be doing when you get to lab. Include a table with the names and formulas of all the chemicals.

EXP 6: What's That Stuff?
        Qualitative Analysis of Chemical Unknowns

39

NOTES
▼

PROCEDURE

SAFETY NOTE

Because you will be working independently, it is especially important that you take responsibility for working safely in the lab. Before attending lab, review the safety rules in the lab text, particularly those that refer to safe chemical handling. Remember that you should never taste any chemical in the lab and to smell the odor of an unknown substance you should wave your hand over the container in such a way as to gently push the vapor towards you while keeping the container itself well away from your face. *Never place your nose directly above a vessel containing laboratory chemicals.*

When you arrive in lab you will be given a test kit containing all of the glassware, equipment, and testing materials necessary for this experiment. The following testing reagents will be provided in your kit:

6 M HCl	0.001 M $KMnO_4$
6 M H_2SO_4	0.1 M $BaCl_2$
6 M NaOH	0.1 M $AgNO_3$

On the benches in the laboratory you will notice several complete sets of the chemicals listed in Table 6-1. These are labeled and identified. Rather than bringing these chemicals to your usual workstation, you will go to the chemicals with your testing kit. Because you are using a common set of chemicals with other students, it is important that you follow some basic laboratory protocols:

• Use the smallest amount of chemicals possible. Dispense reagents with the dropper or spatula supplied with each bottle. No more than 0.5 mL (about 10 drops) of liquid or 0.3 grams (the size of about 3 grains of rice) should be taken for testing.

• Re-cap all reagent bottles and jars after use.

• NEVER return excess materials to the dispensing container due to contamination concerns. Instead, check to see if another student has use for the reagent, or dispose of it in the appropriate waste container.

• Before leaving the lab, leave your testing kit in clean and orderly condition for the next user by closing the test reagent bottle caps and cleaning the well plate and other kit components.

40

EXP 6: What's That Stuff?
Qualitative Analysis of Chemical Unknowns

NOTES

There is no right or wrong way to do this experiment, and the procedure that you follow will be your own. Here are a few tips to get you started.

- Your goal is to narrow the large group of chemical substances down into smaller and smaller subsets until you can uniquely identify each substance. Because some of the substances can be identified by physical observation only, this is a good place to start. Use all of your senses *except taste* to make careful observations of the chemicals in question. Note the physical state, the color, the odor, and any other physical characteristics. From here, you can begin to break the chemicals into smaller groups, such as solids and liquids. From there, you should be able to divide the solid category into smaller subgroups based on physical appearance, and so on.

- Important physical properties of liquids are color, smell, viscosity (resistance to flow), and rate of evaporation.

- After making physical observations, STOP AND ASSESS YOUR DATA. Are there any substances that you can uniquely identify at this point? If so, no further testing is needed.

After observing/testing the physical properties, you can go on to test solubility and chemical properties. Perform the chemical tests on the liquids as well as on the solutions of dissolved solids. As with the physical tests, once you have enough information to identify a substance, there is no need to perform any more tests.

Note that there are a few potentially dangerous reactions to avoid when doing your testing:

$$HCl(aq) + MnO_2(s) \rightarrow [\text{production of a toxic gas—}Cl_2]$$

$$HCl(aq) + KMnO_4(s) \rightarrow [\text{production of a toxic gas—}Cl_2]$$

$$Na_2SO_3(aq) + \text{strong acid} \rightarrow [\text{production of a toxic gas—}SO_2]$$

- Test the water solubility of solids by adding a match-head sized quantity to water in your plastic well plate. It is very important to use only a small quantity of the solid and to be consistent about how much you use. Anything, including table salt, will reach a point where it is no longer soluble if you use too much. It is also a good idea to verify that your solubility tests agree with the solubility rules.

  ONLY IF a substance is insoluble in water, check its solubility in acid.

  Liquid–liquid solubility can also be tested. All of the aqueous solutions will be soluble in water, but non-aqueous solutions may not be.

- Many *cations* have a characteristic color when placed in a flame and their presence can be readily verified by performing a flame test.

EXP 6: What's That Stuff?
Qualitative Analysis of Chemical Unknowns

41

NOTES

- The pH can provide you with valuable information about not just the acids and bases but all solutions, including those made by dissolving solids in water. It should be measured with pH test paper. pH < 7 is acidic, pH > 7 is basic, and pH = 7 is neutral.

- The solubility rules are useful for not only predicting which of the solids will dissolve in water but also for predicting when a precipitation reaction will occur. Remember that when dissolved, ionic substances exist as ions in solution. Some of these ions will react with added ions to form insoluble substances. If you suspect that a particular ion is present, you can test this by adding a *precipitating agent* to test. For example, if chloride ion (Cl^-) is believed to be present, addition of silver ion (Ag^+) will result in the formation of insoluble silver chloride:

$$Ag^+(aq) + Cl^-(aq) \rightarrow AgCl(s)$$

- The tendency to undergo oxidation or reduction reactions is characteristic of many substances, and these reactions are frequently utilized for chemical analysis. This is most conveniently done if there is a color change associated with the redox process. For example, potassium permanganate ($KMnO_4$), a deep purple substance, is a strong oxidizing agent and contains manganese in the +7 oxidation state. When a reducing anion is present, it tends to bleach the color by reducing manganese(VII) to manganese(II).

- Repeat any tests that are ambiguous, making sure that you are able to duplicate your results.

REPORT

There is no report due for this lab. Instead, you will prepare and submit a flowchart that outlines your classification scheme for the chemicals used in this lab. This flowchart, along with your laboratory notebook, will be returned to you for use on the lab practical exam at the end of the term.

Flowcharts are used to create visual maps of a process and should show all steps in the analysis. For this assignment, you should consider the flowchart as a "road map" of laboratory procedures that you will follow to lead you to a correct identification. Your flowchart can be drawn by hand or on a computer using MS Word, MS PowerPoint, or any other flowcharting software application. It is not necessary to fit the entire flowchart on one page, but transitions to other pages should be clearly referenced.

The flowchart that follows represents a scheme to distinguish between five aqueous solutions: $NaCl$, $SrCl_2$, HCl, $NaNO_3$, and HNO_3. These are all clear and colorless and thus cannot be identified by physical observation.

42

EXP 6: What's That Stuff?
Qualitative Analysis of Chemical Unknowns

NOTES

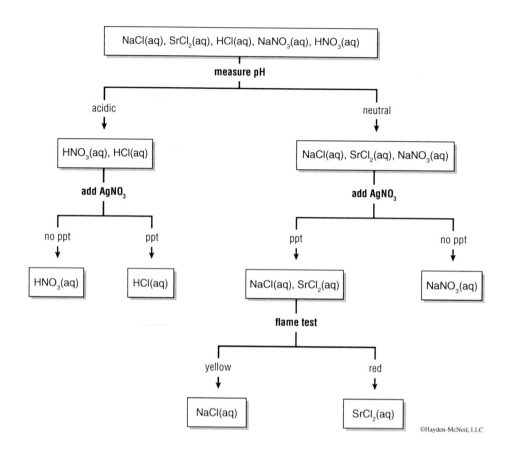

©Hayden-McNeil, LLC

EXP 6: What's That Stuff?
Qualitative Analysis of Chemical Unknowns

43

TABLE 6-1. Substances to Be Identified

Substance	
Mg	magnesium metal
Al	aluminum metal
Zn	zinc metal
Sn	tin metal
Fe	iron metal
C	carbon, solid
S	sulfur, solid
Fe_2O_3	iron(III) oxide, ferric oxide
MnO_2	manganese(IV) oxide, manganese dioxide
$KMnO_4$	potassium permanganate
NaCl	sodium chloride
LiCl	lithium chloride
NH_4Cl	ammonium chloride
$CuCl_2 \cdot 2H_2O$	copper(II) chloride dihydrate, cupric chloride
$SrCl_2$	strontium chloride
NaBr	sodium bromide
$Cu(NO_3)_2 \cdot 3H_2O$	copper(II) nitrate trihydrate, cupric nitrate
$FeSO_4$	iron(II) sulfate heptahydrate
ZnO	zinc oxide
CaO	calcium oxide
SiO_2	silicon dioxide (sand)
$NaHCO_3$	sodium bicarbonate, sodium hydrogen carbonate

Substance	
$CaCO_3$	calcium carbonate
K_2CO_3	potassium carbonate
FeS_2	iron(II) sulfide, ferrous sulfide
$KAl(SO_4)_2 \cdot 12H_2O$	alum, aluminum potassium sulfate dodecahydrate
$CaSO_4$	calcium sulfate
$CuSO_4 \cdot 5H_2O$	copper(II) sulfate pentahydrate
Na_2SO_3	sodium sulfite
$Na_2B_4O_7 \cdot 10H_2O$	borax, sodium tetraborate decahydrate
$C_{12}H_{22}O_{11}$	sucrose, table sugar
$HNO_3(aq)$	1 M solution of nitric acid
$HCl(aq)$	1 M solution of hydrochloric acid
$H_2SO_4(aq)$	1 M solution of sulfuric acid
$HC_2H_3O_2(aq)$	1 M solution of acetic acid
$NaCl(aq)$	1 M solution of sodium chloride
$NH_3(aq)$	1 M solution of ammonia
$NaOH(aq)$	1 M solution of sodium hydroxide
$C_2H_4(OH)_2$	ethylene glycol, 1,2-ethanediol
$C_{15}-C_{40}$ alkane mixture	mineral oil

44  EXP 6: What's That Stuff?
Qualitative Analysis of Chemical Unknowns

NOTES

exp7

Determination of the Heat Exchanged in Chemical Reactions

Co-authored with the assistance of Dr. Brandi Baldock

During a chemical reaction, bonds in the reactant molecules are broken and new bonds are formed in the product molecules. *It takes energy to break chemical bonds. When new bonds are formed, energy is released to the surroundings.*

When energy is released by a chemical reaction (the system), the energy is transferred to its immediate surroundings. When energy is absorbed by a chemical reaction, the surroundings transfer energy to the chemical reaction. A chemical reaction is considered endothermic if the energy required to break the bonds of the reactant molecules is greater than the energy released when the product molecules are formed. The reaction is exothermic if the energy released by the bonds being formed in the product molecules is greater than the energy required to break the bonds of the reactant molecules.

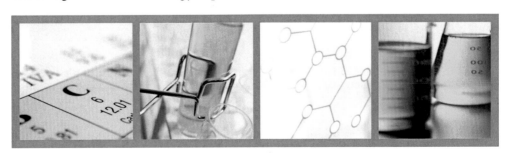

EXP 7: Determination of the Heat Exchanged in
Chemical Reactions

Calorimetry is the study of the heat exchanged during chemical reactions. The chemical reaction is performed inside an insulated container (a calorimeter), and the mass (m) and change in temperature ($\Delta T = T_2 - T_1$) of the reaction solution is determined and recorded. Given the specific heat capacity of the solution (c), the heat transferred to or from the solution (q_{sol}) can be calculated using Eq. (1):

$$q_{sol} = mc\Delta T \tag{1}$$

The heat change of the chemical reaction (q_{rxn}) can then be determined using Eq (2):

$$q_{rxn} + q_{sol} = 0 \tag{2}$$

OVERVIEW

In this experiment, you will determine the heat exchanged when solid magnesium hydroxide reacts with solid citric acid (Eq. 3). The acid will be in the form of citric acid monohydrate. The chemical structure of this acid is depicted in Figure 7-1. Citric acid is referred to as a triprotic acid because it donates three hydrogens, or protons, in acid–base reactions.

$$2H_3C_6H_5O_7(s) + 3Mg(OH)_2(s) \rightarrow Mg_3(C_6H_5O_7)_2(aq) + 6H_2O(l) \tag{3}$$

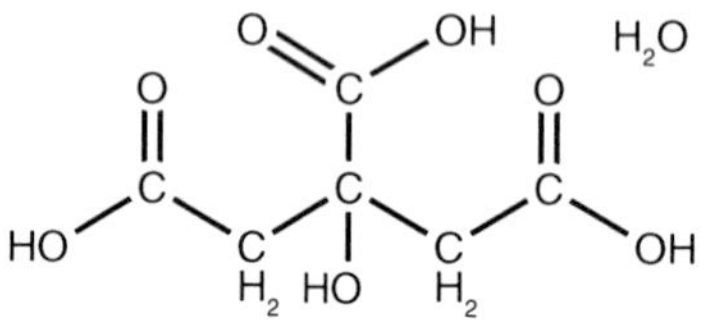

Citric acid monohydrate
210.14 g/mole

FIGURE 7-1. Chemical structure of citric acid

As indicated in Eq. (3), both citric acid and magnesium hydroxide exist as solids in their natural state, making this reaction difficult to study because chemical reactions in the solid state proceed very slowly. However, we can utilize the fact that citric acid is soluble in water (though magnesium hydroxide is not) to perform a series of reactions in water and use thermodynamic information obtained from those reactions to determine the heat of reaction for reaction (3).

You will use a coffee cup calorimeter (Figure 7-2) to determine the heat exchanged during these reactions.

FIGURE 7-2. Coffee cup calorimeter setup

An important consequence of the First Law of Thermodynamics is that the total enthalpy change associated with a chemical reaction is the same whether the reaction occurs in one step or a series of steps. When studying a reaction that is difficult to monitor experimentally (such as reaction (3)) it may be possible to divide the reaction into a series of steps that can be summed to provide the overall reaction. The enthalpy change associated with the individual steps can be experimentally determined and then summed to calculate the enthalpy change for the overall reaction, as shown in Eq. (4).

$$\Delta H_{rxn} = \Delta H_a + \Delta H_b \ldots + \Delta H_n \qquad (4)$$

In Part 1, you will prepare a magnesium hydroxide slurry, Eq. (5a), and determine the heat exchanged during that process (q_a). (A slurry is a mixture of finely divided solid particles suspended in water.)

$$Mg(OH)_2(s) \rightarrow Mg(OH)_2(slurry) \qquad (5a)$$

In Part 2, you will determine the heat exchanged when the magnesium hydroxide slurry reacts with solid citric acid (q_b) according to Eq. (5b):

$$2H_3C_6H_5O_7(s) + 3Mg(OH)_2 \text{ (slurry)} \rightarrow Mg_3(C_6H_5O_7)_2(aq) + 6H_2O(l) \quad (5b)$$

In Part 3, you will determine the heat exchanged when solid citric acid dissolves in water(q_c) according to Eq. (5c):

$$H_3C_6H_5O_7(s) \rightarrow H_3C_6H_5O_7(aq) \qquad (5c)$$

NOTES

In Part 4, you will determine the heat exchanged when solid magnesium hydroxide reacts with aqueous citric acid (q_d) according to Eq. (5d):

$$2H_3C_6H_5O_7(aq) + 3Mg(OH)_2(s) \rightarrow Mg_3(C_6H_5O_7)_2(aq) + 6H_2O(l) \quad (5d)$$

Once you have determined the heat exchanged in each step (q_a, q_b, q_c, q_d) you will need to use it to determine the enthalpy value (ΔH) in kJ/mol for the steps. The enthalpy of a chemical reaction is different than the heat exchanged in that it is a molar quantity and is determined by relating the heat of the reaction (q) to the moles of reaction using Eq. (6):

$$\Delta H_{rxn} = \frac{q_{rxn}}{\# \text{ mol of reaction}} \quad (6)$$

The number of moles of reaction should be determined using the balanced chemical equations (5a–5d), the appropriate coefficients and the number of moles of limiting reactant. For example, let's consider the hypothetical situation when a student, performing reaction (5b), uses 0.11 mol of citric acid and determines that it is the limiting reactant. The stoichiometric coefficients in Eq. (5b) allow us to construct the following conversion factors:

$$\frac{1 \, mol \, reaction}{2 \, mol \, H_3C_6H_5O_7} \Longleftrightarrow \frac{1 \, mol \, reaction}{3 \, mol \, Mg(OH)_2} \Longleftrightarrow \frac{1 \, mol \, reaction}{1 \, mol \, Mg_3(C_6H_5O_7)_2} \Longleftrightarrow \frac{1 \, mol \, reaction}{6 \, mol \, H_2O}$$

Because citric acid has been found to be the limiting reactant in this example, the first of these conversion factors is the one that should be used to determine the number of moles of reaction:

$$\# \, mol \, reaction = 0.11 \, \cancel{mol \, H_3C_6H_5O_7} \left(\frac{1 \, mol \, reaction}{2 \, \cancel{mol \, H_3C_6H_5O_7}} \right) = 0.055 \, mol \, reaction$$

These values can then be used to calculate ΔH_{rxn} for reaction (3).

PROCEDURE

Work in pairs, switching roles at least once.

You will be using Vernier LabPro™ digital temperature probes and Logger *Pro*™ software for data collection and analysis.

You will work with other members of your class to ensure that replicate measurements are made for each part of the experiment. Because class data will be collected you will need to report your raw data on the whiteboard and/or in a Class Data Excel spreadsheet.

Open Vernier LabPro™ and click on the Data Collection icon on the toolbar. Select **Collection** and change the **Duration** to 800 seconds and then click **Done**. *Most runs will be completed in a shorter length of time.*

Part 1—Preparation of Magnesium Hydroxide Slurry

Nest two clean, dry Styrofoam cups in a 250-mL beaker to prevent tipping. Using a clean graduated cylinder, completely transfer 100 mL water into the interior cup. Add a magnetic stir bar and suspend the digital thermometer in the solution so that it is not touching the sides or bottom of the cup (see Figure 7-2).

Begin stirring and press the green start button on the toolbar to start collecting data. The initial portion of the temperature plot should be constant and will appear as a horizontal line on the graph at this point. After about 10–20 seconds, add 5.6–5.8 g of solid $Mg(OH)_2$ to the water. Be sure to record the exact mass of $Mg(OH)_2$ you used in your lab notebook. Record the time of this addition. Monitor the temperature of the slurry until it has been stable for 1 minute and then press the red button to stop temperature data collection. Determine ΔT using the procedure described in Figure 7-3. **Keep this mixture to use in Part 2.**

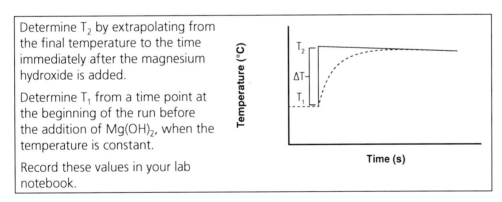

FIGURE 7-3. Determination of ΔT from experimental data

Part 2—Reaction of Solid Citric Acid with Magnesium Hydroxide Slurry

Measure out 7–15 g of solid citric acid and record its exact mass in your lab notebook. To restart data collection, press the green start button again and begin stirring the magnesium hydroxide slurry. If the "Erase data?" dialog opens, select **Erase and Continue** to proceed.

Record the temperature of the magnesium hydroxide slurry for 10–20 seconds, then add the solid acid to it.

Monitor the temperature of the reaction mixture until it has been stable for about 1 minute, then press the stop button.

Determine T_1, T_2 and ΔT as you did in Part 1 (Figure 7-3). Clean and dry your calorimeter cup, stirring bar and temperature probe.

Part 3—Dissolving Solid Citric Acid in Water

Using a clean graduated cylinder, measure 100 mL of water into your clean, dry calorimeter cup and add your stirring bar. Make certain that all the water is transferred to the calorimeter cup. Measure out the same mass of citric acid you used in Part 2.

Following the same procedure as Part 2, restart data collection and record the temperature for 10–20 seconds. Add the acid to the water, and stir. Monitor the temperature of the solution until it has been stable for about 1 minute, then press the stop button.

Determine T_1, T_2 and ΔT as you did in Part 1 (Figure 7-3). Clean and dry your cup, stirring bar and temperature probe.

Part 4—Reaction of Dissolved Citric Acid with Solid Magnesium Hydroxide

Prepare 100 mL of citric acid solution containing the same number of moles of citric acid that you used in Parts 2 and 3:

> In the laboratory, a citric acid stock solution of known concentration will be available. Record the exact molarity of this solution in your lab notebook. Work with your lab partner(s) to calculate the volume of this acid stock solution that contains the desired number of moles. From this, calculate the amount of water that needs to be added to your calculated value of the stock solution to prepare 100 mL of citric acid solution.

> Have your TA check your calculations and then prepare this acid solution in your calorimeter cup.

Measure out 5.6–5.8 g solid magnesium hydroxide. Record the exact mass you used in your lab notebook.

Following the same procedure as Part 2, restart data collection and record the temperature of the citric acid solution for 10–20 seconds.

Add the magnesium hydroxide and monitor the temperature of the reaction mixture until it has been stable for about 1 minute, then press the stop button.

Determine T_1, T_2 and ΔT as you did previously. Clean and dry your cup, stirring bar and temperature probe. Clean up your work station and quit Logger *Pro*.

DATA, OBSERVATIONS AND CALCULATIONS

Raw data should be reported in your laboratory notebook pages but it is not necessary to include the raw data in your lab report. Show a sample calculation for each type of calculation. Results of calculations should be displayed in tables. Values to be calculated include q_{rxn}, mol limiting reactant, mol reaction, and ΔH for each experiment. You can assume that the density of the dilute citric acid solution used in Part 4 is 1.06 g/mL and the density of the water used in the other experiments is 1.00 g/mL. The specific heat of the reaction solutions is 3.853 J/g°C.

Provide balanced chemical equations for each experiment.

Calculate ΔH_{rxn} for the reaction between solid citric acid and solid magnesium hydroxide (Eq. 3) in two different ways. Remember that when summing equations to get to an overall equation, it is necessary to perform the same operations on the ΔH values as you performed on the equations. Include sample calculations.

DISCUSSION/CONCLUSION, ERROR ANALYSIS AND REFLECTION

As usual, follow the generic report writing guidelines that you have been given. In addition, report the major findings of this experiment, including whether each reaction step was endothermic or exothermic. Report the value you calculated for ΔH_{rxn} for reaction (3) and the class average values provided by your TA.

A well-written discussion should address the following questions. Your responses should be incorporated as part of the discussion and not presented in list form.

- Refer back to your introduction. What value were you trying to determine by performing this experiment? If you haven't already reported this in your Claims section, report it here.

- What law in chemistry did you use when you combined the individual ΔH values to find ΔH_{rxn} for reaction (3)?

- Consider the theory behind this experiment. Why were you able to determine the heat of reaction by determining the heat exchanged with the surroundings? What fundamental physical law is behind this? What gained heat and lost heat in each reaction step? Do not use the terms "system" or "surroundings" unless you define what they are.

- There is no information in the literature regarding the value of ΔH_{rxn} for reaction (3). However, the enthalpy value for the dissolution of citric acid (part 3) has been reported to be 19,215 ± 150 J/mol. How does your value compare with this value?

NOTES

▼

Error Analysis

- What are two assumptions you made that could lead to experimental error in this experiment if incorrect? For each assumption, indicate whether it would introduce determinate or indeterminate error to your results. Also, indicate how your values of q and ΔH_{rxn} would be impacted.

- You calculated ΔH_{rxn} using two different sets of data. Theoretically these values should be the same, but given the inherent experimental errors, it is unlikely that you obtained exactly the same values. Consider the likely magnitude of the experimental error and indicate whether the two average values of ΔH_{rxn} for your section were "the same" within what you believe to be reasonable experimental error.

Reflection:

- **Extend.** Propose an idea(s) for further experimentation, with valid reasons. How could the procedure be modified to extend the investigation? Note: This extension is not simply a repeat of the experiment to collect more data. An extension of the experiment is one that would require a new beginning question.

- **Ch 221 lecture topics.** Which lecture topics from CH 221 can be connected to this experiment? Explain briefly.

- **Applications.** How can a concept or technique from this experiment connect to a real-world application? Explain briefly.

- **Related reading.** Confirm, dispute or explain your findings using appropriate literature values or sources. Include appropriate citations for these sources.

Green chemistry. Did this experiment follow the principles of green chemistry? Given that both produce water and a salt, why is it preferable to study this reaction instead of the strong acid, strong base reaction between 10% HCl and solid NaOH?

> ### HINT
>
> $Mg(OH)_2$ is insoluble in water and is the main chemical in "Milk of Magnesia." Solid NaOH is hydroscopic and is the main ingredient in oven cleaner and Drano.

exp8
Water of Hydration

Have you ever wondered about the small packet of "mystery chemicals" that sometimes comes enclosed with certain products such as shoes, medicines, and electronic equipment? The chemicals, which are usually inorganic salts, in these packets are known as desiccants, or drying agents, and they absorb water from humid air. When these compounds absorb water they form **hydrates** and serve to keep the other contents dry. Some common drying agents are alumina—Al_2O_3, calcium chloride—$CaCl_2$, calcium sulfate ("Drierite")—$CaSO_4$, and silica gel—SiO_2. Substances that readily absorb moisture such as this are said to be **hygroscopic**.

Hydrates are not just solids that are wet. Instead, they contain a specific number of water molecules per formula unit of compound. When writing the chemical formula of a hydrate, the formula of the salt is always written first, followed by a raised dot and the numbers of waters of hydration. The dot emphasizes the weak nature of the bonds to the water molecules. Hydrates are named by adding the number of waters of hydration to the name of the salt. In general, Greek prefixes are used to indicate the number of waters. For example, $NiSO_4 \cdot 7H_2O$ is correctly referred to as nickel sulfate heptahydrate. Alternatively, this compound could be identified as nickel sulfate-7-water.

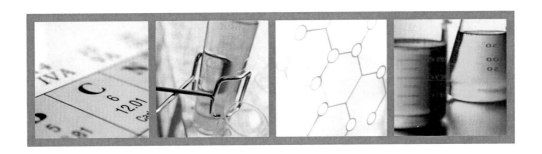

NOTES

One interesting example of a salt that forms a hydrate is cobalt(II) chloride. This compound undergoes a color change when going from the anhydrous form, $CoCl_2$, to the hydrated form, $CoCl_2 \cdot 6H_2O$:

$$6H_2O(g) + CoCl_2(s) \rightarrow CoCl_2 \cdot 6H_2O(s)$$
$$\text{blue} \qquad\qquad \text{red}$$

This process is reversible, depending on the relative humidity, making cobalt(II) chloride a useful component of novelty items marketed to predict the weather.

For many hydrates, heating above 100°C will remove the hydrated water molecules:

$$NiSO_4 \cdot 7H_2O(s) + \text{heat} \rightarrow NiSO_4(s) + 7H_2O(g)$$

The water molecules of other hydrates, such as $FeCl_3 \cdot 6H_2O$, cannot be easily removed, no matter how intense the heat. In this experiment the hydrates to be investigated will be limited to those that are stable at room temperature but that decompose to the anhydrous form on heating. You will determine the mass of a hydrate sample, the mass of water driven off by heating the hydrate, and the mass of the anhydrous salt that remains. By calculating the number of moles of water driven off and the number of moles of anhydrous salt remaining, you will be able to find the empirical formula of the hydrate.

CHEMISTRY IN A SUSTAINABLE WORLD

Gas hydrates, and more specifically methane hydrates, are also known as frozen fuel and could be the world's next great energy source. Methane, CH_4, is a colorless, odorless combustible gas and is the primary component of natural gas. A fossil fuel, methane is formed beneath the Earth's surface by the decomposition of plant and animal matter. Under conditions of near-freezing temperatures and high pressures, such as are found in sediments deep below the ocean surface, the methane molecules are hydrated, sitting inside a crystalline shell made of ice. If warmed or depressurized, the hydrates revert back to water and methane. *If they can be safely extracted*, methane hydrates could become an important fuel source to bridge the gap between a fossil fuel based economy and one that is based on renewable fuels. However, improper or careless methods of extraction could trigger massive tsunamis by causing landslides on the continental slope and, perhaps more importantly, could hasten global warming. This is because methane is a greenhouse gas that is over 20 times more efficient in trapping solar radiation than carbon dioxide when released into the atmosphere. There is currently a great deal of research being done to better understand the nature of gas hydrates, the location of deposits and safe methods of extraction to see if commercial production of methane from hydrates is economically and environmentally feasible. As Tim Collett, co-chief scientist on the *JOIDES Resolution* research vessel and research geologist for the USGS says,

"We're looking at a science that's pretty new. Only after you understand the "where, why and how" of hydrates can you understand the resource potential—or the hazards they represent."[1]

PROCEDURE

1. Obtain a solid stopper and a small (10 × 75 mm) test tube from the front bench.

2. Select a large test tube from your workstation tray. Do not wash or get this wet. Check to make sure the stopper fits into the test tube but don't insert the stopper at this time.

3. Set up an iron tripod with a wire gauze screen on top of it. Position a burner under the wire screen. Place the unstoppered test tube on the wire screen and heat with the burner for approximately 5 minutes. You will find it helpful to curl the screen slightly before heating so as to "cradle" the test tube to prevent it from rolling off. Move the burner around to heat the entire length of the test tube. After 5 minutes, turn off the burner and carefully stopper the test tube.

> ### WARNING
> Hot glass looks exactly like cold glass. Avoid touching.

4. Use a test tube clamp to move the test tube to the benchtop. Leave the test tube "clamped" to avoid rolling.

5. Place the small test tube on the wire screen and heat with a burner for approximately 5 minutes. Using forceps, carefully slide the small test tube into the larger test tube. Stopper the test tube and allow to cool to room temperature before proceeding.

    Try to handle the glassware as little as possible with your fingers. The mass of your fingerprints can make the test tube appear heavier than it is.

6. Take the test tubes and stopper to an analytical balance. Determine the combined mass of the cooled small test tube, larger test tube and stopper. Use this same balance for all remaining measurements.

---

1 Popular Mechanics: Methane Hydrates – Energy Source of the Future? *http://www. popularmechanics.com/science/energy/a12618/2558946/ (accessed 6/2019).*

NOTES
▼

7. After reading the following hints, load the small test tube with two scoops of one of the solid hydrates from the front bench. Be sure to record the identity of the hydrate in your lab notebook.

> **HINTS**
>
> - The solid hydrate needs to be finely ground so it heats uniformly. If it is not already finely ground, use the mortar and pestle to grind up a small amount of solid.
>
> - Using a micro-spatula, load up a "tip full" of solid, slowly slide it about 60% of the way into the small test tube. Roll the spatula in your fingers until the solid is upside down and falls in a small "pile" in the test tube. Withdraw the spatula so as not to disturb the pile. In a similar fashion, put another small pile about 50% down the length of the test tube. You should now have two piles near each other approximately in the center of the test tube.
>
> - Throughout the rest of the procedure do not disturb the piles in the test tube. Keep the test tube horizontal and don't let it roll.

8. Slide the small test tube into the larger test tube and insert the stopper.

9. Take the test tube assembly to the analytical balance and determine the mass. The mass of the solid should be a little over 0.1 g; you may have to add a third small scoop to achieve this mass.

10. Back at your workstation, slide the small test tube out of the larger test tube onto the wire screen, taking care not to spill any of the hydrate. Gently heat the test tube and hydrate so as to drive off the water present in the crystalline solid. This needs to be done slowly and thoroughly. If you heat the hydrate too quickly the solid will erupt out the end of the tube, ruining your results. If water vapor appears, "chase" it out the end of the tube with the flame.

11. Discontinue heating when you think the water has been driven off (it takes about 5–10 minutes).

12. Using forceps and taking care to keep the test tube horizontal, slide the small test tube into the larger test tube and stopper it. Allow the test tube to cool and then take this assembly to the analytical balance and determine the mass. Record the mass.

13. Heat the small test tube again for about 5 minutes, cool and reweigh as above. If the mass is not changed by the second heating (within 0.001 g), the process is complete and no further heating is necessary. If the mass difference between the first and second heatings is greater than 0.001 g, perform a third heating, cooling, and weighing cycle. Repeat the process until two successive weighings do not differ by more than 0.001 g. This ensures that all the water has been removed. You will use the last (lowest) mass in your calculations.

14. When finished, empty the dry solid into the waste bucket and put the used test tube in the labeled container.

15. Repeat the procedure two more times using new samples of the same hydrate.

CALCULATIONS

The goal of the calculations is to determine the empirical formula of your hydrate sample, or, in other words, the moles of water per mole of anhydrous salt. Do the calculations for at least one trial before leaving lab.

1. Determine the mass of water and anhydrous salt:

   mass H_2O driven off by heating = initial mass – final mass after heating
   mass anhydrous salt = final mass after heating

2. Calculate the moles of water and anhydrous salt (use molar masses).

3. Calculate the moles of water per mole of hydrated salt. That is, determine x in the hydrated salt formula:

$$\frac{\text{\# moles water}}{\text{\# moles anhydrous salt}} = \frac{x \text{ moles water}}{\text{mole anhydrous salt}}$$

   When you have completed this calculation, ask your instructor for the correct formula of the hydrated salt.

4. Percentage error:

   Your calculated value of x will probably not be a whole number, even though we know that the correct number of water molecules must be. Use your calculated value of x to determine the percent error in your results:

$$\% \text{ error} = \frac{\left| \text{calculated moles water} - \text{actual moles water} \right|}{\text{actual moles water}}$$

5. Repeat the above calculations for each trial. Do not average your results.

DISCUSSION/CONCLUSION

Report the experimental and actual formulae of your "unknown" hydrate and the % error. Do your experimental results agree within what you would expect to be normal and reasonable experimental error, with the actual value? Propose sources of error that could cause deviations in the number of waters of hydration. As always, follow the guidelines for a well-written lab report.

NOTES

exp9

Graphing Workshop

Special Materials Needed

Bring a calculator to lab.

Background Reading

Read the chapter on *Graphing* in this lab manual before attending lab.

INTRODUCTION

Frequently, the goal of a scientific experiment is to determine how the value of one variable, called the dependent variable, changes as a function of another variable, called the independent variable. For example, a climatologist may monitor the average atmospheric CO_2 level over a period of time in order to gather enough information to predict what the CO_2 concentration will be at some time in the future. Results of this type of experiment are typically presented in two ways: tabular form and graphical form. Though both methods are commonly used, the graphical method is often superior because it provides a visual display for the relationship between the dependent and independent variables.

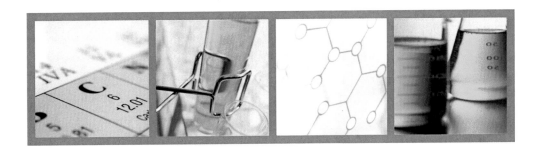

NOTES
▼

Straight line graphs are the most useful in analyzing chemical data because they provide for easy interpolation. However, raw data frequently do not give a straight line when the variables are graphed. In this case, we attempt to *transform* the data in a way that will provide a linear relationship. Transformation is a mathematical manipulation of a variable (x), such as squaring it, taking its inverse (1/x), its logarithm (ln x) or some other mathematical function. For example, consider the following data for the pressure and volume of a sample of gas:

TABLE 9-1. Pressure–Volume Measurements on a Gas Sample[1]

Pressure (atm)	Volume (L)	1/Pressure (atm)
3.215	8.24	0.311
3.747	7.07	0.267
5.027	5.26	0.199
7.858	3.36	0.127
9.156	2.89	0.109
12.275	2.15	0.081
14.300	1.84	0.070
19.160	1.37	0.052
22.312	1.18	0.045
29.871	0.878	0.033

When volume (V) is plotted versus pressure (P), as shown in Figure 9-1, the result is a curve in the form of a hyperbola. While this could be fit to an equation, it doesn't provide us with a useful relationship between pressure and volume.

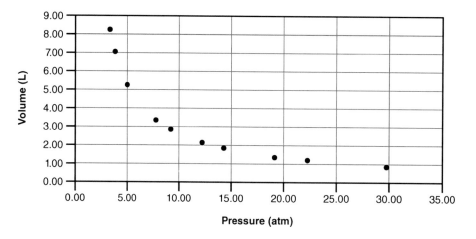

Graph of Volume vs. Pressure

FIGURE 9-1. A plot of V versus P

1 Blancet, A. L.; Hall, K. R. Physica 1970, 47, 75–91.

Let's consider the data in Table 9-1 again. We can see that as the pressure increases, volume decreases. This suggests an inverse relation between pressure and volume. A second graph, this time plotting V versus 1/P, as in Figure 9-2, results in a straight line.

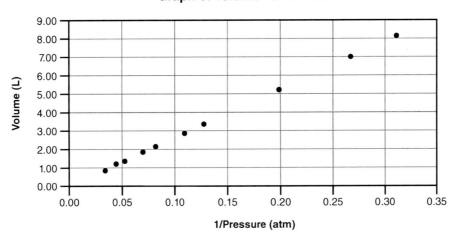

FIGURE 9-2. A plot of V versus 1/P

Linear relationships, such as we observe in Figure 9-2, are characteristic of mathematical equations of the form $y = mx + b$. In the pressure-volume case, $y = V$, m = the slope of the line, $x = 1/P$, and b = the y-intercept. We can derive an equation that relates the volume of a gas to its pressure from this linear relationship:

$$V = k\left(\frac{1}{P} + 0\right)$$
$$y = mx + b$$

In this laboratory workshop on graphing, you will collect a set of data and prepare a graph in lab that allows you to derive the relationship between the Fahrenheit and Celsius temperature scales. Once you have had your graph approved by your instructor, you will graph another set of data that you will use to answer several questions about the system in question.

PROCEDURE

Part A—Temperature Scale Relationships

From your other science courses, you should be familiar with the relationship between the Fahrenheit and Celsius temperature scales, $°F = 9/5°C + 32$ or $°C = (°F−32)5/9$. In this section of the lab you will make a series of temperature measurements and perform a graphical analysis of your data to see how this relationship can be derived. Your goal is to derive the equation that will allow you to convert any temperature in °C to °F (or, in other words, $°F = ?$). Work with a partner to collect data and plan the graph, but construct your graph independently. All data should be tabulated and submitted with your graph.

1. Use a digital thermometer to record the room temperature in both °F and °C.

2. Place about 200 mL water into a 600-mL beaker. Place the beaker on a piece of wire gauze on a metal tripod. Heat the water to boiling using a Bunsen burner, and record the temperature of the boiling water in °F and °C. Turn off the Bunsen burner. Add some ice chips to the water, stir, and record the new temperature in °F and °C. Continue to add ice and record the temperature until you have at least 5 more temperature readings. For the final reading, add ice until you have an ice/water slurry.

3. Construct (by hand) a graph of your experimental data. The first step in construction of a graph is determination of the axes. Consider what you are trying to learn from your graph and decide what to plot as the dependent and independent variables. In this case you are trying to answer the question, $°F = ?$ Then, examine your data; do the variables appear to be directly related or inversely related? Will it be necessary to perform a transformation of the data before graphing? Once you have decided on the axes, follow all instructions in the Graphing guidelines to prepare your graph. Determine the value of the slope and intercept and derive the mathematical expression for the temperature scale relationship.

4. Use the equation of your line graph to answer the following questions:

   a. At what temperature do the two scales intersect—that is, at what temperature does $°F = °C$? (Hint: this is a 2-equation, 2-unknowns problem.)

   b. What is the temperature in °F when the temperature is 200°C?

5. Have your graph approved by your instructor and correct any deficiencies before proceeding to Part B.

NOTES
▼

Part B—Atmospheric Carbon Dioxide Measurements

The amount of carbon dioxide in the atmosphere has been increasing steadily since the start of the Industrial Revolution. This is concerning because an increase in atmospheric CO_2 leads to an increase in global temperatures. As the amount of CO_2 in the atmosphere increases, the solubility of CO_2 in water also increases. Observe the demonstration of CO_2 in water and record your observations in your notebook. How will an increase in CO_2 in the world's oceans affect the pH?

Atmospheric carbon dioxide measurements have been made at the Mauna Loa Observatory in Hawaii since 1959. This is an ideal location for monitoring constituents in the atmosphere due to its remote location, undisturbed air and minimal influences from vegetation and human activity. Table 9-2 shows the average annual CO_2 concentrations in parts per million (ppm). This information is also located in a folder on the laboratory computer desktop.

Using Microsoft Excel, copy the data on the computer into your own spreadsheet. Follow the instructions in the Excel graphing guidelines to prepare a graph of annual CO_2 levels versus. (See Appendix D.)

To predict future levels of CO_2, we would like to have an equation that fits the data, which we can generate using the curve-fitting feature of Excel. Because we don't know the relationship between the variables, we will have to try a few different options and see which gives us the best result. Start by following the instructions to insert a *linear trendline*. When doing so, select the option to display the equation and value of R^2 on the chart. R^2 is a parameter that tells you whether the relationship that you are using is a good fit to the data. The closer this value is to 1.00, the better the fit.

Does the linear relationship seem to be a good fit? Try inserting another trendline, this time with an exponential fit. Again, display the equation and R^2 on the chart. Finally, try a second order polynomial fit. The curves and equations can be customized to display in different colors to help you distinguish which is which. Print a copy of your graph.

    a.   Which trendline provides the better fit? Explain why.

    b.   Many atmospheric scientists believe that the upper safety limit for atmospheric CO_2 is 350 ppm, a value that was reached in 1988. Beyond this level, it may not be possible to preserve a planet similar to that on which civilization developed and to which life on Earth is adapted.[2] In 2015 global CO_2 levels sailed past the 400 ppm threshold, accompanied by increases in average global temperatures. Does the year 2015 agree with the year predicted by your best fit trendline? To answer this question you will need to increase the number of significant figures in your trendline equation to four or five decimal places before doing the calculation.

    c.   Consider the differences between extrapolation and interpolation and the dangers associated with extrapolating beyond the limits of the data.

---

2 *Hansen, J., et al.* Target Atmospheric CO_2: Where Should Humanity Aim? Open Atmos. Sci. J. *2008, 2, 217–231.*

Part C—Atmospheric Oxygen Measurements

Atmospheric O_2 abundance has been monitored by Scripps Research Institute since 1989. The main goal of atmospheric O_2 monitoring has been to quantify the yearly global O_2 loss to improve understanding of the processes controlling the buildup of atmospheric CO_2. By comparing the change in O_2 with the expected change due to fossil-fuel burning it is possible to assess the strength of land sinks for CO_2.[3]

Table 9-3 shows the January O_2 readings measured at the Mauna Loa Observatory since 1991. These values are given in **per meg** units. These units report the *changes in the O_2/N_2 ratio of air relative to the O_2/N_2 ratio in the mid-1980s.* The values are negative because the O_2/N_2 ratio of the air has decreased since the mid-1980s. One per meg equals 0.0001 percent.

The information in Table 9-3 is also stored in the folder on the laboratory computers. Because it is much easier to see trends in data by graphing, these data should also be graphed following the same instructions that you followed for the CO_2 graph. Fit the data to a linear model and display the equation and R^2 on the graph.

> **NOTE**
>
> The data points that you are graphing in this section are negative and Excel may place the horizontal (x) axis at the top of the graph, rather than the bottom. To change this, double click on the vertical (y) axis. The dialogue box that opens up will give you an option to set the value for where the horizontal axis crosses the vertical axis. Change this from 0.00 to the value that you would like to have at the bottom of your graph. This will move the y-axis to the bottom.

a. Could you have graphed the O_2 data on the same graph as the CO_2 data? Why or why not?

b. Assuming that the trend has been constant, determine the reference year for the O_2/N_2 ratio. Because the per meg units reflect the change in the ratio from the reference year, the per meg unit value for the reference year ratio would be zero.

c. Some scientists hypothesize that the decrease in the O_2/N_2 ratio is due to the burning of fossil fuels. Do the data that you graphed support this hypothesis? Explain your answer fully using balanced chemical equations where appropriate. You can find further information to support your arguments at this web site: http://scrippso2.ucsd.edu/faq.

---

3 *http://scrippso2.ucsd.edu/introduction (accessed 6/2019)*

NOTES
▼

REPORT

You will write a "Slim Report" for this lab. Refer to the guidelines posted on Canvas for further information on what is expected.

TABLE 9-2. Annual Mean Concentrations of CO_2 at the Mauna Loa Observatory[4]

Year	CO_2 Concentration (ppm)	Year	CO_2 Concentration (ppm)
1959	315.97	1989	353.07
1960	316.91	1990	354.35
1961	317.64	1991	355.57
1962	318.45	1992	356.38
1963	318.99	1993	357.07
1964	319.62	1994	358.82
1965	320.04	1995	360.80
1966	321.38	1996	362.59
1967	322.16	1997	363.71
1968	323.04	1998	366.65
1969	324.62	1999	368.33
1970	325.68	2000	369.52
1971	326.32	2001	371.13
1972	327.45	2002	373.22
1973	329.68	2003	375.77
1974	330.18	2004	377.49
1975	331.08	2005	379.80
1976	332.05	2006	381.90
1977	333.78	2007	383.76
1978	335.41	2008	385.59
1979	336.78	2009	387.37
1980	338.68	2010	389.85
1981	340.10	2011	391.63
1982	341.44	2012	393.82
1983	343.03	2013	396.52
1984	344.58	2014	398.65
1985	346.04	2015	400.83
1986	347.39	2016	404.24
1987	349.16	2017	406.55
1988	351.56	2018	408.52

4 *ftp://ftp.cmdl.noaa.gov/ccg/co2/trends/co2_annmean_mlo.txt (accessed 6/2019)*

NOTES
▼

TABLE 9-3. January Concentrations of O_2 Measured at the Mauna Loa Observatory[5]

Year	O_2 Concentration (per meg)
1991	−102.9367
1992	−108.1877
1993	−119.6115
1994	−139.1075
1995	−158.3165
1996	−178.0519
1997	−199.9775
1998	−214.0102
1999	−227.0527
2000	−241.437
2001	−262.1184
2002	−280.9342
2003	−302.3377
2004	−323.6647
2005	−342.8027
2006	−363.8835
2007	−383.4666
2008	−404.9102
2009	−426.8643
2010	−448.0126
2011	−474.7146
2012	−495.4693
2013	−518.8701
2014	−543.7159
2015	−565.5842
2016	−589.8758
2017	−617.2345
2018	−641.0757

---

5 http://scrippso2.ucsd.edu/osub2sub-data (accessed 6/2019)

exp10

Emission Spectroscopy

Special Material Needed

Spectroscope construction kit: this includes a cardboard box, two plastic aperture pieces, a piece of replica diffraction grating (handle by edges only!), a small piece of graph paper, a ruler, a construction template, and safety instructions.

INTRODUCTION

This experiment provides an opportunity for you to make basic observations that are similar to those which helped form the foundation of modern atomic structure theory. Prior reading of the chapter of your general chemistry text dealing with atomic spectra is necessary to support your understanding of this experiment. In turn, the experiment will support your understanding of atomic theory.

> "The most directly compelling evidence for the quantization of energy comes from the observation of the frequencies of light absorbed and emitted by atoms and molecules."
>
> —P. W. Atkins

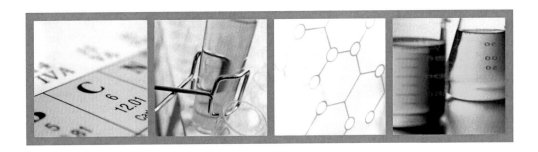

NOTES

▼

Spectroscopy is the study of the interaction of electromagnetic radiation (EMR) with matter. When matter is energized (excited) by the application of energy, electromagnetic radiation is often emitted as the matter relaxes from the excited state back to its original, or ground, state. The emitted EMR is often in the form of visible light. We may perceive the released light energy as only general colors (for example, excited Na appears yellow, excited Ne appears red, and excited Hg appears bluish-white). In these cases the full range of individual color components may be better observed by using a spectroscope. The spectroscope is a device which breaks the light up into its component colors and allows the measurement of the wavelengths of specific bright lines being emitted as the excited atoms lose their energy and return to the ground state. The resulting spectrum of radiation emitted by a substance that has absorbed energy is called an emission spectrum, and the science is appropriately called emission spectroscopy.

Spectroscopy is a powerful and sensitive form of chemical analysis, as well as a method of probing electronic and nuclear structure and chemical bonding. The key to interpreting this spectral information is the knowledge that certain atomic and molecular processes involve only specific energy ranges. For example, radiation emitted in the visible and near-UV regions involves transitions of valence shell electrons. On the other hand, X-rays arise from transitions of inner-shell electrons and microwave radiation is the result of molecular rotations.

As you have learned, atoms and molecules contain electrons that occupy discrete energy levels. The actual energy of each state (level) is dependent upon several factors: the nuclear charge, the distance of the electron from the nucleus, and the number of electrons between the nucleus and the electron in question. Since these various factors are different for every atom or molecule, it follows that the energy levels are unique for any given atom or molecule.

The transition of an electron from one level to another must be accompanied by the emission or absorption of a discrete amount of energy. The magnitude of this energy depends on the energy of each of the levels between which the transition occurs. The relationship between energy and light radiation was proposed by Einstein in 1905 and represented by the equation:

$$\Delta E = E_2 - E_1 = hc/\lambda \tag{1}$$

where:

ΔE = change in energy from the excited state (state 2) to the ground state (state 1)

h = Planck's constant (6.6262×10^{-34} J•s)

c = the velocity of light in a vacuum (2.9979×10^8 m/sec)

λ = the wavelength of the observed light

As mentioned above, the atomic spectra that are observed for the excited atoms consist of radiation given off as electrons cascade down from higher to lower energy levels. The number and type of these transitions depend on the particular structure of the energy levels in a given chemical species and on various quantum selection rules. The emission spectra are characteristic of specific gaseous atoms or molecules whether observed in the laboratory, your home town, or on another planet. (In other words, each element produces its own characteristic emission spectrum.) If the value of ΔE lies within the visible region of the total electromagnetic spectrum, then the frequency corresponds to visible light, and the emission can be seen by the eye. The wavelength of emitted light can be measured using a spectroscope. Then, using Eq. (1), we can calculate the amount of energy released for various transitions and so "map" the energy levels available to the electrons in the atom.

The separation of light into its spectral components can be done by refraction or diffraction. In this laboratory experiment, the separation of light into its component colors is accomplished by diffraction in a device called a spectroscope. A spectroscope is simply a box, with a slit at one end (to let light in) and a light-separating device at the other end. The separating device you will be using is called a transmission diffraction grating, and it consists of a sheet of transparent plastic that has thousands of tiny grooves ruled on it. The way in which the grating works to separate light into colors is by wave interference. The actual details of this process won't be covered in this discussion.

Three common terrestrial sources of visible radiation from atomic emissions are electrical discharges in gases, thermal energy from combustion, and heated metals. A convenient source in the laboratory is the electrical discharge tube. This is a glass tube that contains metal electrodes at each end and is filled with a gas, such as hydrogen, helium, or mercury, at a low pressure. A high voltage is placed across the electrodes, and when the current is switched on, a stream of fast-moving electrons shoots through the gas from the cathode to the anode. Energy is transferred from the electrons to the gas atoms, and the electrons in the gas atoms are excited to higher energy levels. The return of excited electrons to the ground state results in the emission of light, which may be analyzed with a spectroscope. Some practical gas discharge devices are the common fluorescent light (mercury vapor), "neon" lights, and street lights (mercury or sodium vapor).

Many solid substances (sodium chloride, for example) may be excited by the thermal energy (heat) of flames. The heat comes from the exothermic combustion reaction occurring in the flame. Solid sodium chloride consists of sodium ions (Na^+) bonded to chloride ions (Cl^-). In a Bunsen burner flame, these ions are dissociated, and the separated Na^+ ions combine with free electrons in the flame to form sodium atoms:

$$Na^+ + e^- \rightarrow Na$$

NOTES

▼

Electrons within the neutral sodium atoms can then be excited to higher energy levels by the heat of the flame:

$$Na + thermal\ energy \rightarrow Na\ ^* \text{ (an excited sodium atom)}$$

The excited atoms then "relax" back to the ground state and emit light in the process:

$$Na\ ^* \rightarrow Na + h\nu \text{ (light)}$$

The light which is emitted is characteristic of the electronic transition which occurs. Spectroscopic analysis of the light gives the atomic emission spectrum of sodium.

The Bohr Model of the Hydrogen Atom and the Balmer Series of the Hydrogen Spectrum

The energy of emitted radiation (Eq. 1) in Bohr's model of the hydrogen atom is given by:

$$\Delta E = - R_H \left(\frac{1}{n_i^2} - \frac{1}{n_f^2} \right) \tag{2}$$

where:

R_H = Rydberg's constant for hydrogen (joules)

n_f = quantum number of the final state

n_i = quantum number of the initial state

Several series of emission lines have been observed for the hydrogen atom. For example, if we let $n_f = 1$, and let n_i vary from 2–6, we obtain the Lyman series lines for hydrogen. The Balmer series results from transitions in which n_i varies from 3–10. The quantum numbers and wavelength (in nm) of the associated radiation are given below for the lines that occur in the visible region of the spectrum.

TABLE 10-1. Balmer Series of Hydrogen Emissions

n_i	Wavelength (nm)	Color
3	655	red
4	486	turquoise
5	430	blue-violet
6	410	violet*

*The violet line in the hydrogen spectrum is difficult to see. Many people only observe 3 hydrogen lines (n_i = 3, 4, 5).

In this experiment you will construct a simple but fairly accurate spectroscope containing a built-in quantitative calibration system. The spectroscope will be used to obtain various atomic line spectra and the wavelength and energy of emitted light. The Balmer emission spectrum for the hydrogen atom will be used to determine the value of the Rydberg constant and the value of the quantum number in the final state of the Balmer series.

CHEMISTRY IN A SUSTAINABLE WORLD

Whenever you turn on a light, whether incandescent or fluorescent, you take advantage of the quantum phenomena described in the previous section. Incandescent light bulbs contain a tungsten filament surrounded by an inert gas such as argon. When heated to approximately 2,400°C the tungsten becomes "white hot" as the atoms are promoted to higher energy levels. When they return to the ground state they emit visible light. While relatively simple and cheap, incandescent bulbs are not very efficient because most of the energy is released in the form of heat rather than light. For this reason, fluorescent light bulbs are a much more sustainable source of visible light than incandescent bulbs.

Fluorescent bulbs function in essentially the same way as the mercury discharge tubes used in this experiment. These bulbs contain mercury as well as a small amount of an inert gas. When excited, mercury atoms emit light in both the visible and ultraviolet regions. The ultraviolet photons are absorbed by a phosphor coated on the inside of the bulbs which then emits even more light in the visible region. Incandescent bulbs produce ultraviolet radiation as well but this is not converted to visible light, thus wasting valuable energy. In addition, fluorescent bulbs lose far less energy to heat emission, making them three to four times more efficient than incandescent bulbs.

There is an environmental trade-off associated with the use of fluorescent lighting. Mercury is toxic and these light bulbs must be recycled at the end of their lifetime. Without this step, mercury can be released into the environment and contribute to air and water pollution.

PROCEDURE

Part A—Construction of a Spectroscope

The spectroscope will be constructed from a cardboard "shirt-box." Both the bottom and top of the box will probably have to be taped in the inside corners so that they will not flatten in use.

A diagram of the important features of the spectroscope is shown below in Figure 10-1. These features are:

- an entrance slit which allows a controlled amount of light to enter the box and also gives the light a characteristic slit shape,

- a sighting hole through which you'll look to see the spectrum. The sighting hole also holds the diffraction grating,

- a piece of graph paper which makes it possible to calibrate the spectroscope so that wavelengths can be read from it, and

- an illuminating slit behind the graph paper so that you can see the lines on the graph paper "in the dark."

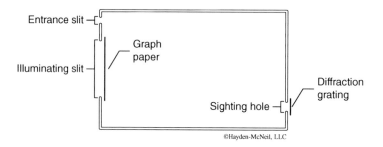

©Hayden-McNeil, LLC

FIGURE 10-1. The "shirt-box" spectroscope

1. Follow the directions on the "construction instruction" sheet (included inside the box) to cut the entrance slit, sighting hole, and illuminating slit.

> **CAUTION**
> Please be careful. The box knife blades are sharp!

2. Center the graph paper on the inside of the box bottom over the illuminating slit. Carefully number every tenth line for reference later, then tape the paper in place. The numbers should be directly over the illuminating slit.

3. The diffraction grating is now mounted over the sighting hole, oriented so that the spectrum observed will consist of colored replicas of the slit seen on the graph paper. This orientation may be found by holding (by the edges!) the grating in place over the sighting hole and aiming the spectroscope toward the

room lights. You should see the colored images of the slit on the graph paper. If you've put the grating over the hole with the wrong orientation, you'll see a blur of light above and below the entrance slit (rotate the grating 90 degrees in that case). When the proper orientation is found, tape the grating in place over the sighting hole.

4. Refinement of the entrance slit, as well as adjustment of the width, can now be made by utilizing two plastic or cardboard aperture pieces. They should be taped to the outside of the box top. The separation between the edges of the aperture pieces can then be adjusted to give optimum intensity and resolution; usually the optimum is near one millimeter. This is about the thickness of the cardboard box, so the piece of cardboard removed when cutting the slit may be utilized as a spacer between the aperture pieces when taping the second piece in place. Try to keep the slit absolutely vertical.

Part B—Exploring Spectroscope Specifications

It is always wise to explore the good points and the limitations of any instrument before launching out and spending time and money (your tuition, in this case!) using it. Obviously, the spectroscope which you have built has many limitations. However, the nice thing about an inexpensive, simple, self-built instrument is that you should have no inhibitions about using it, breaking it, changing it, or fixing it. In fact, you have a unique opportunity to write the specifications of your own spectroscopic instrument. Spend a few minutes familiarizing yourself with your spectroscope and experiment as necessary to answer the following questions.

*   Were you confused at any step of the construction—and where? How could the instructions for building the spectroscope be improved. (For example: Can they be made shorter?)

*   Observe the laboratory fluorescent lights with your spectroscope. Hold it so that the source (fluorescent light) is visible through the slit when you look through the grating. When the source and slit are properly aligned you will see a single line or a number of lines, depending on the source, appearing on the graph paper. This is the spectrum of the fluorescent light.

*   This may seem like a silly question, but it's not. What is the actual location of the spectrum? Is it really inside the box? (To answer this, try taking the lid off your spectroscope and observing the graph paper without looking through the grating.)

*   Can you predict what differences in the spectrum you would see if the spectroscope were made out of a giant pizza box?

*   Now let's change some things. Vary the slit width by unpeeling one of the pieces of electrical tape and repositioning it onto the box. If you make the slit larger or smaller, what happens to the fluorescent light spectrum? Draw a few simple pictures in your lab book to illustrate what you see.

NOTES

▼

- Does the slit have to be a long thin rectangle?
- What is the relationship between the distance of the source from the spectroscope and the characteristics of the spectrum?
- Give your spectroscope a rating (1–10) for
  a. craftsmanship
  b. aesthetics
  c. spectroscopic efficiency
- Compare your spectroscope to the commercial spectroscope.

Part C—Calibration of the Spectroscope

Each spectroscope will be slightly different from any other, so each instrument must be individually calibrated. The lines of light observed when using the spectroscope are the transmitted beams that are diffracted, or bent, by the grating and then strike your eye. The spectrum is not reflected or projected to the graph paper. Consequently, the spectroscope must be calibrated from at least two observed and known lines. We will use the mercury lines as the calibration standard. There are four emission lines in the visible spectrum of mercury. The first three are easy to observe but the fourth, at 404.7 nm, may be more difficult. If you see only one line at the blue end of the spectrum, it is almost certainly the 435.8 nm blue line. Observation of at least two known lines will give the exact position of particular wavelengths on the scale and enables you to find how many nm units correspond to one division on the scale.

TABLE 10-2. Mercury Emission Wavelengths and Colors

Wavelength (nm)	Color
578.0	yellow-orange
546.1	green
435.8	blue
404.7	violet

Prepare a table in your lab notebook: record the positions in millimeters (read from the graph paper taped inside the box) of the observed lines of the mercury spectrum. In a second column record corresponding wavelength (in nm) of the spectral lines (see above).

> **NOTE**
>
> The next portions of this experiment can be performed in any order. The sources for these experiments are in various places in the room. Check for accessibility and go ahead! For each atomic line spectrum observed, record the overall color of the emitted light and prepare a table to record the color of the spectral lines, the intensity (strong, weak, etc.), and the position in mm (from the graph paper).

Part D—Spectra of Gases

Using the gas discharge lamps, observe the spectrum of hydrogen and record the positions of the spectral lines. (The hydrogen lamp is filled with H_2, but the diatomic gas dissociates so that you observe the atomic spectrum of H and not the molecular spectrum of H_2.) You may find it advantageous to increase the slit width to about 1.5 to 2.0 mm and to view the lamp quite closely, perhaps about 10–20 cm away.

Repeat with the tubes containing helium gas and at least one other gas. (You may see as many as 8 spectral lines from the helium lamp!) It is not necessary to record the positions of these lines, merely your observations.

Part E—Spectra of Metals

You will do this section of the experiment with the other members of your lab table group.

You are already familiar with performing flame tests on metal cations in which the metals produce a distinctive color when heated in a flame. Flame emission spectroscopy takes this a step further, providing a powerful method for qualitative identification and quantitative determination of many elements. As you are working on this section of the experiment, remember that one of the most common flame emissions is that from atomic sodium. Because it is so prevalent, it may contaminate some of the other emission spectra that you are trying to observe.

- Position the metal shield behind the burner so as to block out as much outside light and air movement as possible.
- Hold a cotton swab (Q-tip) over a crystallizing dish and add one of the metal salt solutions dropwise until the swab is fully wet. Take care to avoid contaminating the swab because any contaminations could also appear in the flame. Only use one solution per swab.

NOTES

▼

- Light the lab burner and adjust to obtain a steady blue flame. Before performing the flame test, position both the box spectroscope and the commercial spectroscope so that the flame is clearly visible through the viewing windows.

- When ready, place the tip of the saturated swab into the burner flame. This should be positioned at the lower edge of the flame, between the inner and outer cones.

- Repeat as necessary until the spectrum has been clearly visualized. Record the color of the flame as well as the colors of the light as observed through the spectroscope(s).

- Repeat procedure with each of the salt solutions.

A positive potassium flame test can be difficult to observe due to interference from the more intense sodium emission that is often present as a contaminant. Viewing the emission through blue cobalt glass, which filters out the sodium emission, can solve this problem.

- Repeat the potassium flame test while holding a piece of blue cobalt glass close to your eye. How does the appearance of the flame change? (It is not necessary to use a spectroscope for this part of the procedure.)

- Does the cobalt glass change the appearance of any of the other flame tests?

Part F—Qualitative Analysis Using Spectroscopy

In previous experiments you have learned a variety of ways to identify chemical unknowns, including the use of flame tests. Spectroscopy provides you with another tool.

- Perform a flame test on the unknown sample(s) that are in the lab. The unknown will be at least one of the substances that you viewed previously and it could be a mixture. What color do you observe? Does the flame test provide you with enough information to confidently identify the unknown? Note: for the sake of this exercise, you aren't allowed to compare the unknown flame test with the known compounds.

- If you are uncertain of your identification, view the emissions with a spectroscope. What do you observe? Based on your observations, what must be present in the unknown sample?

- Of the three methods (naked eye, homemade spectroscope, plastic commercial spectroscope), which is "best" for determining the identity of the metal(s) responsible for the flame color?

- After assessing your unknown using the spectroscopes, follow the instructions provided in lab to do an instrumental emission analysis. Based on this new information, can you make a new claim about the identity of your unknown? Does it differ from your earlier claim?

Clean-Up

- Discard used swabs in the container in the hood.

- Clean your work area, rinsing out the crystallizing dish and discarding any trash. If you do not want to keep the constructed spectroscope, place it on the window counter for recycling.

CALCULATIONS

Following instructions provided in lab, enter your data into the class data bank. This must be done before leaving lab.

As with any situation in which a series of repetitious calculations must be made, the Spectroscopy lab calculations can be made less tedious through the use of a spreadsheet. You may need to review Using Excel: A Summary of Basic Spreadsheet Operations and Graphing with MS Excel before beginning.

Part C—Calibration of the Spectroscope

Using MS Excel, set up Table 1:

Columns:

- Column A: observed color of Hg line

- Column B: wavelength of Hg line (in nm) (see Table 10-2)

- Column C: Hg line position from spectroscope (in mm)

Fill in the table using your data and known wavelengths.

Prepare a spectroscope calibration curve by plotting position (mm) vs. wavelength (nm). Since we are observing visible light in this experiment, the wavelength axis should cover the visible light region, approximately 400–700 nm. Perform a linear regression analysis to determine the equation for the line.

Parts D and E—Spectra of Gases and Metals

The purpose of this portion of the experiment is to determine the wavelength of all observed emission lines and the energy of the hydrogen lines. You will need to set up a second table in the same spreadsheet that you are already working on.

Table 2:

Columns:

- Column A: element identity

- Column B: observed color of line

- Column C: line position from spectroscope (in mm)

NOTES
▼

- Column D: wavelength of line (nm)
- Column E: energy of hydrogen line

Fill in columns A, B, and C using your data.

Column D: The wavelengths of the lines are calculated values. (Refer to "Entry of formulas" in the basic Excel instructions if necessary.) Rearrangement of the equation of the calibration curve obtained in Part C yields:

$$\text{wavelength (nm)} = \frac{\text{position (mm)} - \text{(y intercept)}}{\text{slope}}$$

Click on the cell of column D that correlates with the first observed emission line. If, for example, the first line position (in mm) is in cell C13, you will be working in cell D13.

To enter the formula for the wavelength calculation,

=(C13-y intercept)/slope

where slope and y intercept are the numerical values obtained from the calibration curve. Press enter and the answer for the calculation will be displayed in cell D13.

Follow the instructions for Filling Down (in the basic Excel instructions) to calculate all of the wavelength values.

Column E: Calculate the energy of the hydrogen lines (only!) in column E. Given that energy $=hc/\lambda$, you can use the wavelength value calculated in column D to calculate the energy. Click on the appropriate cell in column E. If, for example, this is cell E13, you will use the wavelength calculated in cell D13. Type:

=6.63E-34*2.998E8/(D13*1E-9)

Press enter and the calculated energy value will be displayed. Again, use the fill down feature to calculate the energy of the remaining hydrogen lines.

The Balmer Series

Equation (2) can be rearranged and written as

$$\Delta E = - R_H \left(\frac{1}{n_i^2} \right) + \frac{R_H}{n_f^2} \tag{3}$$

Eq. (5) has the general form of the equation of a straight line. Thus, a plot of ΔE versus $1/n_i^2$ should yield a line with slope $= -R_H$ and y intercept $= R_H/n_f^2$. The value previously calculated in Column E is the energy difference (ΔE) between the initial (n_i) and final (n_f) energy levels of the electron transition. Prepare this graph using the n_i values from Table 10-1 (x-axis) and your calculated energy values (y-axis). Determine the Rydberg constant and verify that n_f is 2 using the slope and y-intercept. (Be sure your graph displays 3 significant figures for the Rydberg constant. See page 288 for instructions.)

2.18×10^{-18} J is the accepted value for R_H. Calculate the percentage error between your calculated value and the accepted value. (See the section on Uncertainty, Error, and Precision in Quantitative Measurements on page xxiv if you have forgotten how to calculate percentage error.)

When finished, save your work and print. These printed tables should be included with your lab report.

DISCUSSION/CONCLUSION

Since this laboratory experiment differs from the traditional chemical reactions which you have become familiar with, you may be feeling confused as to what your discussion should include. However, the basic guidelines for writing a good discussion are still the same, in that your goal is to demonstrate an understanding of the processes that you have been studying and report your results. Here are some questions to get you started:

What are you studying when you study spectroscopy? What is the source of the spectral lines? What is the relationship between the color, the wavelength, the frequency, and the energy of the spectral lines? You have calculated values for the energy of the lines—what does this energy represent?

Include your results and the class results in your lab report. Compare your value and the class value to the literature value of R_H (2.18×10^{-18} J). Are the differences between these values significant? Remember that anytime a measurement is more than about three standard deviations from the accepted value, there is significant error present. Does having a large number of measurements increase your confidence in the result? Finally, assess this laboratory technique in terms of the class results.

What are the limitations and requirements of your spectroscope (Part B)? Given the value of the Rydberg constant which you calculated and your spectroscope assessment from Part B, evaluate the quality of the "shirt-box" spectroscope which you constructed. What are some practical applications of spectroscopy?

How can applications of the principles and phenomena observed in this experiment contribute to the goal of achieving improved energy efficiency leading toward energy sustainability? What is the downside in terms of environmental impact?

NOTES

exp11

Molecular Models

Valence-Shell Electron Pair Repulsion (VSEPR, commonly pronounced "vesper") theory is a model that allows us to predict the shapes of molecular (covalent) compounds and polyatomic ions. According to this theory, valence electron pairs, both bonding and non-bonding, around the central atom will align themselves in such a way as to minimize the electrostatic repulsion between them. VSEPR occasionally fails but in general, it provides us with a powerful predictive tool for determining molecular geometry. In this laboratory exercise you will use Lewis Structures and VSEPR theory to predict shapes of small molecules and polyatomic ions and construct 3-dimensional models of these species using a molecular modeling kit.

PRE-LAB READING

Review the sections of your textbook on Lewis Structures and VSEPR theory.

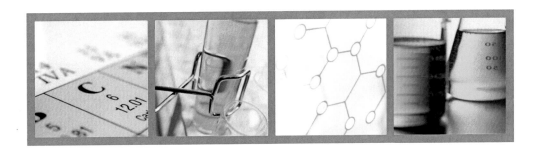

NOTES

▼

PROCEDURE

Part A—Basic Modeling

Access the course Canvas site for the list of molecules and polyatomic ions that you will be modeling for this lab. ***Before attending lab***, complete steps 1–3 for each species, using the worksheets accompanying this lab procedure.

1. Determine the total number of valence electrons in each molecule.

2. Draw the Lewis Structure of the molecule.

3. Determine the number of bonding electron pairs and non-bonding electron pairs around the central atom(s).

In lab:

4. Determine the electronic and molecular geometry around each centralized atom in the molecule from the Lewis Structure and VSEPR theory.

5. Construct an exact geometric model of the molecule. (You may work with a partner to construct models.)

6. Sketch an exact 3-D representation of the molecule from the model.

7. Indicate whether the molecule is polar or not. Obtain your TA's initials.

exp12

Physical Behavior of Gases

INTRODUCTION

Samples of a gas are commonly described by four physical properties: the volume, the pressure, the temperature and the quantity, or more specifically, the number of moles. Because there is empty space between gas molecules, a gas in a balloon will expand when heated and contract when cooled. Using a pressure pump, one can increase the pressure inside of a bicycle tire. We observe that when one of the physical properties of a gas (P, V, T, n) changes, the values of the others are able to change as well. Early experimenters realized that most gases exhibit nearly "ideal" behavior at ambient temperatures and pressures and as such, comply with the ideal gas law.

Ideal gas law: $PV = nRT$

where P = pressure, V = volume, n = number of moles, and T = absolute temperature.

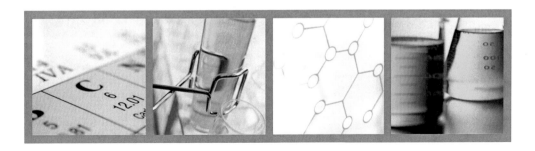

NOTES

▼

You may be wondering what is meant by ideal behavior, and what is the difference between ideal gases and real gases. Kinetic theory assumes that an ideal gas is composed of individual particles in constant random motion, that the gas particles have essentially no volume compared to the volume of their container and that the particles do not exert or experience any intermolecular forces of attraction with one another. Deviations from ideal behavior occur when these assumptions are no longer valid, that is, under conditions of high pressure where the volume of the individual gas molecules is no longer negligible and at low temperatures when the effect of intermolecular attractions becomes relevant, ultimately causing the gas to condense into a liquid. The temperature where gases condense to liquids varies greatly amongst different substances. For example, water vapor condenses to a liquid at 100°C and nitrogen condenses to a liquid at −196°C.

In this experiment, you will investigate the relationships between the different physical properties of gases and how a change in one property may affect the others. You will also consider whether the gases you investigate exhibit ideal gas behavior. Different pairs of students will be working with different gases and sample sizes. It will be necessary to pool your data to create a large data set. You and your colleagues will work together to construct several graphs. You will consider how the data represented in the graphs exhibits relationships among variables. Students will need to apply the skills acquired for making graphs in a previous lab experiment to this experiment.

A NOTE TO THE STUDENT

Your instructors know reading the technical procedures for this laboratory exercise may present a challenge because you have not previously seen and worked with gas collection equipment. Therefore, you might not understand all of the steps in the procedure. Do the best you can in writing the pre-lab for this laboratory. Your laboratory TA will provide specific pre-lab instruction on how to use the equipment and be with you during the lab to help you correctly use the equipment. When writing your pre-lab, you do not need to make data tables for parts B and C. An empty data table for these sections will be provided for you to complete in lab. (A data table is still necessary for part A.)

PROCEDURE

Part A: Generating Hydrogen and Examining the Relationship between **Moles of Gas** and **Gas Volume** at Constant Temperature and Pressure

Work Assignments

There are four sizes of magnesium ribbon to be studied. At your lab table, one pair of students will do three trials, using two different-sized pieces of magnesium (one duplicate). The other pair of students at your lab table will do three trials using the other two sized pieces of magnesium to ensure that all four sizes are investigated by your table group.

Before beginning the data collection, work with the members of your table group to answer these questions in your laboratory notebook:

1. Write the balanced chemical equation for the reaction between solid magnesium and hydrochloric acid. (Hint: This reaction is very similar to the one studied in the Galvanized Nail experiment during fall term.)

2. Assuming that magnesium is the limiting reactant and hydrochloric acid is in excess, how many moles of hydrogen gas are produced from the complete reaction of 0.0376 g of magnesium? (Show all work.)

3. What observation would indicate that magnesium is the limiting reactant when you look at what is in the test tube at the end of the experiment?

4. What is the current atmospheric pressure? Look at the barometer on the wall. Record the current atmospheric pressure.

Data Collection Procedure

Watch the video found at https://youtu.be/Z2pPvA34hyM and TA demonstration of proper technique before beginning.

1. Fill an 800-mL beaker with water to within about 1 inch of the top and position it below the gas measuring tube held by a buret clamp on a ring stand.

2. One tall plastic cylinder is shared per bench. Fill this with DI water. This will be used to equalize the generated gas in the measuring tube to atmospheric pressure after the reaction is complete. Because of the height, you should place this in a sink basin for use.

3. Select a piece of pre-cleaned Mg ribbon and weigh this on the analytical balance. Record the mass. To avoid transferring skin oil to the Mg ribbon, wear gloves, use forceps to pick up the ribbon, and use weigh paper when weighing.

NOTES

4. Attach the Mg ribbon to the copper wire with one of the two methods shown in Figure 12-1 and described by your TA. Test your assembly by holding it vertically and inverting—it must be secure in both positions. If the ribbon becomes dislodged from the "basket" before it completely dissolves, you will most likely have to repeat the run. The "hook" end will initially be used to hang it from the tube end. The magnesium should be in the vicinity of the 50-mL line of the gas measuring tube.

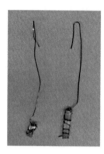

FIGURE 12-1. Copper wire hangers and magnesium ribbon. Left: "basket" style for short Mg. Right: "closed spiral" for long Mg

5. Add 10 mL of 6 M hydrochloric acid directly to the measuring tube using the pump dispenser at the reagent station (Figure 12-2). **Caution: Use gloves when working with the acid solution as it is corrosive.** Re-clamp the measuring tube to the ring stand.

FIGURE 12-2. Adding HCl to the measuring tube

6. Carefully fill the measuring tube with DI water. Do this slowly using the funnel to direct the water down the inside of the tube. Your goal is to minimize mixing so as to keep the acid at the bottom of the tube. Note: Initially you may observe some mixing eddy currents, but these should cease as the water column rises.

7. Carefully place the Mg ribbon assembly into the tube, leaving it suspended from the lip by the hook end. **Do not allow the Mg ribbon assembly to fall**

into the tube; the reaction with the un-mixed acid in the bottom of the tube can be sufficiently vigorous to eject material from the open end of the measuring tube. Wet a size 00 holed rubber stopper and gently insert this into the end of the measuring tube with twisting motion—do not force the stopper in. Some water should be forced out and the tube should be completely full of solution. As you prepare to invert the tube assembly, verify that the holes in the stopper are full to the top with water: it not, fill them using your DI bottle.

8. Cap the holes with finger pressure, invert the tube, and place the stoppered end into the beaker so that the stoppered end is about 1 inch below the surface before removing your finger (Figure 12-3). Your partner then clamps the tube in this position. Note: The reaction will begin ~30 seconds after the tube is inverted, so be prepared to do the inversion and re-clamping steps in a timely manner.

FIGURE 12-3. Charged tube inverted to start reaction, prior to clamping

9. When no more bubbling is observed, **record the volume** of the liquid in the measuring tube.

10. After the reaction ceases, you will need to determine the pressure of the hydrogen gas inside the cylinder. This can be done by inverting the measuring tube in a large cylinder of water and allowing the levels of liquid in the measuring tube and cylinder to equalize. When the level of liquid in the measuring tube is equal to the level of water in the large cylinder, we can assume the pressure inside the measuring tube is equal to the pressure outside the measuring tube. In other words, the pressure equals atmospheric pressure at this point.

Begin by moving the measuring tube to the tall clear plastic cylinder. One person, wearing gloves because the solution in the measuring tube is now acidic from the displaced unreacted hydrochloric acid, caps the stoppered holes with finger pressure while the other releases the buret clamp. With the holes covered, move the measuring tube to the water cylinder and immerse the stopper below the water surface before removing your gloved finger. Raise or lower the measuring tube so that the level of solution in the tube matches that of the water in the plastic cylinder. The pressure inside the tube is now equal to the pressure outside the tube. **Record the gas volume** at this pressure.

NOTES

▼

11. You will also need to record the room air pressure and gas temperature. We will assume the system is at thermal equilibrium with the surroundings and the gas temperature is equal to the room temperature. Remember to account for the correct number of significant figures and units of measure for the graduated devices.

12. Prepare your equipment for the next trial: Collect acid solution from the gas measuring tube and its first rinse in the 1000-mL poly beaker. The measuring tube is expensive and doesn't fit in the sink for cleaning under the faucets. Instead, use beakers of DI to rinse it; after the initial rinse, all other rinse water can go down the drain. The inside does not need to be dried. If the 800-mL beaker becomes too full, excess acid solution can be poured into the poly waste beaker.

13. Repeat steps 4–10 two more times, once with the same sized magnesium sample and once with a second sample of a different size.

14. When finished with all trials, clean up as before. Leave the rinsed gas measuring tube inverted in the buret clamp. Rinse the copper wire and leave it un-twisted for the next user. Empty the poly waste beaker and the 800-mL beaker into the spent products bucket in the hood and leave the workstation orderly as found.

Calculations and Graphing for Part A:

Each pair of students should prepare one spreadsheet and graph.

a. Open a new Excel spreadsheet to record data and perform calculations.

b. The first column should indicate the run number (1, 2, 3… etc.).

c. Enter the mass of magnesium in the second column and calculate the moles of magnesium in the third column.

d. Refer to the balanced molecular equation and enter the moles of hydrogen gas generated in the fourth column.

e. Enter the volume of hydrogen gas collected in the fifth column.

f. Prepare a graph of volume of hydrogen gas collected vs. moles hydrogen gas collected.

g. Analyze your graph. Is the relationship between moles of gas and volume clearly demonstrated? If you have any outlying data points, check with your TA to see if they should be eliminated. You need at least four good data points so you will need to obtain data from other students in the lab who used the same size of metal to replace any eliminated data point(s).

h. Enter all "good" data into the class data sheet.

Part B: Examining the Relationship between **Pressure** and **Volume** of Different Quantities of Various Gases at Constant Temperature

Work Assignments

One pair of students at your lab table will work on the pressure–volume relationship in part B and the other pair will work on part C. Decide amongst your tablemates who will be doing which section. Both pairs will use the same gas, as will be assigned and dispensed by your TA. You will need to gather data from your classmates and complete the data table, providing you with a full set of data for analysis.

Setup and Data Collection Procedure

Pressure Sensor and Logger *Pro* Setup

1. The pressure sensor has already been connected to the computer.

2. Open Logger *Pro* by clicking on the Vernier icon in the application menu bar. The software will recognize the sensor. Pressure will be reported in kPa units.

3. To configure the software, click on the data collection icon in the Logger *Pro* menu bar. From the Mode menu that opens, select **Events with Entry**. Then set the **Name** as "Volume" and "mLs" as the **Short Name**. Then select **Done**. The sensor and software are now ready for data collection.

P-V Gas Syringe Setup

1. Collect your bench's assigned gas balloon from you TA and record the gas type.

2. Practice moving the plunger on the 24-mL luer-lock syringe. The volume is measured on the blue scale at the edge of the plunger disk.

3. When you are comfortable with the syringe operation, press the plunger to empty the syringe and connect it to the balloon via the mating luer-lock fitting (Figure 12-4).

> **WARNING**
>
> Do not over-tighten! The plastic threads are easily damaged and will leak. The luer-lock assembly is designed to be air and water tight with only light finger force and about a half turn.

4. Open the valve on the balloon by turning the handle so that it is parallel to the assembly. Pull the plunger back to about the 20-mL mark. Now close the valve by turning the handle so that it is perpendicular to the assembly. Then unscrew

the balloon and depress the plunger to the 15-mL mark, and immediately attach it to the pressure sensor (Figure 12-4). Observe the same cautions with the luer-lock.

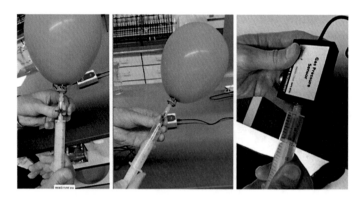

FIGURE 12-4. Attaching the gas balloon, filling the syringe to 10 mL, and then connecting to pressure sensor for data collection. The valve on the gas balloon is kept closed between fillings

Data Collection

1. One person will operate the syringe, and the other will enter data into the computer. It will take two hands and and some force to hold the plunger in place to collect data as the volume moves further from the fill point. Your goal is to get at least six pressure–volume data points per run.

2. Press the ▶ button to start data collection. Push the syringe in about 1 mL and hold. Press the ✺ Keep button; the pressure at this point will be saved and you will be prompted to enter the mL volume.

3. Now push the plunger in another mL and log the pressure and volume. Repeat with lesser volumes until the pressure approaches 200 kPa. Caution: Do not exceed 200 kPa as the sensor will be damaged.

4. Then work with reduced pressure. Release the plunger, and take a duplicate reading near the starting volume. Now pull the plunger out a mL and take another reading. Continue until it becomes difficult to pull the plunger.

5. Press the ▭ button and record the pressure–volume data in your notebook.

6. Disconnect the syringe, and repeat the above with an initial 10-mL gas fill and then again with an initial 5-mL fill.

7. When done, disconnect the syringe and leave it on the tray in the closed position. To de-power the sensor, Logger *Pro* must be turned off. From the upper menu bar, click on **Logger *Pro*** in the upper left-hand corner. From the drop-down menu box, select **Quit Logger *Pro***. Do not save files.

Calculations and Graphing for Part B:

Each pair of students should prepare one spreadsheet and graph.

    a. Find the other pair(s) of students in the lab that used the same gas. Share your data with these groups to give you a complete set of data for the gas you are studying.

    b. Open a new Excel spreadsheet. In the title for this new spreadsheet, be sure to record the identity of the gas your group investigated, as well as a descriptor of what the experiment was investigating.

    c. Enter the volume for your first trial in the first column.

    d. The volume needs to be corrected to account for the volume of gas in the sensor's tubing, which is 0.7 mL. In the second column, calculate the actual gas volume by adding 0.7 mL to the volume in the first column. *] equation*

    e. In the third column, calculate the inverse of the volume (1/V).

    f. Enter the measured pressures from your first trial in the fourth column.

    g. Prepare a graph of gas pressure vs. the inverse volume of gas.

    h. Repeat these steps for the second and third trials, placing all of the curves on the same graph. If you are unsure how to do this, refer to the Graphing document in Appendix D on page 289. Equations should be displayed on the graph and the graph should contain a key indicating the identity of each curve.

Enter your data in the class data Excel spreadsheet.

Part C: Examining the Relationship Between **Pressure** and **Temperature** for Various Gases at Constant Volume

Work Assignments

This section is to be done by the pair of students at each laboratory table that did not do part B. Both pairs will use the same gas, as will be assigned and dispensed by your TA. Data will be pooled and all students in the class must have a complete set of data to analyze at the end of lab.

In this procedure, we heat a gas sample in a closed vessel of known volume from room temperature to about 90°C while recording the gas pressure and temperature.

NOTES

Setup and Data Collection Procedure

Pressure and Temperature Sensor and Logger *Pro* Setup

1. The pressure and temperature sensors have already been connected to the computer.

2. Open Logger *Pro* by clicking on the Vernier ⟋ icon in the application menu bar. The software will recognize the sensor. Pressure will be reported in kPa units.

3. To configure the software, click on the data collection ⊡ icon in the Logger *Pro* menu bar. From the Data Collection box, select **Time Based** from the Mode menu. Then set the **Length** to **40 minutes** and the sampling rate to **1 samples/minute**.

4. The sensor and software are now ready for data collection.

P-T Equipment Setup

1. Evacuate air from the gas vessel (125-mL or 250-mL Erlenmeyer flask fitted with a stopper, hose, and valve assembly) with help from your TA at vacuum pump station. Your TA will oversee connecting the vessel to the vacuum pump and will operate the pump. Keep the valve closed until the next step. The flask has been labeled with the measured volume of the complete apparatus (flask with stopper, tubing, valve and connections to pressure sensor); record this value as you will need it for data analysis.

2. At your workstation fill the gas vessel with the assigned gas (nitrogen or argon):

    a. Connect the tubing to the balloon via the mating luer-lock fitting.

    > ### WARNING
    >
    > Do not over-tighten! The plastic threads are easily damaged and will leak. The luer-lock assembly is designed to be air and water tight with only light finger force and about a half turn.

    b. You will obtain the gas from a balloon kept in the fume hood. Open the valve on the balloon by turning the handle so that it is parallel to the assembly, and then open the valve on the tubing. See Figure 12-5. Gas will immediately flow into the flask. Then close both valves by turning the valve handles so that they are perpendicular to the valve body. Carefully unscrew the connector on the flask hose assembly.

FIGURE 12-5. Configuration for filling the flask with gas from a balloon

3. Set up the water bath: fill a 1 L beaker about ¾ full with deionized water, add a stir bar, and place the beaker on the hot plate (no heat or stirring yet).

4. Secure the gas vessel in the clamp, with the lip of the flask centered between the upper and lower edge of the clamp. See Figure 12-6. This position will allow the flask to be submerged more completely, which will improve the accuracy of the data.

FIGURE 12-6. Clamped flask

NOTES
▼

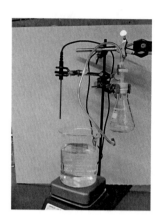

FIGURE 12-7. Equipment assembly for Part C

5. Lower the vessel into the water, securing the clamp where it just touches the lip of the beaker. Now add water to the beaker until the water level is as high as possible without overflowing.

6. Open the valve at the end of the tube attached to the gas vessel, and connect the tube to the Vernier pressure sensor. Because the tubing is briefly open to the atmosphere, the contained gas will now be at room pressure.

7. Place a Vernier temperature probe in the water bath. The probe should not touch the side of the beaker or the gas vessel. See Figure 12-8.

FIGURE 12-8. Flask in water bath with temperature probe

8. Begin stirring the water bath, and turn the heat all the way up. Start pressure—temperature data collection in Logger *Pro*. As the water bath heats up, use a poly pipet to withdraw water as needed to prevent overflow due to thermal expansion.

9. When the water temperature reaches about 90°C, halt data collection and turn off the hot plate (continue stirring to prevent localized boiling).

10. Record the value for the volume of the apparatus that you and your partner used.

11. When finished, empty and clean up the equipment.

Calculations and Graphing for Part C

Each pair of students should prepare one spreadsheet and graph.

a. Find the other pair(s) of students in the lab that used the same gas. Share your data with these groups to give you a complete set of data for the gas you are studying.

b. Open a new Excel spreadsheet. In the title for this new spreadsheet, be sure to record the identity of the gas your group investigated, as well as a descriptor of what the experiment was investigating.

c. Cut and paste the pressure and temperature data into this spreadsheet.

d. For this analysis, and all experiments involving gases, it is necessary to use Kelvin temperatures. In another column, calculate the Kelvin temperature by adding 273 to the values in the column marked C.

e. Prepare a graph of pressure vs absolute temperature for your gas sample.

GRAPHING

In addition to the graphs you already prepared using your individual data, you will also need to prepare graphs using class data to allow you to do a complete analysis. Please note that all data must be entered in the class Excel spreadsheet. It will be in your best interest to complete all graphs in the lab rather than at home so your TA can check your work and ensure that you have a complete data set.

The following graphs should be created and submitted as part of your lab report. All graphs must be at least a half page or larger.

Part A, volume and mole relationship

1. Your mole/volume data, including at least four data points.

2. Class mole/volume data.

Part B, volume and pressure relationship

3. Pressure/volume data for Ar (3 curves).

4. Pressure/volume data for a N_2 (3 curves).

Part C, pressure and temperature relationship

5. Pressure/temperature data for Ar.

6. Pressure/temperature data for N_2.

REPORT

A slim report is required for this laboratory.

Your slim report should include these components:

Introduction

See the Generic Guidelines for further information on this section.

Calculations and Graphs

- Show *one example* calculation for each of the following:

    1. Part A: Stoichiometric relationship to convert Mg (g) to to mol of H2

    2. Part B: Converting recorded volume to corrected volume

    3. Part C: Converting recorded temperature from Celsius to Kelvin

- Include all six graphs generated for this experiment in your report. Recommended printing style: half-page or full-page graphs with all appropriate headings/captions and features. Refer to the guidelines on page xxxi of your lab text to ensure your graphs are properly formatted.

    Part A, volume and mole relationship

    1. Your mole/volume data, including at least four data points.

    2. Class mole/volume data.

    Part B, volume and pressure relationship

    3. Pressure/volume data for Ar (3 curves).

    4. Pressure/volume data for a N_2 (3 curves).

    Part C, pressure and temperature relationship

    5. Pressure/temperature data for Ar.

    6. Pressure/temperature data for N_2.

ANALYSIS

The goal of this lab is to find the different relationships between quantity, pressure, volume and temperature of gases. You will be able to do this by analyzing the graphs you have created. Indicate which graph(s) support your answers to the following questions. What is the relationship between the number of moles of a gas and the volume? What is the relationship between the pressure of a gas and the volume, and does the relationship change depending on the initial volume? What is the relationship between the temperature of a gas and the pressure? Does the identity of the gas (N_2, Ar) matter, or do all gases apparently exhibit the same behaviors under similar conditions? Explain. What evidence do you have to support the claim made in the introduction of this lab write-up that most gases behave ideally under ambient conditions?

Extra Credit (5 points): On your own, with no assistance from a TA, use the data collected to determine R, the Ideal Gas Constant. Compare with the literature value (including a reference), report your % error and comment on your findings.

NOTES

exp13

Spectrophotometric Determination of a Food Dye

INTRODUCTION

Food additives, such as artificial colors and flavors, are ubiquitous in the American diet. There is often concern about whether these substances are safe to consume, or more importantly, whether they are safe to consume in the quantities that are present. It is not the purpose of this experiment to determine the safety or efficacy of food dyes but rather, to determine the amount that is present in several popular drinks. This experiment introduces **spectrophotometry** as a method for quantitative analysis.

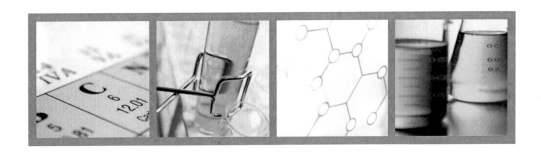

NOTES

BACKGROUND

Spectrophotometry

Read Appendix E, *Spectrophotometry*.

The Beer-Lambert law states:

$$A = \varepsilon bc$$

where

A is absorbance (unitless)

ε is the molar absorptivity coefficient ($M^{-1}\,cm^{-1}$)

b is pathlength (cm)

c is concentration (M)

We can see that using this relationship, the concentration of a solution is directly proportional to its absorbance.

To find the concentration of an unknown, a standard (or calibration) curve is made by measuring the absorbance, A, of several **standard solutions**, which are solutions of known concentration. Note that when A is plotted versus c, a straight line passing through the origin and with a slope of (εb) results. The concentration of the unknown is determined by using this equation and the absorbance of the unknown.

It should be noted that when solution concentrations are too high or too low there are deviations from Beer's law and there is no longer a linear relationship between absorbance and concentration. In this case it is no longer possible to utilize a standard curve to determine concentration and solutions must be diluted until their absorbance is within the linear range.

Food Dyes

Coloring agents have been used as food additives for centuries. They help us to identify foods visually. For instance, lime and orange sherbets would be nearly indistinguishable based on appearance if not for the added green and orange colors. They add a festive appearance to foods—M&M's candies would still taste just the same if they were all colored gray, but where's the fun in that? They are also added to foods because we have very strong expectations about what colors should be associated with certain foods. All else being equal, would you be more likely to buy a bright orange-colored orange, or one that is a mottled brown-green?

Coloring agents have been added to foods for less legitimate reasons as well. At the beginning of the 20th century, when there was no regulation of color additives in this country, coloring agents were added to food to mask inferior or spoiled foods, and some coloring agents marketed for inclusion in food were just flat out poisonous. Since passage of the Federal Food, Drug, & Cosmetic (FD&C) Act of 1938, color additives in the US have been the responsibility of the Food and Drug Administration (FDA). A recent controversy in the news concerns the addition of a dye, canthaxanthin, to farm raised salmon. The dye gives the fish the deep red color consumers expect. After a lawsuit was filed in Seattle by a consumer advocate group, local grocery chains were forced to label all fish containing the dye.

The FDA splits coloring agents into two categories: "certifiable" and "exempt from certification." The former are derived primarily from petroleum; the latter includes agents derived largely from mineral, plant, or animal sources. Certified colors are further broken down into water-soluble "dyes" and water-insoluble "lakes," with most colors being available in both forms. At this time (2014) there were nine color additives certifiable for food use. Three of these will be used in this lab.

Red food dyes have a history of controversy. In 1960, additions to the FD&C Act of 1938 included the so-called Delaney amendment. This amendment prohibits the marketing of any coloring agent that has been found to cause cancer in animals or humans, *no matter what the dose*. For many years, FD&C Red No. 3 was the most important red dye used in foods. But, in 1983, a single study found that FD&C Red No. 3 could be associated with thyroid cancer in male rats. On the basis of that study, the FDA banned all uses of Red Lake No. 3 and several uses of Red Dye No. 3.[1] FD&C Red No. 2 met a similar end several years earlier,[2] with the curious result that, for a time, there were no red M&M's candies. As of today, Red Dye 3 remains certified for use in foods. However, food manufacturers have almost entirely abandoned this dye in favor of FD&C Red No. 40.

You can read more about color additives in foods, drugs, and cosmetics, at

> https://www.fda.gov/food/food-additives-petitions/color-additives-food
> (last accessed June 2019)

CHEMISTRY IN A SUSTAINABLE WORLD

Food dyes and other colored substances owe their color to the presence of *chromophores*, the part of a molecule that absorbs visible light. For reasons that are beyond the scope of this book, chromophores are frequently found in organic molecules containing alternating single and double bonds, such as exist in Allura Red. Complexes containing metal ions can also be chromophores. Some of these metal ions, particularly those that are referred to as *heavy metals*, are of concern in the

---

1 Dept. of Health and Human Services, FDA, Federal Register 1990, 55(22), 3515–3543.

2 U.S. Food and Drug Administration, Color Additives Fact Sheet, https://www.fda.gov/industry/color-additives-cosmetics/color-additives-and-cosmetics-fact-sheet (last accessed June 2019)

environment due to their toxicity to plants, animals, humans, wildlife, and aquatic life. Chemists are engaged in an on-going effort to mitigate the effects of these pollutants in the environment, and more importantly in terms of global sustainability, to minimize their use.

Traditionally, students studying the Beer-Lambert law performed experiments using brightly colored solutions of heavy metal ions such as copper, cobalt, or chromium. This resulted in the generation of large quantities of waste that required hazardous waste disposal. To eliminate the problem of toxic waste and to enact green chemistry principles, this experimental procedure has been modified to use food dyes, relatively harmless substances that can safely be washed down the drain when the experiment is finished.

The drive to replace heavy metal chromophores with less hazardous substances is not limited to academic teaching laboratories. Red, orange, and yellow pigments for the paint industry and others have historically been created using toxic heavy metals such as lead, chromium, and cadmium. In response to concerns about these compounds in the environment, Engelhard Organic Pigments has developed an environmentally friendly line of pigments for use in packaging and entirely phased out its use of heavy metals. Prior to this transition, the company produced 6.5 million pounds of metal containing pigments per year. In addition to eliminating heavy metals, a water-based manufacturing process was incorporated instead of using the organic solvents typically associated with the creation of pigments. For this, Engelhard Organic Pigments (now BASF Corporation) received the 2004 Designing Safer Chemicals Green Chemistry Achievement Award from the Environmental Protection Agency.[3]

PROCEDURE

CAUTION!

Although the material used in this experiment are food dyes, treat them with the same respect that you would show for any chemical unknown: do not taste, do not inhale the dust, and minimize skin contact.

There are 3 different food dyes that will be used this week, FD&C Yellow No. 5, FD&C Red No. 40 (Allura Red), and FD&C Blue No. 1. You will work individually to prepare solutions and make a Beer's Law graph for one of the dyes, as assigned by your lab instructor.

---

3 http://www2.epa.gov/green-chemistry/presidential-green-chemistry-challenge-winners (accessed 6/2019)

Part A: Preparation of Stock Solution

1. Using the information in Table 13-1, calculate the mass of your assigned food dye that is necessary to produce 500 mL of a solution of the target molarity. To check your work, verify that your calculated value is less than the mass shown in the last column of the table.

TABLE 13-1. Food Dye Information

Dye	Molar Mass (g/mol)	Target Molarity	Mass should be less than:
FD&C Yellow No. 5	534.37	1.75×10^{-4} M	0.06 g
FD&C Red No. 40	496.42	1.90×10^{-4} M	0.06 g
FD&C Blue No. 1	792.86	3.65×10^{-5} M	0.02 g

2. Before carrying out the next steps, make sure your hands are clean and *dry*! Take a 500 mL volumetric flask to the balance with you.

3. Place a square of weighing paper on the balance and tare the balance. Carefully weigh to the nearest 0.0001 g the quantity of food dye calculated in step 1. (Start with a very small scoop of material—the total quantity required is comparable in size to your small fingernail.) Don't walk away from or re-tare the balance yet.

4. Quantitatively transfer the food dye to the 500-mL volumetric flask. Place the weighing paper (now devoid of food dye) back on the same balance and record the mass. Take the weighing paper back to your station with you.

5. Fill the volumetric flask to the line with deionized water and mix well. This constitutes the stock solution from which you will prepare standard solutions. Dribble a few drops of water on the area of the weighing paper where the food dye sat. Record what you see.

Part B: Preparation of Standard Solutions

1. Clean and dry four containers of at least 100 mL capacity and label them A, B, C, and D.

2. Refer to Table 13-2 for the recommended quantity of stock solution to use to prepare your standard solutions. Transfer some of your stock solution to a small beaker and pipet from this beaker during steps 3 and 4. Because of the risk of contamination you should never pipet directly from the stock solution flask.

NOTES

TABLE 13-2. Quantity of Stock Solution for Preparing Standard Solutions

Dye	Solution A	Solution B	Solution C	Solution D
FD&C Yellow No. 5	1 mL	5 mL	10 mL	15 mL
FD&C Red No. 40	1 mL	5 mL	10 mL	15 mL
FD&C Blue No. 1	2 mL	5 mL	10 mL	15 mL

3. Prepare standard solution A by pipetting the quantity of stock solution given in Table 13-2 into a 100-mL volumetric flask. Dilute to volume and mix well. Transfer this to your container marked A, where it will be stored until you need it later.

4. Repeat, using the quantities in Table 13-2 for solutions B, C, and D to prepare the remaining three standard solutions. The standard solutions will be used to generate the calibration curve, and to determine λ_{max}. For convenience, the standard solutions will hereafter be referred to as std. soln. A, std. soln. B, etc.

Part C: Collection of Absorption Spectra and Determination of λ_{max}

λ_{max} is the wavelength at which a sample absorbs most strongly, i.e., at which the absorbance is the largest. Whatever their concentration, all samples of the same substance have the same wavelength of maximum absorbance (λ_{max}). The *amount* of light absorbed may vary, but the *energy*, or *wavelength*, of light absorbed remains the same. To determine λ_{max} for the food dye you are using, an absorbance spectrum is collected over the visible wavelength range and the wavelength with maximum absorbance is determined to be λ_{max}.

It is always necessary to use a "blank solution" when calibrating a spectrometer. This is a solution that contains all species that may be present *except* the species of interest. In the case of an aqueous solution, such as the food dye solution, the blank is deionized water. By calibrating with a blank, you are ensured that the measured absorbance is only due to the species of interest.

Standard Solutions

1. Start the Logger *Pro* 3.4.5 software.

2. To calibrate the Spectrometer, select **Experiment > Calibrate > Spectrometer**. The calibration dialog box will display the message: "Waiting ... seconds for lamp to warm up." Allow the spectrometer to warm up for at least three minutes. Follow the instructions in the dialog box to complete the calibration. The small container used to hold the sample is referred to as a "cuvette." For this experiment, where water is the solvent, fill the "blank" cuvette about ¾ full with de-ionized water. When handling the cuvette, touch the ridged sides only to avoid getting fingerprints on the windows. Insert the cuvette in the

spectrometer with the non-ridged sides facing top and bottom (toward the words "Vernier Spectrometer"). Click **Finish Calibration**, and when that is finished Click **OK**.

3. Fill a cuvette about ¾ full of your "std. soln. D." Place the sample in the cuvette holder of the Spectrometer and click **Collect** (*green* button).

4. Click **Stop** (red button) to end data collection.

5. To optimize the view of the absorbance spectrum that you have just collected, select **Analyze > Autoscale > Autoscale**.

6. Fill a cuvette about ¾ full of your "std. sol. C," place in the cuvette holder and click **Collect**. When the dialog box opens, click the blue button "Store Latest Run"; this will allow you to show (overlay) your "std. sol. C" on the same screen as your "std. sol D." Click **Stop** (red button) to end data collection.

7. Repeat with "std. sol. B" and "std. sol. A."

8. Now all 4 absorbance spectra should be on the screen, with "std. sol. D" the "highest" and 'std. sol. A' the "lowest" peak.

9. To change the absorbance spectrum colored lines to black, **Double-click** on the box just above the colored row of data you want to change ("Abs" box), click on the **Options** radio button, then on the **Color** tab, then the "scroll arrows," scroll down to the bottom to **Black** and click. Repeat for remaining colored lines.

10. To find the wavelength of maximum absorbance (λ_{max}), select **Analyze > Examine**. This will bring up a line on the screen that you can move to the wavelength of maximum absorbance. Record this value. It will also bring up a box with the Wavelength and Absorbance values that you can "grab" and move anywhere on the graph, and by **Double-clicking** in this box you can increase the font size also. Notice that moving the mouse moves the line.

11. **Double-click** anywhere else on the graph to bring up the "Graph options" box to type your name in the title box.

12. Once you have your graph with the line at exactly maximum absorbance (λ_{max}), without moving the mouse, type Command (⌘) P to print the absorbance spectrum.

13. The data can now be selected in the data table to the left, copied, and pasted into Excel for further analysis.

Part D: Concentration of Food Dye in Commercial Drinks

There are samples of 6 commercial drinks on the center bench. These drinks contain either one food dye (single component dye) or a combination of two of the food dyes that you and your classmates have made calibration curves for. Working

$$C_1 V_1 = C_2 V_2$$

NOTES
▼

with the other person at your table who used the same food dye as you, use a 50-mL beaker to obtain about 30 mL of the single component drink that contains "your" food dye. You can get more later if needed.

Consider the intensity of the color of this drink and decide whether the absorbance of the drink will fall within the range of your standard solution data. If uncertain, make a measurement of the absorbance using the previous procedure.

If the absorbance is not within the standard solution range, prepare a dilution of the drink solution to obtain one that is within the data range. Be sure to record the dilution factor that you used because you will need to use it in your calculations to determine the concentration of the food dye in the original solutions.

Once you have prepared a solution that is within range, measure and record the absorbance at λ_{max} of that solution.

Working with all of the others at your lab bench, use a 50-mL beaker to obtain about 30 mL of the drink that contains both of the food dyes used at your lab bench. Repeat the above process to determine the concentrations of both of the food dye components in the drink. It may be necessary to prepare different dilutions to measure the different dyes.

CALCULATIONS

Prepare a data table that, for each standard solution (including std. soln. D), includes concentration and measured absorbance at λ_{max}. Remember to give a sample calculation for the determination of concentration.

Generate a calibration curve by plotting absorbance vs. concentration. Perform a linear regression analysis and plot the line of best fit.

Use the equation for the line and the absorbance of the drink solution to determine the molarity of the food dyes in the drink. Remembering that the drink mixes were diluted and weaker than the normal drinks would be, calculate the concentration of the food dyes present in the beverage when consumed at their normal concentration.

REPORT

In addition to the normal components of every lab report, your report for this experiment should include the identity of the dyes that you studied, the spectrum (absorbance vs. wavelength) used to determine λ_{max}, the calibration curve, the molar absorptivity coefficient of the food dye that you studied, the molarity of the food dyes in the diluted drink solutions and the molarity of the food dyes in undiluted drinks. Additional items to consider in your discussion:

• Why do we want to know / use λ_{max}?

- When you weighed and then transferred the food dye to the volumetric flask, you made the assumption that the quantity you weighed all actually made it into the flask—that's what "quantitative transfer" implies. The point of re-weighing the empty weighing paper and then dribbling water on it was to help you evaluate the goodness of that assumption. *Did* all of the food dye get into the flask? If not, can you estimate (order of magnitude) how much did not? How does all of this affect the concentration of your stock solution?

- According to the Beer-Lambert law the calibration curve should be perfectly linear. The amount of "scatter" in the points is a reflection of experimental error. Comment on the linearity of your data and suggest a major source of error that would account for the scatter.

QUESTIONS

1. A student finishes with her std. soln. A and properly, thoroughly rinses out the 100-mL volumetric flask using distilled water. Then, however, she immediately proceeds to prepare her second standard solution without making any attempt to dry or shake out the residual water in the flask. What effect will this have on her std. soln. B? Will the concentration be too large? Too small? Explain.

2. Many common materials that we ingest (table salt, aspirin), though quite safe in reasonable quantities, become toxic when taken in very large doses. A measure of toxicity is the LD50 value (Lethal Dose, 50%). It is the quantity of material, expressed in mg of material per kg of subject-body-weight that, if administered to a population of subjects, will cause 50% of the population to perish. The LD50 value for FD&C Yellow No. 5 is 12,750 mg/kg in mice, FD&C Red Dye No. 40 is > 10,000 mg/kg in rats and for FD&C Blue No. 1 it is > 2,000 mg/kg in rats.

   Assume that the LD50 value for humans is the same as for mice and rats. Calculate the number of mg of food dye present in an eight-ounce glass of the single component beverage you used in this lab. How many such glasses would a typical adult human have to ingest in order to reach the LD50 concentration? Be sure to state explicitly any major assumptions you make in order to do the calculation. Considering only the potential acute toxicity of the food dye and neglecting anything else that may be present in the drink, do you believe that the beverage you analyzed is a safe product?

3. Calculate the volume of aqueous waste that you produced while completing this experiment. Use this value to calculate the volume of aqueous waste that would be produced by a General Chemistry course with 800 students enrolled.

   This lab procedure has frequently been performed using copper sulfate pentahydrate ($CuSO_4 \cdot 5H_2O$) instead of a food dye. Consult the MSDS (Material Safety Data Sheet) for copper sulfate pentahydrate to determine the concerns associated with this compound and appropriate methods of disposal. Would you be able to pour this waste down the drain as you did the food dye waste?

NOTES
▼

exp14

A Fatty Acid Monolayer

Avogadro's number is named after the Italian physicist and lawyer Almedo Avogadro, who, though he conceived the basic idea, never knew the actual value. Avogadro's number, N_A, is defined as the number of atoms in exactly 12 g of carbon-12 and according to the National Institute of Standards and Technology, the current accepted value for N_A is $6.02214129 \times 10^{23}$. The quantity of a substance that contains Avogadro's number of particles (atoms, molecules, formula units, etc.) is known as a mole of the substance.

Since it is clearly not possible, even with the fastest computer, to count all of the atoms in a mole, you may be wondering how Avogadro's number has been determined. Perhaps surprisingly, it isn't that difficult and over the years there have been many different experimental methods developed to measure this value. One technique, a variation of which we will be using in this laboratory experiment, counts the number of molecules present in a sample of compound with a known mass. Multiplication of the number of molecules per gram by the molar mass of the compound then yields Avogadro's number. In this experiment we will determine the number of molecules required to form a film of an oily substance, stearic acid, one molecule thick (a monolayer) on a water surface.

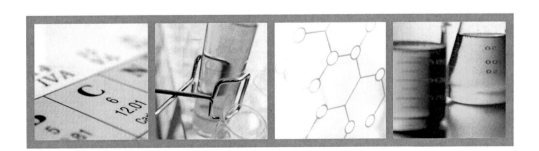

NOTES

Stearic acid ($C_{17}H_{35}COOH$) is a member of a class of substances known as fatty acids due to their presence in many natural fats. Fatty acids are long "hydrocarbon chains" which terminate in a carboxylic acid group (−COOH). The polar carboxylic acid group is strongly attracted to water (hydrophilic, or "water loving") through hydrogen bonding interactions. On the other hand, the long hydrocarbon chains are greasy and are repelled by water (hydrophobic, or "water hating"). Due to the presence of the long hydrophobic hydrocarbon chains, fatty acids are generally insoluble in water. When a solution of stearic acid in a volatile hydrocarbon solvent is placed on water, the stearic acid molecules spread out on the surface of the water with the hydrophilic "heads" (−COOH) stuck into the water and the hydrophobic "tails" projecting out into the space above the water. The water insoluble hydrocarbon solvent evaporates, leaving behind a monolayer of stearic acid. Additional stearic acid solution will cause the monolayer to spread until the entire water surface is covered. Subsequent addition of solution will float on top of the existing monolayer to form a lens-shaped droplet that is readily visible. The exact number of drops of stearic acid solution required to form the monolayer is readily apparent from the number of drops required to see the lensing effect.

CHEMISTRY IN A SUSTAINABLE WORLD

Several factors were considered in the selection of a solvent for this experiment. The first requirement is that the solvent be capable of dissolving stearic acid. Secondly, because the solvent/stearic acid layer has to float on the surface of water, the solvent must be insoluble in water. Lastly, the solvent needs to evaporate quickly (i.e., volatile). These requirements dictate that an organic solvent be used. Organic solvents exist in liquid form at room temperature, are volatile, are capable of dissolving fats and other non-polar substances, and are fairly insoluble in water. These solvents are carbon based, containing at least one carbon atom and one hydrogen atom, and are widely used in industrial and cleaning applications. There is often a risk associated with their use and many are recognized as carcinogens, teratogens, and neurotoxins. After testing several solvents, hexane, C_6H_{14}, was chosen. In addition to meeting the above requirements, when released into the air hexane can react with oxygen and break down relatively quickly. Hexane has low acute toxicity, meaning that the immediate risk associated with low short-term exposure is slight though long-term chronic exposure can lead to neurological problems.[1] When handled properly in a laboratory with adequate ventilation there is minimal risk associated with its use.

The selection of hexane as a solvent is an example of the complexities associated with green experimental design. There are organic solvents that are more benign than hexane but when tested, these provided unsatisfactory results. There are other solvents, such as chloroform and benzene, that have more desirable solubility properties but these are much more hazardous to human health and the environment.

---

1 *Agency for Toxic Substances and Disease Registry, United States Public Health Service.* Toxicological Profile for Hexane 7/99. *http://www.atsdr.cdc.gov/toxprofiles/tp.asp?id=393&tid=68 (accessed 6/2019).*

NOTES
▼

Due to procedural requirements we are unable to eliminate the need for an organic solvent but by using hexane we can achieve our experimental goals in the greenest manner possible.

PROCEDURE

> **SAFETY NOTE**
>
> Avoid skin contact with hexane. Avoid breathing the fumes and use the fume hood as instructed.

This can be a very unforgiving lab if sloppy methods are used. Pay careful attention to portions of the procedure pertaining to cleaning the watch glass and dropping technique. Part B (on the following page) can be done before Part A if it becomes crowded near the sinks and washing area.

Part A—Preparation of the Watch Glass

Fatty acids are very similar in structure to other "oily" substances, such as body oils and also soap. Because you are trying to determine the number of molecules of stearic acid required to form a monolayer on a water surface, it is very important that your glassware is completely clean before you start. The presence of either bodily oils (fingerprints) or soap will have disastrous effects on your results.

Measure and record the diameter of a 125-mm watch glass. Measure several different directions to see if the watch glass actually is round. Calculate the average diameter if it is not. You now need to clean the watch glass, which is the most critical portion of this lab. First, wash your hands and rinse off all soap. Then scrub the watch glass thoroughly with hot water and a clean paper towel. Do not use any soap. After scrubbing, avoid touching the inside surface of the watch glass. Rinse thoroughly (2 min.) with LOTS of tap water and then give a final rinse with deionized water. Clean and rinse a 150-mL beaker using the same care.

Place the clean watch glass on a 600-mL beaker. This will be the holder for the watch glass from now on. Using the cleaned 150-mL beaker, put some deionized water into the watch glass. Position the beaker-watch glass assembly so that you can see the overhead lights reflected in the water's surface. Then fill the watch glass to the edge with deionized water from the 150-mL beaker. Ensure the watch glass is completely full by filling until the water spills over the edge.

NOTES

▼

Part B—Calibration of the Pipet

The purpose of the calibration is to determine the volume of a drop delivered from the pipet. It is therefore important that your drops are of consistent size. To help ensure this, note the following dropping tips:

- Consistent drop size can be maintained only if the pipet is held completely vertical while dropping.

- Form and release the drops in "good time" with a steady rhythm. Use a very gentle squeeze so that back pressure isn't built up in the pipet bulb.

- Never tip up the pipet and allow the solution to run into the bulb. If this happens, the hexane will dissolve anything in the bulb and this will be added to your solution, thus ruining the experiment. Recall that accurate results depend on having a monolayer composed of stearic acid molecules only.

- Hexane in the pipet will evaporate readily at normal body temperatures, thus altering the composition of the solution. To avoid having the heat from your hands vaporize the hexane, fill the pipet partially full and handle by the top and bulb only.

- Take care to keep the solution from contacting the rubber pipet bulb, as this may dissolve some of the rubber and ruin the experiment.

Obtain a clean Pasteur pipet. These are new and have never been handled. Without touching it, check the pipet tip to be sure that it isn't broken, chipped, or cracked. (The bottom of the tip should be at right angles to the sides of the pipet.)

Weigh a clean, dry weighing bottle with the lid.

Place about 3 mL pure hexane (located in the large laboratory hoods) in a small graduated cylinder. Practice your dropping technique by pulling up some of the hexane into your pipet and dropping it back into the graduated cylinder. Then, use the Pasteur pipet to add 25 drops of hexane to the weighing bottle. Because the hexane evaporates very quickly, immediately cover the weighing bottle after the 25 drops have been added.

Weigh the bottle, lid, and hexane. (Avoid jostling the bottle when carrying it, as this will speed up the evaporation.) After weighing, return the hexane to the graduated cylinder and repeat this process 2 more times. Then, dispose of the hexane in the waste container in the hood.

Part C—The Monolayer

Use a weighing bottle to obtain a small amount of stearic acid/hexane solution from the hood area. Keep it covered when not in use. Record the concentration of this solution (including units).

Quickly rinse the Pasteur pipet several times with the stearic acid/hexane solution. Then, add the solution, one drop at a time (remember technique!), to the center

of the water in the watch glass. You must add the drops to a portion of the water's surface in which you see the overhead lights mirrored so that you can see what happens to each drop.

Counting the drops and waiting about 10 seconds after each drop is added (for the hexane to evaporate), continue adding until a drop will not disperse. You should be able to see each drop spread out until this last one, which should remain as a lens-shaped drop (which looks like a bead of oil) in the middle of the watch glass for about 5 to 10 seconds. (It will disappear as the hexane evaporates off.) Record the number of drops required to form the monolayer. (The number of drops required to form the monolayer is one less than the number required to observe the lens effect.)

> **NOTE**
> Everyone's technique is a little different, but it generally takes 10–20 drops to form the monolayer. If you observe a lensing effect after only one drop, your glass is not clean.

Because all the hexane has evaporated off, you may dispose of the water/stearic acid mixture down the drain.

Repeat Parts A and C two more times (3 trials). It is not necessary to repeat the pipet calibration.

Dispose of used pipets in the broken glass container.

CALCULATIONS

The goal of your calculations is to determine an experimental value of Avogadro's number (molecules/mole). To find the number of moles of stearic acid, you will first determine the mass of stearic acid from the measured volume and known concentration of the stearic acid solution. The number of moles of stearic acid in the monolayer is determined using its molar mass.

The surface area of the water covered by each stearic acid molecule is approximately 0.21 nm^2.[2,3] The total number of stearic acid molecules in the monolayer can be determined from the measured area of the monolayer. Avogadro's number is then obtained by dividing the number of stearic acid molecules by the number of moles of stearic acid.

2 Smith, H. A., Hurley, R. B. J. Phys. Colloid. Chem., *1949, 53, 1409.*

3 Adamson, A. W., Physical Chemistry of Surfaces; *John Wiley and Sons: New York, 1976.*

NOTES

▼

> **NOTE**
>
> When doing your calculations, be careful with unit conversions. It is probably easiest to convert all distances to meters before doing any calculations. If converting from a value such as cm² to m², remember to perform the same operation on both the number and the units in the conversion factor. For example, the volume of a 1 m³ cube in cm is not found by performing the following calculation:
>
> $$1\,\cancel{m^3}\left(\frac{100\ cm^3}{\cancel{m^3}}\right) = 100\ cm^3 \quad \textit{(Wrong!)}$$
>
> Rather, this value is found as follows:
>
> $$1\,\cancel{m^3}\left(\frac{100\ cm}{\cancel{m}}\right)\left(\frac{100\ cm}{\cancel{m}}\right)\left(\frac{100\ cm}{\cancel{m}}\right) = 1\,\cancel{m^3}\left(\frac{100\ cm}{\cancel{m}}\right)^3 = 1 \times 10^6\ cm^3$$

Part A—Determination of the number of molecules (N) in a monolayer:

1. Calculate the surface area (A) of the monolayer in the watch glass (where d = diameter of the watch glass):

$$A = \frac{\pi d^2}{4}$$

2. Calculate the number of stearic acid molecules (N) in the monolayer. Assume that the area each stearic acid molecule covers is 0.21 nm2 and that there are no spaces between the molecules.

$$N = \frac{A}{0.21\ nm^2/molecule}$$

Part B—Determination of the number of moles:

3. Calculate the average mass of 25 drops of hexane from calibration (Part B).

4. The number of drops per mL is calculated from the average mass of the drops counted into the weighing bottle (previous step) and the density of hexane (0.667 g/mL).

$$\frac{drops}{mL} = \frac{density\ of\ hexane\ (g/mL)}{average\ mass\ of\ drops\ (g)} \times 25\ drops$$

5. Calculate the volume (V) of stearic acid solution required to form the mono-layer. The volume can be found by using the number of drops of stearic acid solution needed to form the layer and the value for the number of drops per milliliter obtained in the previous calculation.

$$V = \frac{\text{number of drops}}{\text{number of drops per milliliter}}$$

6. Calculate the mass (m) of stearic acid from the calculated volume of solution and the concentration given in g/mL.

$$m = (\text{concentration}) \times V$$

7. Calculate the number of moles (n) of stearic acid (molar mass = 284.5 g/mol).

$$n = \frac{m}{284.5 \text{ g/mol}}$$

Part C—Calculate the number of stearic acid molecules per mole. This is the experimental value for Avogadro's number.

$$\text{number of molecules per mole} = \frac{N}{n} = N_A$$

DISCUSSION/CONCLUSION

Report your values of N_A and the mean and standard deviation. Compare your value to the accepted value of Avogadro's number. Consider the following when doing so: What are the largest source(s) of error? Were the results for each of your trials consistent? How do the different sources of error impact the results? What assumptions were made when doing this laboratory experiment? Can you use these assumptions to explain any unexpected results?

Green chemistry does not require that questions remain unanswered or products be abandoned due to environmental or waste concerns. Rather, it accepts that the end goal is a given and then seeks to find ways to achieve that goal in a manner that adheres to the twelve principles of green chemistry. Discuss how this statement is relevant in the context of this experiment.

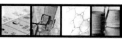

NOTES

exp15

Forensic Analysis of Ink Using Thin-Layer Chromatography

INTRODUCTION

Chromatography is a technique used to separate and/or analyze complex mixtures. There are several different types of chromatography and all involve distributing the substance to be analyzed between two phases, one of which moves and is called the moving phase, and the other which does not and is called the stationary phase. Each component in the mixture being separated spends some time sorbed (the process is called sorption) on the stationary phase, and some time desorbed in the moving phase. Components desorbed in the moving phase are carried along by the moving phase. The essence of the separation technique is that a component that spends much of its time desorbed will be carried further in a given interval of time than a component that spends much of its time sorbed onto the stationary phase.

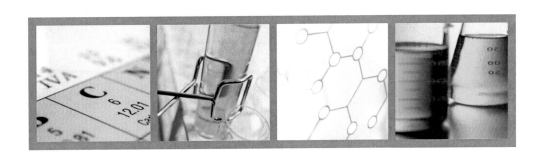

NOTES

One of the oldest forms of chromatography is adsorption chromatography. In this form, the stationary phase is a solid (the adsorbent) and the moving phase is a liquid. The stationary phase is a porous medium with very large surface area, such as silica gel ($SiO_2 \cdot H_2O$), cellulose, or finely divided alumina (Al_2O_3) (see Table 15-1). The stationary phase can be packed into a glass column (column chromatography) or may be in the form of a thin layer spread onto a sheet of plastic or glass backing material (thin-layer chromatography, or TLC). The moving phase is a liquid that passes down through the column by gravity, or through the thin-layer by capillary action. Usual laboratory practice is to select an appropriate solid adsorbent and then vary the polarity of the liquid solvent to achieve maximum separation of the components in the mixture. Solvent polarity is easily controlled by either choosing a pure solvent of a given polarity or by mixing solvents of different polarity to achieve the desired polarity (see Table 15-2).

TABLE 15-1. Solid Adsorbents for Thin-Layer Chromatography

Solid Adsorbents	
paper	increasing
cellulose	polarity
calcium sulfate	↓
silica gel	
alumina	

TABLE 15-2. Liquid Solvents for Chromatography

Liquid Solvents	
cyclohexane	increasing
carbon tetrachloride*	polarity
benzene*	↓
methylene chloride*	
diethyl ether	
ethyl acetate	
acetone	
pyridine	
ethanol	
methanol	
water	
acetic acid	

*Suspected carcinogens.

In this experiment you will separate ink, which is a mixture of colored substances, into its different components using adsorption chromatography. When that has been accomplished, you will be able to identify which of several suspect pens was used to write a threatening letter. TLC is a primary tool for rapid qualitative analysis of mixtures and is extremely effective and convenient for this purpose. A microscopic amount of sample is applied at one end of a small plate covered on one side with a thin coating of adsorbent (a technique known as spotting). The plate is then dipped into a shallow pool of solvent which rises on the coated layer by capillary action, permitting the compounds of a mixture to move with the solvent to differing heights. This is known as developing the chromatogram. In this process, the various components of the mixture are separated. They can then be detected as separate spots along the plate. The separation is based on the different rates at which the individual components of the mixture advance upwards along the plate. The stronger the affinity or "binding" of the chemicals in the mixture to the adsorbent, the less rapidly they will move up the ascending chromatogram with any given moving solvent. In general, the adsorbent is strongly polar and strongly binds polar substances. The moving phase is generally less polar and most easily transports substances that are less polar or non-polar. To summarize, on a polar adsorbent, the most polar substances will advance only slightly, if at all, while non-polar substances will travel further and more rapidly.

Determining the compounds in a mixture is done by inspecting the movement of the spots of the compounds to varying heights on the TLC plate. Spots that are pigmented may be seen visually. Non-pigmented spots can be detected by treating the developed TLC plate with iodine vapor or by illuminating the plate with an ultraviolet lamp. Many substances, particularly certain organic compounds, will show a bright fluorescence under ultraviolet light that may have a characteristic color. Yet another way to make the spots more visible on the plate is to use an adsorbent layer that contains a trace of fluorescent dye. Compounds that are fluorescent will show up as bright spots on a light background; any others will appear as dark spots, since they absorb the ultraviolet light and prevent fluorescence of the dye.

For identification of a specific compound in a mixture, the TLC behavior of the mixture and that of a known sample are compared on the same plate. A given compound will move on the plate to the same extent relative to the solvent front (a ratio known as the R_f value) under the same conditions (sample quality, solvent, temperature, and coating). Because these conditions are not often rigidly controlled, comparison of two samples on the same plate is therefore essential. In addition to identifying a compound based on its position on the plate in relation to a known sample, the appearance of the compound on the plate may also aid in identification if distinctive color or fluorescence can be developed.

NOTES

Forensic document examiners are often called upon to scientifically examine inks. Suppose, as part of a criminal investigation, a threatening note such as a bomb threat or a ransom demand is discovered. A suspect is arrested and is found to have a pen in his/her pocket. By examining the ink from both the threatening note and the suspect's pen, it can be determined if the inks are of the same chemical formulation. While this is not definitive proof that the suspect wrote the note, it does add to the body of circumstantial evidence against the suspect.

Ink samples are examined both physically and chemically. Physical examination includes looking at the color of the ink, whether it fluoresces under ultraviolet light, and whether it absorbs or transmits under infrared light. Some manufacturers deliberately add a particular pigment or fluorescent substance to their dyes to make them more readily identifiable. Chemical examination is typically done using TLC. A tiny sample of the writing is removed from the sample. The ink is then extracted from the paper using a suitable solvent. For waterproof ballpoint pens, pyridine is usually the solvent of choice. For water-soluble felt tip pens a solution of 50% ethanol in water can be used. The extracted ink is then applied to a TLC plate along with a sample of ink from the suspect's pen. After the chromatogram has been developed, a comparison of pigments and R_f values from the two samples can determine whether the inks are of the same formulation.

CHEMISTRY IN A SUSTAINABLE WORLD

Thin-Layer Chromatography has been used in research, commercial and teaching laboratories for many years. It is utilized in the General Chemistry laboratory course to provide students with an introduction to the procedure and to prepare them for the Organic Chemistry laboratory where the technique is used to monitor the progress of chemical reactions. For our purposes, the only requirement is that the mixture to be analyzed contains components that can be separated and visualized. The previous version of this experiment analyzed a mixture of the heavy metal ions Cd^{2+}, Cu^{2+}, Pb^{2+}, Fe^{2+}, Co^{2+}, and Ni^{2+} and used n-butanol, acetone, concentrated HCl, NH_3, Na_2S and dimethylglycine as solvents and visualizing agents. While the metal ions were colorful and readily visualized, the experiment was decidedly "non-green." In recognition of the green chemistry principles to prevent waste and use safer solvents whenever possible, the procedure was changed to one that is greener and more relevant without making any compromises to the pedagogical goals of the course.

PROCEDURE

A threatening letter has been received by the Office of Public Safety. The only information they have to go on is that it was sent from someone associated with a radical campus student organization. The investigating officer has obtained pens from several members of the group and would like us to analyze the inks and compare them to the inks used on the letter.

Part A—Determining the Best Solvent System

Work with the members of your group to determine the best solvent system for this analysis.

The best solvent (or eluent) for a TLC analysis is generally not known in advance and must be determined by the experimenter through a process of trial and error. The solvent selected should be one that

- does not allow any of the compounds to remain on the baseline,
- does not allow any of the compounds to travel with the solvent front, and
- maximizes the differences in the R_f values for the compounds being separated.

1. Using one of the suspect pens provided in lab, draw a line about one inch long on a piece of paper, cut it into small pieces and place into a well on a spot plate. Add 50% ethanol to fill the well about half full. Allow about 10 minutes for the complete extraction of the ink. Stir periodically with a glass stir rod.

2. Obtain 7 developing jars. Number the jars 1–7. Place approximately 3 mL (1/4″ depth) of each of the solvent solutions from the table below in the correspondingly numbered jar.

> **SAFETY NOTE**
> The solvents used in this lab are fairly volatile. Therefore, keep chromatography jars capped when not actually transferring TLC plates.

Jar #	Solvent composition
1	100% ethyl acetate
2	50% ethyl acetate/50% ethanol
3	50% ethyl acetate/25% ethanol/25% water
4	100% ethanol
5	25% ethyl acetate/25% ethanol/50% water
6	50% water/50% ethanol
7	100% water

3. While waiting for the extraction to be completed, obtain 7 pieces of filter paper. Lightly pencil in a horizontal line approximately 1 cm from one of the short edges of the plate (do not use a pen or mechanical pencil).

4. Fill the tip of a micropipet by dipping into the extracted ink solution. Capillary action will fill the pipet. To spot the filter paper, touch the micropipet lightly and briefly to each piece of paper on the pencil line. Allow the solvent to dry. The extracted ink should be spotted repeatedly until the spot is a medium-dark

gray. This may require spotting up to 10 times. The smaller the spot, the better the separation, so try to keep the size of your spot small—approximately 2 mm in diameter.

5. Place one piece of the spotted filter paper in each jar and cap the jar. Make certain the level of the developing solvent in the jar is below the origin marked on your filter paper. When placing the paper in the jar, take care not to jiggle the jar to avoid splashing solvent onto the plate and causing erroneous results. Allow the chromatogram to develop until the solvent front is approximately 1 cm from the top. Remove the filter paper from the jar and immediately mark the solvent front with a pencil by drawing a horizontal line across the width of the paper at the height to which the solvent has advanced. Circle each spot with a pencil. In your lab book, sketch the plates, indicating the location and color of the different spots or bands of color. (This is important because the plates fade as they dry.)

6. With your group, determine the best solvent to use for the separation of the ink components of the pen that you used. Before proceeding to Part B, verify your choice of solvent with your TA.

7. Dispose of waste in the marked containers in the fume hoods. Do not pour solvents down the drain.

Part B—Analysis of Unknown

Work independently for this portion of the lab.

1. Cut out a sample of handwriting from the incriminating correspondence (10–12 characters should be sufficient). Cut the sample into small pieces and transfer to a well plate for extraction. Extract the ink using the same procedure as used previously. Your solution should be very dark. If not, add more of the writing sample in order to extract more ink. On a piece of scrap paper, write a word or two with each of the suspect pens. Do not use the extracted ink from Part A—this process should be repeated for the pen used previously. Again, extract the inks using 50% ethanol. Allow 10–15 minutes for complete extraction of the inks. Periodically agitate the paper with a glass stirring rod for a more complete extraction.

2. Obtain a silica gel plate. Notice there is a shiny side and a dull, rough side, which is the adsorbent side. Take care to not touch the adsorbent side with your fingers. On the rough side of the TLC plate, *lightly pencil* in a horizontal line approximately 1 cm from one of the short edges of the plate (do not use a pen or mechanical pencil). You will be placing four samples on the plate, as shown in Figure 15-1.

3. Fill the tip of the micropipet by dipping into one of the solutions to be examined. Spot the TLC plate following the same procedure as used in part A. You may first want to practice your spotting technique on a practice TLC plate.

4. Rinse the micropipet with water by allowing capillary action to fill the pipet. Blow out the excess water with a pipet bulb. Repeat the spotting process with the other samples rinsing after each ink sample.

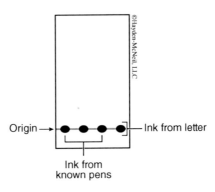

FIGURE 15-1. Chromatography plate

5. Put approximately ½ cm of the developing solvent (determined in Part A) in a beaker. This should be enough to cover the bottom, but not so much that the solvent level is higher than the spots on the TLC plate. Place the TLC plate in the beaker and cover with a piece of aluminum foil. Make certain the level of the developing solvent in the beaker is below the origin marked on your TLC plate. Again, to avoid erroneous results, take care to avoid splashing solvent on the plate. Allow the chromatogram to develop until the solvent front is approximately 2 cm from the top.

6. Remove the TLC plate from the jar and immediately mark the solvent front on the dull side of the plate with a pencil by drawing a horizontal line across the width of the plate at the height to which the solvent has advanced. After doing this, view the plate under a UV lamp and draw a light pencil circle around any spots that you observe. After returning to your work station, circle each colored spot on your TLC plate with a pencil. In your lab book, sketch the plate, indicating the location and color of the different spots or bands of color. By comparing the R_f values (see Figure 15-2) and the colors of the pigments in the inks from each of the samples, determine which type of pen was used to write the incriminating letter.

7. Dispose of waste in the marked containers in the fume hood.

CALCULATIONS

Calculate R_f values for all spots. These values are determined as shown in Figure
15-2 using the following equation:

$$R_f = \frac{\text{distance from the origin to the center of a spot}}{\text{distance from origin to the solvent front}}$$

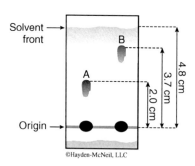

FIGURE 15-2. Determination of R_f values

DISCUSSION/CONCLUSION

Report the solvent used and your basis for selecting it. Discuss the different solvents
in terms of polarity and what your results indicate about the degree of polarity that
seems to be best for this particular analysis. Discuss the solvent selection in terms
of green chemistry. Would it have been possible to accomplish your experimental
goals with a greener solvent that could have perhaps gone down the drain at the
end of the experiment?

Report the identity of the pen that was used and your basis for identification.
Imagine that you have been called on the witness stand to defend your identification. What sources of error exist which may weaken your analysis?

Discuss the chromatography procedure which you performed, considering such
factors as why some pigments rise higher on the plate than others and what conditions are necessary to get a good separation of components.

Include your silica gel TLC plates with your report. It is not necessary to include the
filter paper chromatograms from Part A.

exp16

Freezing Points of Solvents and Solutions

Ice cream makers, automobile antifreeze and arctic fish all take advantage of the same phenomenon to alter the point at which freezing would be expected to occur. Any time a solution is formed by dissolving solute in solvent, the freezing point of the solution is different than that of the pure solvent.

If we define $T_{f(\text{solvent})}$ as the freezing point of the pure solvent and $T_{f(\text{solution})}$ as the freezing point of the solution, the change in the freezing point, in °C, is given by:

$$\Delta T_f = \left| T_{f(\text{solvent})} - T_{f(\text{solution})} \right| \qquad (1)$$

In this laboratory experiment, as a class, you will design experiments to observe and measure the effect that the amount of solute has on the freezing point of a solvent and use your data to determine the molar mass of the solute.

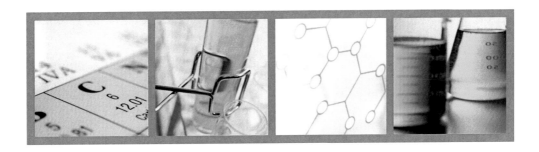

135

Because it is difficult to determine the temperature at which a substance solidifies, you will need to collect data and graph a cooling curve by recording the temperature of the cooling sample as a function of time. Ideally the temperature of the pure solvent should decrease at a steady rate until it reaches its freezing temperature, hold for some time while all the sample solidifies and then cooling should resume at a steady rate. This behavior is illustrated in Figure 16-1.

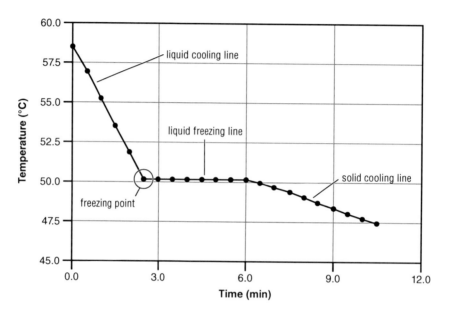

FIGURE 16-1. Ideal cooling curve

In actual practice the curves may look more like Figure 16-2 and the point where freezing actually begins isn't as easy to observe. The freezing point of the sample is obtained by drawing the best straight line through the steady declining points as the liquid is cooling and another line through the data points that remain constant as the sample is freezing. The intersection of the lines is taken as the freezing point.

You also may observe supercooling before the sample begins to freeze, indicated by a brief drop in temperature below the freezing point. The freezing point is determined in the same manner.

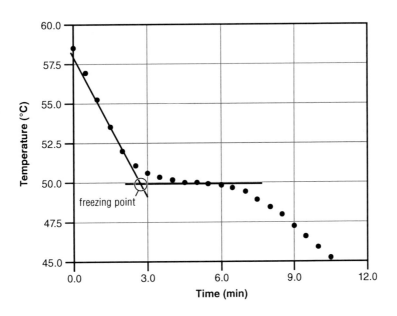

FIGURE 16-2. Cooling curve of a pure solvent

Figure 16-3 illustrates a cooling curve when an impurity is present. The slight slope that occurs as the sample is cooling is due to the presence of the impurities. The freezing point of the sample is obtained by drawing the best straight line through the steady declining points of the liquid and another line through the slightly sloped "plateau" which occurs as the sample freezes. The intersection of the lines is taken as the freezing point.

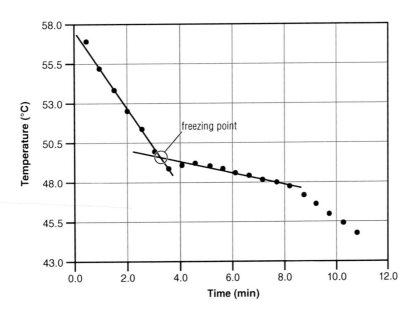

FIGURE 16-3. Cooling curve of an impure solvent

CHEMISTRY IN A SUSTAINABLE WORLD

The procedure for this experiment previously called for the use of naphthalene and p-dichlorobenzene as "unknown" solutes. You may be familiar with these substances as they are used as insecticides and pest repellents and have very strong odors that you may associate with mothballs or toilet bowl deodorizers. In addition to their toxicity to moths and other insects, they are both suspected human carcinogens and moderately poisonous. Naphthalene is in a class of compounds known as polycyclic aromatic hydrocarbons and has been classified as a primary pollutant by the U.S. Environmental Protection Agency. Because of the risks associated with naphthalene and p-dichlorobenzene, they have been replaced in this experiment with another substance that may also have a familiar odor to you. This compound is widely used in cooking and consumer products such as Vicks VapoRub™, is abundant in the oils of coniferous trees and other plant species and is only poisonous when ingested in large quantities. You will learn the name of this green replacement after you have collected your data for this experiment.

PROCEDURE

For this laboratory, you will be using Vernier LabPro™ digital temperature probes and Logger *Pro*™ software for data collection and analysis. You will be collecting data in pairs—be sure to switch roles at least once.

> **SAFETY NOTE**
>
> Cyclohexane is as explosive as gasoline. There must be no sparks or flames in the lab! Test tubes containing cyclohexane should be stoppered when not in use.

Part A—Freezing Point Determination of a Pure Solvent

As a class, you need to determine if the freezing point of a pure solution is dependent on the amount of solvent that is present.

Note that water is a contaminant in this experiment and test tube(s) must be clean and dry before use.

Experimental System

Conduct the experiments using the large test tubes that are in the lab.

1. To prepare your sample, use a No. 1 rubber stopper to lightly seal the test tube. Place in a 100-mL beaker and use the beaker to support the tube during weighing and while you are carrying it. Weigh the tube, stopper, and beaker on the analytical balance, add cyclohexane and weigh again. Quantities of cyclohexane to be used should be in the range between 3 and 7 grams. Because cyclohexane is fairly volatile, avoid heating the test tube with your hands.

2. You will cool down the cyclohexane in a salt-ice bath. Fill a small beaker with about 250–300 g of rock salt and transfer into a 1000-mL beaker. Fill the beaker about two thirds full with ice and add approximately 100 mL water. Stir until a very thick slushy mixture forms. The presence of ice on the outside of the beaker indicates that the bath is cold enough. To maintain this slushy mixture throughout the experiment, add more ice as needed.

3. If Logger *Pro* is not open on your computer, start the program by clicking on the Logger *Pro* icon on the desktop. Go to **Experiment** > **Data Collection** and verify that you are in the **Time Based** mode, then set the time as 600 seconds. Click **Done**.

4. Prepare the Logger *Pro* program for data collection by setting the data collection parameters. In the graph window, click on each axis, select **Graph Options** and then **Axis Options**. Select **Manual** from the scroll down **Scaling** box and enter the appropriate values for the maximum and minimum values. Reasonable choices for this procedure are a temperature range of −15°C to 30°C and a time scale of 0 to 600 seconds. Click on the title and re-title the graph, including your name or initials.

5. When ready to start data collection, begin stirring the cyclohexane in the test tube with the temperature probe. While placing the test tube into the salt-ice bath, click the green **Collect** button. Stir the cyclohexane gently and continuously in a circular fashion (not up and down). At the same time, stir the test tube itself in the salt-ice bath. (The goal is to have a smooth cooling curve. Anomalous jumps in temperature are generally caused by poor stirring technique or inconsistent temperatures within the salt-ice bath.) Continue to stir until you have passed the freezing plateau and stirring becomes difficult.

6. When the cooling curve is complete, click the red **Stop** button.

Vernier Analysis

1. Determine the section of the curve to which you would like to fit a straight line (see Figures 16-1 and 16-3). Place the cursor over the beginning of that portion of the curve. Only try to fit the linear sections of the curve and ignore the irregular points near the intersection of the two lines. Click and hold while dragging the cursor to the end of the section you would like to fit. Release the mouse key.

2. Pull down the **Analyze** menu and click **Linear Fit**.

3. Repeat steps 1 and 2 for the second portion of the graph to which you wish to fit a straight line.

4. Pull down the **Analyze** menu again and click **Interpolate**. You will see a small circle on each line. Move the cursor to the point where the two lines meet. The small circles will also merge. Notice how the *x* and *y* coordinates for these

NOTES ▼

circles change as you move the cursor. Your goal is to overlay the two circles and find the point where the two lines intersect. Each circle should have the same x and y coordinates, or as close to the same as possible. The y value at this point is the freezing point of pure cyclohexane. The literature value for the freezing point of cyclohexane is 6.5°C. If the value you obtained was not in this range, you may want to assess whether you properly fit the lines to your data in the previous steps.

5. Print the cooling curve.

6. Enter your values into the class database.

Part B—Freezing Point Determination of a Solution

As a class, you need to determine how different amounts of solute impact the freezing point of a solution.

1. Stopper the tube containing the cyclohexane and warm in water until the cyclohexane has completely melted.

2. Meanwhile, work with your group to determine what mass of unknown to use for the analysis. Samples should be between 0.1 and 0.4 grams and the class should be sure to cover this full range. Weigh two samples of unknown on the analytical balance using weighing paper and store each weighed sample on the paper until it is used.

3. "Revive" your salt-ice bath if necessary by pouring off excess water and adding more ice and/or salt.

4. Pull down the **Data** menu and select **Clear All Data**. (If for some reason you wish to save your data, select **Hide Data Set**.)

5. Add the first sample of unknown to the cyclohexane in the test tube, making sure that none sticks to the sides and fails to dissolve. When the unknown has been completely dissolved in the cyclohexane, repeat steps Procedure A5 and A6 with the cyclohexane/unknown mixture.

6. Repeat the data analysis procedure (Vernier Analysis steps 1–5) to determine the freezing point of the solution.

7. Stopper and place the test tube in room temperature water until it melts, then discard the solution in the waste container provided.

8. Using the second test tube, prepare a fresh sample of cyclohexane (step A2). Repeat the entire procedure with the second fresh cyclohexane sample and the second weighed quantity of unknown solute. (You do not need to repeat the procedure to determine the freezing point of pure cyclohexane.)

9. Dispose of cyclohexane waste in the container provided. The ice water bath can be disposed of down the drain.

CALCULATIONS/GRAPHING

1. Use the results of your graphical analysis to determine the freezing point depression (ΔT_f).

2. Calculate the molar mass of the unknown for each of your trials and enter your results into the class database. Do not calculate an average value.

3. Using your calculated value of the molar mass, calculate the molality of the solutions that you prepared.

Class data

Part A: Refer to the class data graph of mass vs. freezing point temperature. Summarize the class findings. Does the quantity of material that you started with affect the freezing point? Does this agree with what you would predict? Why or why not?

Part B: Refer to the class data graph of freezing point depression vs. molality to see how the amount of solute added affects the freezing point of a pure solution. Is the relationship linear? What is represented by the slope of the line? How does this value compare with the expected value?

DISCUSSION/CONCLUSION

Report what you have learned about the relationship between amount of a substance and it's freezing point, as well as the amount of a solute and the freezing point of a solution. Look up the freezing point for cyclohexane and compare it with your value. Why might there be a discrepancy? What is represented by the slope of the line for the graph of freezing point depression vs molality? How does this compare to the expected value? Report the mean value of the unknown molar mass. Obtain the identity of the solute from your laboratory instructor and compare your value for the molar mass with the expected value. Discuss sources of "noise" or unevenness in the data. If your sample of pure cyclohexane did not achieve a flat, freezing point plateau, suggest reasons why this might occur. As usual, consider sources of error and uncertainty in this laboratory experiment. Assess the solvent and solute in terms of green chemistry and why this solute was used rather than those that were used in the past.

NOTES

exp17

Kinetic Exploration

As you may have noticed in earlier experiences in the laboratory, chemical reactions occur at varying rates. While the rate of some reactions is explosively rapid, others occur so slowly that we might be tempted to conclude that no reaction has occurred.

The *rate of reaction* is defined as the change in the quantity of a reactant or product in a specific period of time. Experimentally, this is found by monitoring the change in concentration (usually in moles per liter, M) of one or more of the reactants or products over time. For the hypothetical reaction, $A \rightarrow B$, the average rate of chemical reaction over a given period of time is expressed either in terms of the disappearance of reactants, rate $= -\dfrac{\Delta[A]}{\Delta t}$, or the appearance of products, rate $= \dfrac{\Delta[B]}{\Delta t}$. The change in concentration is followed by measuring some chemical or physical property, such as pressure changes in gas phase reactions or changes in color intensity, as the reaction proceeds. The choice of which experimental variable to measure is arbitrary and generally dictated by experimental convenience.

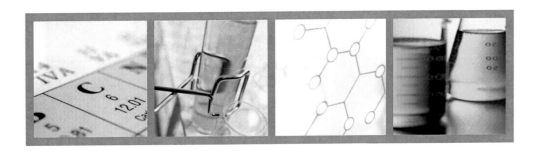

143

NOTES

OBJECTIVES

Your goal in this week's experiment is to work with your classmates to decide on beginning questions addressing how the concentration (Part A), presence of a catalyst (Part B), and temperature (Part C) affect the rate of a reaction. You will need to consider how you will determine the answers to your questions. As you are designing the experiments, keep in mind that it is important to keep most variables constant and only change one variable in any given experimental trial. Otherwise you won't know what is causing the observed results. It is necessary to perform duplicate and replicate trials and to identify the independent and dependent variables in each experiment.

You will be investigating the kinetics of the reduction of MnO_4^- to Mn^{2+} in aqueous solution. The reducing agent is oxalic acid, $H_2C_2O_4$:

$$2MnO_4^-(aq) + 5H_2C_2O_4(aq) + 3H_3O^+(aq) \rightarrow Mn^{2+}(aq) + 5CO_2(aq) + 7H_2O(aq) \qquad (1)$$

Because MnO_4^- is purple and Mn^{2+} is almost colorless, it is convenient to study the rate of this reaction by monitoring the change in color. As the manganese is reduced from an oxidation state of $+7$ in MnO_4^- to $+2$ in Mn^{2+} you may observe several different colors associated with different oxidation states. The endpoint of this reaction may be difficult to assess and it is important to be consistent in your determinations.

PROCEDURES

You will work with a partner for this experiment. Each student needs to be actively involved with doing the experiments, making measurements, and doing the calculations.

SAFETY NOTES

Oxalic acid occurs naturally in foods but at much higher levels it can be toxic to humans. Like most acids, oxalic acid is corrosive to skin. In this lab it is mixed with 1M H_2SO_4, and the solution has a NFPA hazard rating of 3-0-0 for being a corrosive. Glove use is appropriate for handling.

KMnO$_4$ stains are difficult to remove. Avoid getting this on your skin or clothes and clean up spills and glassware immediately. Low levels of manganese do not have negative health effects for humans but Mn^{2+} may have adverse effects on the mortality of young fish.

NOTES

▼

Part A—Concentration Effects

1. There are four containers of $KMnO_4(aq)$ solutions in the room with varying concentrations. Your TA will tell you which concentration to use to ensure that replicate measurements are made. Identify independent and dependent variables for this experiment.

2. So that measurements are consistent, the entire class needs to agree on when it is appropriate to start the stopwatch or timer for the timing of each trial. Will you start as you start pouring the solution or will you start when the last contents of the solution have been poured?

3. Place 40 mL of $KMnO_4$ solution into a 125-mL Erlenmeyer flask using a graduated cylinder to measure. Add a stir bar to the solution. Be sure to record the concentration of the $KMnO_4$ solution.

4. Rinse the graduated cylinder used to measure the $KMnO_4$ as soon as possible to avoid staining.

5. Place the flask on a stirring hot plate and begin stirring. You may find that placing a clean white piece of paper under the flask will aid in observing the colors.

6. Collect 40 mL of oxalic acid/H_2SO_4 solution in a clean graduated cylinder.

7. Add the oxalic acid/H_2SO_4 solution to the reaction flask containing the $KMnO_4$ solution and start the stopwatch.

8. Measure and record the temperature as you make observations (before, during and after).

9. Continue until the solution becomes colorless and record the time.

10. Dispose of waste in a waste beaker on your table and then in the waste bucket in the hood when you are finished.

11. Repeat using the same concentration of $KMnO_4$. (This is a duplicate trial, not a replicate. What is the difference?) To hasten this section of the experiment you can begin this duplicate trial while timing your first trial.

12. Enter your data for each individual trial into the class database. Calculate the average reaction time for each of the different concentrations.

take inverse of slope to find rate

+

conc.

NOTES

Part B—Effect of a Catalyst

1. What is(are) your beginning question(s)? How will you determine the answers to these questions? Be sure that your plan includes duplicate and replicate measurements. Identify independent and dependent variables for this experiment.

2. Perform the experiments as you did in Part A, this time adding one drop of the catalyst, $MnCl_2$, to the oxalic acid before mixing the chemicals. Repeat.

3. Enter your data for each individual trial into the class database. Calculate the average reaction time for each of the different concentrations.

0.002M

Part C—Temperature Effects

1. What is(are) your beginning question(s)? How will you determine the answers to these questions? Be sure that your plan includes duplicate and replicate measurements. Identify independent and dependent variables for this experiment.

2. The experiment should be run using at least four different temperatures. Suggested temperatures are 30°C, 35°C, 40°C, and 45°C (± 2°C). Your TA will tell you which temperature to use to ensure that *replicate* measurements are made. Identify independent and dependent variables for this experiment.

3. You and your partner will have two hot plates to work with. Place 100 mL– 150 mL water into each of two 600-mL beakers and heat on the hot plates to the desired temperature. Be careful not to overheat.

4. Prepare 125-mL flasks with the reactant solutions as described in Part A. Place a stir bar in the $KMnO_4$ solution. Use 0.002 M $KMnO_4$ for this part of the procedure.

5. Set *both flasks* in the warm water on the hot plates, one in each water bath. Put a thermometer in each and bring both solutions up to the target temperature.

6. Transfer the oxalic acid solution to the $KMnO_4$ flask and start the timer using the agreed on procedure for starting the timing. Record the time when the solution becomes colorless and record the temperature again. If temperatures didn't remain constant determine the average of the initial and final temperatures.

7. Repeat using the same target temperature. This is a *duplicate* trial.

8. Enter your data for each individual trial into the class database. Calculate the average time for the reaction at each of the different temperatures.

Part D—Cleanup

Empty waste and clean glassware, turn off thermometers and hot plates and organize the tray station before doing the computer graphing work.

ANALYSIS

To be completed before leaving class.

- Prepare a graph that shows how the reaction time varies as the concentration of $KMnO_4$ is changed, using the average reaction times calculated from class data.

- Prepare a graph that shows how the reaction time varies when a catalyst is added. Include a data point from Part A for a trial with zero catalyst. Use the average reaction times calculated from class data.

- Prepare a graph that shows how the reaction time varies with temperature. Use the average reaction times calculated from class data.

- Work with your TA to discuss how reaction rates could be determined from your graphs. Does this method work for the data that you collected today? Why or why not?

REPORT

For this laboratory you will be writing a "Slim Report." Your slim report should include these components:

Beginning Questions

What beginning questions did your class choose to investigate? Were there any other questions that you were able to investigate?

Claims

What claims can you make based on the results of your experiment? Claim statements can also be answers to BQs.

Evidence

Provide evidence (graphs) and a written argument (interpretation of graphs) to support your claim(s).

Graphs

Attach three graphs:

Part A: average reaction time vs. concentration

Part B: average reaction time vs. concentration with and without a catalyst

Part C: average reaction time vs. temperature

Continue to next page

NOTES
▼

ANALYSIS

1. Construct the table below in your lab report. Complete the table using class data from Part A. Show a sample calculation for how you determined the *rate* of reaction for each trial.

Trial #	Initial Concentration (M)	Final Concentration (M)	Time for Reaction to Complete (s)	Calculated Rate (M/s)
1	0.0015			
2	0.001			
3	0.0005			
4	0.00025			
Average rate =				

2. Comment on the relationship between concentration and average rate of the reaction based on the data and calculated values in the previous table.

3. Comment on the relationship between the time of reaction and the temperature, and the time of reaction and the presence of a catalyst. How does the rate of reaction change with an increase in temperature or the addition of a catalyst?

4. For the reaction $A(g) \rightarrow B(g)$, sketch two graphs/curves on the same set of axes showing:

    a. the consumption of reactant (A) as a function of time.

    b. the formation of product (B) as a function of time.

REFLECTION

a. **EXTEND:** Propose an idea(s) for further experimentation. How could the procedure be modified to extend the investigation? Note: This extension is not simply a repeat of the experiment to collect more data. An extension of the experiment is one that would require a new beginning question.

b. **CH 221/2/3 LECTURE TOPICS:** Which lecture topics from CH 221/2/3 can be connected to this experiment? Explain briefly.

c. **APPLICATIONS:** How can a concept or technique from this experiment connect to a real-world application? Explain briefly.

d. **RELATED READING:** Confirm, dispute or explain your findings using appropriate literature sources. Include appropriate citations for these sources.

e. **GREEN CHEMISTRY:** Identify relevant principles of green chemistry and briefly explain how they were implemented or addressed in this experiment. (Note: This should not be limited to comments about waste disposal.)

exp18

A Kinetic Study of the Bleaching of Allura Red

Allura Red ($C_{18}H_{14}N_2O_8S_2$), also known as FD&C Red Dye No. 40, is a commonly used commercial food dye. As is true of all seven of the certified food dyes in use in this country, it is an organic molecule with a system of alternating single and double bonds. The delocalization of electrons in this π-bonding system, known as a chromophore, is responsible for the color of these dyes.

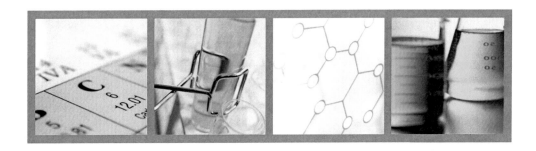

NOTES

Allura Red
(FD&C Red Dye #40)

Common household bleach is an aqueous solution of 3–6% sodium hypochlorite, NaOCl. The OCl⁻ ion oxidizes the chromophores in colored materials, breaking the double bonds and forming new molecules that do not absorb visible light, thus "bleaching" the colored material. In the process, the hypochlorite ion is reduced to chloride and hydroxide ions:

$$OCl^-(aq) + H_2O(l) + 2e^- \rightarrow Cl^-(aq) + 2OH^-(aq)$$

In this laboratory experiment you will study the kinetics of the reaction between Allura Red and bleach.

$$C_{18}H_{14}N_2O_8S_2(aq) + NaOCl(aq) \rightarrow products$$

(This reaction has not been investigated to determine the exact products formed.)

As the reaction proceeds, the intense color of Allura Red will fade. We would like to learn the rate law for this reaction and because we are working with a colored solution, we can use spectrophotometric methods to monitor the course of the reaction. From that, we can determine how the concentration changes with time and use that information to find the rate law for the reaction.

The average rate of a chemical reaction over a given period of time is expressed either in terms of the disappearance of reactants, rate $= -\dfrac{\Delta[A]}{\Delta t}$, or the appearance of products, rate $= \dfrac{\Delta[B]}{\Delta t}$. The choice of what to monitor experimentally is arbitrary, depending on which species lends itself to easy measurement. Because Allura Red is the only colored species in the reaction, we can monitor the rate of reaction by recording the decrease in the color of the solution with time.

The rate law for a chemical reaction is an expression that relates the rate of a reaction to the concentration of the reactants and the rate constant. For this reaction

$$\text{rate} = -\frac{\Delta[\text{Allura Red}]}{\Delta t} = k[\text{Allura Red}]^x[\text{NaOCl}]^y$$

The exponents x and y represent the reaction order of the corresponding compounds and k is the rate constant for the reaction at a given temperature. These values must be determined experimentally, the objective of this experiment.

Imagine a situation in which the concentration of the bleach is in large excess over the concentration of Allura Red. For example, say we prepare the system such that initially, at time = 0,

$$[\text{NaOCl}]_o = 2.0 \text{ M, and } [\text{Allura Red}]_o = 0.001 \text{ M.}$$

Then, when the reaction has run to completion (at time = infinity),

$$[\text{NaOCl}]_i = [\text{NaOCl}]_o - [\text{Allura Red}]_o = 2.0 \text{ M} - 0.001 \text{ M} = 1.999 \text{ M} \approx 2.0 \text{ M}$$

In this case, the concentration of bleach did not change appreciably during the course of the reaction and can be considered to remain constant. In this case, the rate law simplifies to

$$\text{rate} = -\frac{\Delta[\text{Allura Red}]}{\Delta t} = k'[\text{Allura Red}]^x$$

where $k' = k[\text{NaOCl}]^y$ and is referred to as the pseudo-first order rate constant.

This rate law expression can be mathematically converted into an integrated rate law, the form of which depends on the value of x.

zeroth order: $[\text{Allura Red}]_t = -k't + [\text{Allura Red}]_o$

and a plot of [Allura Red] vs time will give a straight line plot with the slope = $-k'$.

first order: $\ln[\text{Allura Red}]_t = -k't + \ln[\text{Allura Red}]_o$

and a plot of ln[Allura Red] vs time will give a straight line plot with the slope = $-k'$.

second order: $\dfrac{1}{[\text{Allura Red}]_t} = k't + \dfrac{1}{[\text{Allura Red}]_o}$

and a plot of 1/[Allura Red] vs time will give a straight line plot with the slope = k'.

NOTES

By measuring the concentration of Allura Red at various times during a reaction and graphing the results, the relationship between concentration and time that gives a linear fit allows you to determine the order of reaction with respect to Allura Red (i.e., a value for x).

A second set of rate data, collected for reactions where the concentration of Allura Red is held constant and the initial excess concentration of bleach is varied in a simple ratio between trials will allow you to determine the order of reaction with respect to bleach (i.e., a value for y).

For example, since $k' = k[NaOCl]^y$, if $[NaOCl]$ is doubled and the rate doesn't change, the bleach is not involved in the rate determining step of the reaction. On the other hand, if the observed rate doubles, y must be 1 and if the observed rate increases by a factor of 4, then $y = 2$.

The concentration of Allura Red will be determined spectrophotometrically using a Beer's law calculation, as was done previously. You will use the values of lambda max and the molar absorptivity coefficient that you previously determined when you did the Spectrophotometry lab. If you missed this experiment, check with your instructor to obtain these values.

CHEMISTRY IN A SUSTAINABLE WORLD

One of the 12 fundamental principles of green chemistry is that chemical processes should be designed to prevent waste, leaving no hazardous products to treat or clean up. All of the products and excess chemicals from this laboratory procedure are safe to be washed down the drain at the end of the experiment, thus adhering fully to this important green chemistry principle.

PROCEDURE

You will be measuring concentration changes over time for five different sets of reactant concentrations. These data will be exported to Microsoft Excel for analysis.

1. The stockroom has prepared a 1.0×10^{-4} M stock solution of Allura Red and a 4.0×10^{-3} M solution of bleach. Using separate 100-mL beakers, obtain 45 mL of each solution from the cup dispensers at the front bench.

2. Open Vernier Logger *Pro*™ by clicking the [icon] icon in the computer dock.

3. Calibration of Spectrometer:

    •   Insert "blank" cuvette into spectrometer. (Note: The "blank" cuvette should be filled with deionized water.) Remember that the cuvette should only be touched on the ridged sides and should be inserted into the spectrometer with the non-ridged sides facing top and bottom (toward the words "Vernier Spectrometer"). Be sure to wipe the outside of the cuvette with a Kimwipe to remove any smudges.

- Select Experiment > Calibrate > Spectrometer. The calibration dialog box will display the message: "Waiting … seconds for lamp to warm up." Allow the spectrometer to warm up for one minute. Follow the instructions in the dialog box to complete the calibration.

4. Click on the Configure Spectrometer Data Collection icon on the toolbar. From the window that pops up, select Abs vs Concentration. Deselect the wavelength that the program has selected and select 502 nm (or your λ_{max} for Allura Red as previously determined). Click OK.

5. Click the data collection button on the menu bar. Change the Mode to Time Based. Make the length 540 seconds. Deselect the check mark for Sample at Time Zero. In the section titled Sampling Rate, enter 30 seconds/sample (NOT 30 samples/second). Click Done.

6. Refer to Table 18-1, trial 1. Using a different graduated pipet for each substance, transfer the quantities of Allura Red from column A and water from column B into a 50-mL beaker and swirl to mix.

7. Transfer the quantities of bleach from column C and water from column D into a second 50-mL beaker and swirl to mix.

8. *Simultaneously*, pour the bleach quickly into the beaker containing Allura Red and start the data collection by clicking the green Start button. (By pressing the green start button at the same time as mixing the solutions, data will automatically be recorded at T = 30 seconds and every 30 seconds thereafter until 540 seconds.)

9. Stir the solution rapidly using the tip of a transfer pipet. Use this pipet to fill the cuvette about ¾ full. Wipe with a Kimwipe and place in the spectrometer in time for the data recording at thirty seconds.

10. If the absorbance drops below 0.03 before 540 seconds is over, you may press the red Stop button to end data collection.

11. Cut and paste your data into Microsoft Excel.

12. Discard the solution in the cuvette and 50-mL beakers down the drain. Rinse and dry beakers for use in subsequent mixing. Rinse cuvettes and return to drying rack on front bench.

13. Select Experiment > Clear Latest Run

14. Repeat steps 6–13 four more times using the quantities for trials 2–5 in Table 18-1.

NOTES

TABLE 18-1. Reagent Quantities

Trial	A Stock Dye (mL)	B H₂O for Dye (mL)	C Stock Bleach (mL)	D H₂O for Bleach (mL)
1	2.5	7.5	10	—
2	5	5	10	—
3	10	—	10	—
4	5	5	5	5
5	5	5	2.5	7.5

CALCULATIONS AND ANALYSIS

Before proceeding with the calculations, be sure that you have read and understand the introduction to this experiment. Without this background, this method of rate law determination may seem confusing.

Use the stock solution concentrations and the values in Table 18-1 to calculate the initial concentrations of Allura Red and NaOCl for trials 1–5.

Determination of the reaction order with respect to Allura Red:

To find the reaction order with respect to Allura Red, you will need to prepare three graphs using data from trials 1–3. These graphs will represent:

- [Allura Red] vs time
- ln[Allura Red] vs time
- 1/[Allura Red] vs time

Data for all three trials should be included on the same graph. In other words, you will have three graphs with three curves on each. To prepare these graphs, set up another column for each trial to calculate concentration from the absorbance readings using Beer's law and the molar absorptivity coefficient for Allura Red that you determined in the Spectrophotometry experiment. Remember that you will need to manually calculate the concentration of Allura Red at zero seconds from the stock solution concentration, the aliquot taken, and the total reaction solution volume.

Create new columns for each trial to calculate ln[Allura Red] and 1/[Allura Red].

Create the three graphs and determine the reaction order for Allura Red based on which graph yields a linear relationship.

NOTES
▼

Determination of the reaction order with respect to Sodium Hypochlorite:

To determine the reaction order with respect to Allura Red, we held the concentration of sodium hypochlorite constant and noted how the rate changed as a function of the concentration of Allura Red. To determine the order with respect to sodium hypochlorite, we will reverse the process and hold the concentration of Allura Red constant while varying the concentration of NaOCl. Because NaOCl is colorless, it is not possible to monitor the experiment as was done previously. However, because k' is directly proportional to rate, we can determine how the rate changes by comparing k' for trials 2, 4, and 5.

Did you determine that the reaction was first order for Allura Red and the graph of ln[Allura Red] vs time yielded linear results? The slope of the curves on those graphs is $-k'$. Prepare another graph of ln[Allura Red] vs time using data from trials 4 and 5. Find k' from the slopes of the two lines. Determine the reaction order with respect to sodium hypochlorite by noting how the values of k' change for trials 2, 4, and 5.

Determination of the rate constant, k:

Recall that $k' = k[NaOCl]$. Determine the value of k for trials 2, 4, and 5 using the k' values derived from the linear relationships.

REPORT

There is no report for this experiment. Instead, complete the worksheet pages that are posted on Canvas and submit at the end of lab, along with your pre-lab pages and four graphs per pair of students.

REFERENCE

Henary, M.M.; Russell, A.A.; *J. Chem. Educ.* 2007, 84, 480–482.

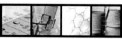

NOTES

exp19

The Cobalt Chloride Equilibrium System

When reactants in a chemical system combine they eventually form a mixture of reactants and products that exist in a state of dynamic equilibrium. At this point, it appears that no further reaction is occurring. However, if you could observe this equilibrium on a microscopic scale, you would see that two reactions were occurring—a forward reaction in which reactants combine to form products, and a reverse reaction in which products react to form the original reactants. No net change is apparent because the rates of the forward and reverse reactions are equal at equilibrium and the concentrations of the reactants and products remain constant.

In this laboratory experiment, you and your classmates will be studying the equilibrium that exists between cobalt(II) and chloride ions. Cobalt(II) ions and chloride ions interact in solution as described by equation (1).

$$Co(H_2O)_6^{2+}(aq) + 4Cl^-(aq) \rightleftarrows CoCl_4^{2-}(aq) + 6H_2O(aq) \tag{1}$$

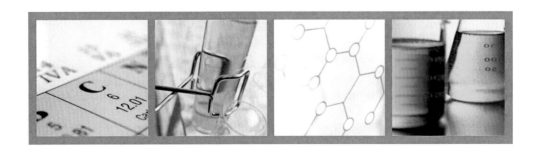

These are the questions that you and your classmates will be investigating:

- Assuming that reaction (1) correctly represents the reaction between cobalt(II) and chloride ions, what is the result of the addition of increasing the chloride ion concentration?

- If the concentration of water in the system is decreased, will the system react to form more products or to use up products to form more reactants? What experimental observations support this conclusion?

- What is the effect of heating the solutions? Is the effect the same for both the aqueous and alcoholic solutions? Why or why not?

- How can your observations be explained in terms of Le Châtelier's principle?

- What colors are the Co^{2+} and $CoCl_4^{2-}$ ions.

- What is the difference in composition between aqueous and alcoholic solutions that are the same color?

- Is reaction (1) exothermic or endothermic?

- Is reaction (1) reversible?

- The cobalt chloride system is often used in novelty weather indicator devices. How do these weather devices work?

PROCEDURE

SAFETY NOTE

The hydrochloric acid used in this experiment is very corrosive to skin and clothing. Wear your safety goggles at all times! Due to irritable HCl fumes, contact lenses should not be worn. Avoid breathing the fumes or spilling on your skin. If you accidentally get some on your skin, immediately rinse with copious amounts of water. Report all acid spills to your instructor for clean-up. As always when working with acids, add acids to water, rather than water to acids.

Part A—Preparatory

1. Clean 10 small test tubes, rinse with deionized water and invert in a test tube rack to drain.

2. Begin heating water on a hot plate to use in Part D of this procedure.

3. Use a 50-mL beaker to obtain approximately 15 mL of 1 M cobalt chloride solution from the stock bottle on the side laboratory bench. Cobalt salts are toxic. Handle the cobalt solutions carefully and dispose of them properly.

4. **Using water, practice using a 10-mL graduated pipet. Familiarize yourself with the graduations on the pipet (they may seem backward to you).** Fill the pipet and practice using it to sequentially deliver 1.0, 2.0, 3.0, and 4.0 mL volumes of water without refilling.

5. When you are ready to begin, use a 50-mL Erlenmeyer flask (carried in a 250-mL beaker) to obtain slightly more than 20 mL of concentrated hydrochloric acid from the poly squeeze bottles in the fume hoods. Label the beaker "con HCl."

6. Wet a piece of filter paper with several drops of your 1 M cobalt chloride solution. What color is the paper? Allow the paper to air dry. What color is the paper when dry?

Part B—Aqueous Solvent

Label five of the test tubes B1–B5. Arrange in a row in the test tube rack. Use a one-milliliter pipet to measure 1 mL of 1 M cobalt(II) chloride solution into each test tube. Use a ten-milliliter pipet to transfer to these test tubes the volumes of deionized water and concentrated hydrochloric acid that are called for in Table 19-1. Mix the contents of the test tubes well with a glass stir rod. Note: Try to avoid drawing any solutions into the pipet bulb. If this happens, you should rinse the bulb thoroughly by pulling water into it with the pipet and swirling.

TABLE 19-1.

Deionized Water and Concentrated Hydrochloric Acid Volumes	Test Tubes				
	B1	B2	B3	B4	B5
1 M CoCl$_2$, mL	1.0	1.0	1.0	1.0	1.0
DI water, mL	7.0	6.0	5.0	4.0	3.0
conc. HCl, mL	0.0	1.0	2.0	3.0	4.0

Record your observations in tabular form. Do not discard solutions yet.

Part C—Alcoholic Solvent

All of the reagents you will use in this experiment contain water. The 1 M cobalt chloride solution is mostly water. Concentrated hydrochloric acid solution is at least 50% water and isopropyl alcohol contains 30% water. By changing the solvent system from water to isopropyl alcohol, you will be able to observe the effect that a smaller total percentage of water has on the position of equilibrium.

Use a 50-mL beaker to obtain approximately 30 mL of isopropyl alcohol from the side laboratory bench. (Note: isopropyl alcohol = isopropanol = IPA = 2-propanol = rubbing alcohol.)

Label five of the test tubes C1–C5. Arrange in a second row in the test tube rack. Use a one-milliliter pipet to measure 1 mL of 1 M cobalt(II) chloride solution into each test tube. Use a 10-mL pipet to transfer to these test tubes the volumes of isopropyl alcohol (IPA) and concentrated hydrochloric acid that are called for in Table 19-2. Mix the contents well with a glass stir rod.

TABLE 19-2.

Isopropyl Alcohol and Concentrated Hydrochloric Acid Volumes	Test Tubes				
	C1	C2	C3	C4	C5
1 M CoCl$_2$, mL	1.0	1.0	1.0	1.0	1.0
IPA, mL	7.0	6.0	5.0	4.0	3.0
conc. HCl, mL	0.0	1.0	2.0	3.0	4.0

Record your observations in tabular form. Do not discard solutions yet.

Part D—Temperature Effects

1. Your TA will perform a demonstration involving the addition of HCl to water. Record your observations.

2. Fill a 250-mL beaker about halfway with water. Place on a hot plate and heat to almost boiling. Meanwhile, use a disposable pipet to transfer one half of the solution in test tube B4 into another test tube. Place one of the test tubes containing solution B4 into the hot water bath. Reserve the second test tube as a control to which you can compare the hot solution. After a few minutes, examine the hot solution, compare it the control, and record your observations. Allow the sample to cool to room temperature and record your observations.

3. Choose the alcoholic solution that most closely matches in appearance the unheated aqueous solution in test tube B4. Again, use a disposable pipet to transfer one half of the contents of the chosen test tube into another test tube. Place one of the test tubes into the hot water bath. Reserve the second test tube as a control to which you can compare the hot solution. After a few minutes, examine the hot solution, compare it to the control, and record your observations.

4. Remove the test tube from the hot water bath and immediately place only the bottom third of the tube into an ice bath for about 60 seconds so that the bottom half of the solution is in ice and the top half is not. Occasionally, remove the test tube from the ice very briefly and record your observations.

Part E—Group Data Comparison

1. Compare your solutions in test tubes B1–B5 and C1–C5 with others in your laboratory group. If there are any contradictory or ambiguous results, think of ways to resolve the problems and try them. Be sure that you have enough data recorded to answer the questions that follow. If there are any other tests that you would like to try, check with your teaching assistant and if approved, carry them out.

2. Dispose of all solutions in the waste containers provided.

DISCUSSION/CONCLUSION

Your goal in this laboratory experiment is to develop an interpretation of the cobalt chloride equilibrium system that will explain all or most of your observations. The questions posed at the beginning of this chapter should help guide your discussion.

REFERENCE

Bell, J. A., *Chemical Explorations*, D.C. Heath and Company, Lexington, MA, 1993.

NOTES

exp20

Conductivity and pH of Aqueous Solutions

1. INTRODUCTION

Life on earth exists because of chemical reactions that occur in aqueous solutions. In aqueous solutions, water is the substance present in the greatest amount, and is therefore considered the solvent. Other components dissolved in the water are considered solutes, because they are present in lesser amounts. Solutes can be classified as strong electrolytes, weak electrolytes, or non-electrolytes by their degree of ionization in solution. For example, an aqueous solution of sodium chloride consists primarily of ions (cations and anions) surrounded by water molecules, rather than molecules of NaCl, as shown in Figure 20-1. When strong electrolytes dissolve in water the ions are 90–99% dissociated or ionized. Therefore, NaCl is classified as a strong electrolyte.

$$NaCl \rightarrow Na^+(aq) + Cl^-(aq)$$

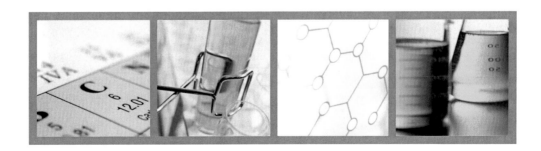

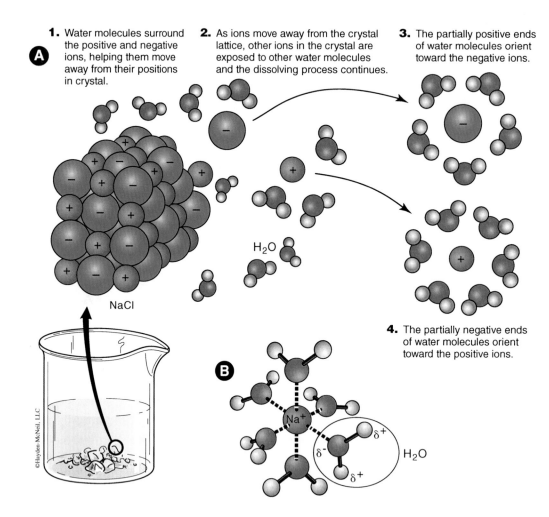

1. Water molecules surround the positive and negative ions, helping them move away from their positions in crystal.

2. As ions move away from the crystal lattice, other ions in the crystal are exposed to other water molecules and the dissolving process continues.

3. The partially positive ends of water molecules orient toward the negative ions.

4. The partially negative ends of water molecules orient toward the positive ions.

FIGURE 20-1. Dissolution of NaCl

Solutions containing strong electrolytes conduct electricity when they are subjected to a difference in electrical potential, due to the movement of their ions in solution. A solution's conductivity increases as a function of the concentration of dissolved ions. A conductivity meter can be used to determine the concentration of ions present an aqueous solution. Siemens (S) is the SI unit of the electrical conductivity of solutions. For dilute solutions, conductivity is measured in units of milli-Siemens (mS) or micro-Siemens (μS). The conductivity meter in a 0.1 M NaCl solution will measure a higher micro-Siemens value compared to a 0.05 M NaCl solution due to the greater number of ions in the solution (Figures 20-2a, 20-2b).

Solutions containing weak electrolytes, such as $H_2SO_3(aq)$, exhibit lower conductivity because these solutions contain relatively few ions (Figure 20-2c). When H_2SO_3 dissolves, most of the particles still exist as molecules. An equilibrium system equation to represent this weak electrolyte system can be written as follows:

$$H_2SO_3(aq) \rightleftharpoons H^+(aq) + HSO_3^-(aq)$$

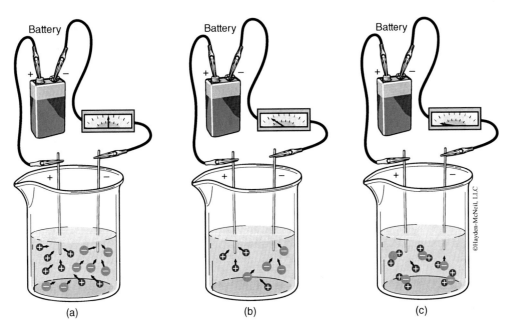

FIGURE 20-2. Conductivity of three aqueous solutions. Figure 20-2(a) represents a 0.1 M NaCl(aq) solution, Figure 20-2(b) represents a 0.05 M NaCl(aq) solution and Figure 20-2(c) represents 0.10 M H_2SO_3(aq) solution. Water molecules are omitted for clarity.

The pH of Water and Acids

Water itself is a very weak electrolyte, and auto-dissociates to form low concentrations of positively charged hydronium ions and negatively charged hydroxide ions, according to the following chemical reaction equation:

$$2H_2O(l) \rightleftharpoons H_3O^+(aq) + OH^-(aq) \qquad K_w = 1 \times 10^{-14}$$

At 25°C, pure water is neither acidic nor basic, it is neutral. The concentration of hydronium ions and hydroxide ions are both 1.00×10^{-7} M.

When an acid is dissolved in water, it reacts with the water molecules to form hydronium ions. The concentration of hydronium ions is inversely related to the pH of the solution, which is calculated using the following equation:

$$pH = -\log[H_3O^+]$$

The pH of a solution can be measured using acid–base indicators or a pH meter.

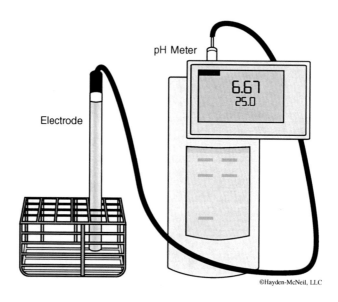

FIGURE 20-3. Representation of a simple pH meter

The numerical pH scale is used to describe the acidity (or basicity) of an aqueous solution (Figure 20-4). Solutions are considered acidic if their pH is less than 6, and basic (also known as alkaline) if their pH is 8–14. A pH of 7 indicates a neutral solution.

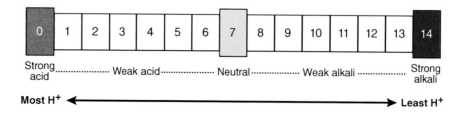

FIGURE 20-4. The pH scale

Figure 20-5 depicts molecular level representations of particles in 0.1 M HCl and 0.1 M HF solutions. These solutions contain the same concentration of acid, yet their pH (and the concentration of hydronium ions they contain) are very different. This difference arises because HCl is a strong acid that disassociates completely in water, whereas HF is a weak acid that disassociates partially.

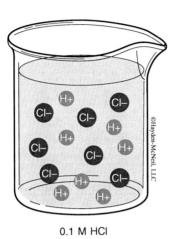
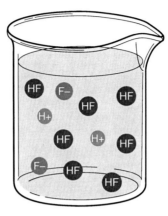

0.1 M HCl   0.1 M HF

FIGURE 20-5. Molecular-level diagrams of solutions containing 0.1 M HCl and 0.1 M HF. Water molecules are omitted for clarity.

Because HF is a weak acid, we can write the following equilibrium reaction to describe the reaction bewteen HF and water:

$$HF(aq) + H_2O \leftrightarrows H_3O^+(aq) + F^-(aq) \qquad K_a = 7.2 \times 10^{-4}$$

In the above equation, HF is the acid, H_2O is the base, H_3O^+ is the conjugate acid of H_2O and F^- is the conjugate base of HF.

NOTES
▼

CONDUCTIVITY AND pH OF AQUEOUS SOLUTIONS

Name

_____

GTF

_____

Lab Day and Time

2. OVERVIEW AND OBJECTIVES

In this experiment, you and your classmates will develop your understanding of the reactions that occur in aqueous solutions by measuring the conductivity and pH of aqueous solutions containing various solutes and relating your observations to what is happening on the molecular level.

In Part I, you will familiarize yourself with conductivity and pH meters and measure the conductivity and pH of some familiar solutions. In Part II, you will measure the conductivity and pH of conjugate pairs, and in Part III, you will mix these conjugate pairs and measure the conductivity and pH of the resultant solutions. Finally, in Part IV, you will measure the effect on the pH of adding a strong acid or base to the solutions you have prepared.

Since there are far too many solutions for any one student to test and analyze on his or her own, you will need to work cooperatively with your classmates at your table and with the class as a whole. Every student must contribute to sharing his or her data so that everyone will have a full set of data at the end of lab.

It is not necessary to write a pre-lab in your laboratory notebook for this experiment. Instead, read the procedure and write a minimum of three Beginning Questions that you would like to investigate given the equipment and solutions provided in the space below. Additionally, complete the first two blank columns (Type of Substance and Type of Electrolyte) in Table 20-1 before attending lab.

Beginning Questions:

3. SAFETY

The 2 M acid and base solutions in dropper bottles on your lab bench are corrosives. Wear gloves to avoid skin contact with these solutions. Alert your GTF if you have a spill on yourself or elsewhere.

4. PROCEDURE AND ANALYSIS

Part I. Conductivity and pH of Familiar Solutions

As part of your pre-lab, examine the substances listed in Table 20-1, and use information available in your general chemistry textbook to designate what type of substance (strong acid, weak acid, strong base, weak base, neutral salt, acidic salt, basic salt or covalent compound) and type of electrolyte (weak, strong, or non-electrolyte) each substance is.

During the lab, work with your tablemates to test the conductivity and pH of solutions containing various concentrations of KNO_3, HCl, $C_{12}H_{22}O_{11}$ (sucrose), and NaOH. Each pair of students (A and B or C and D) will be responsible for collecting data regarding four different concentrations of *two* of these substances. By dividing the work in this manner, your table group will collect all of the necessary data for these 16 solutions.

Part I A: Conductivity Measurements

Your TA will demonstrate how to use the conductivity meter. Be sure to rinse the electrodes with deionized water and wipe the electrodes with ChemWipes after testing each solution.

Using a well plate, collect about 15 mL of each of the four solutions that you will be testing. (Enough to fill the cells of the well plate about three-quarters full.) Measure the conductivity of each solution. Record the values from your table in Table 20-1. Save the solutions to use in Part IB.

TABLE 20-1.

Student	Solution	Type of Substance	Type of Electrolyte	Measurement	Concentration 0.0010M	0.010M	0.10M	0.15M
Example	Formic acid	Weak acid	Weak	Conductivity (mS)	0.200	0.600	1.800	2.000
				pH	3.3	2.6	2.2	2.2
A	KNO_3			Conductivity (mS)				
				pH				
B	HCl			Conductivity (mS)				
				pH				
C	$C_{12}H_{22}O_{11}$			Conductivity (mS)				
				pH				
D	NaOH			Conductivity (mS)				
				pH				

Part I B: pH Measurements

Measure the pH of the same four solutions that you used in Part IA. Note: The laboratory pH meters don't work well when there are no ions present in solution (i.e., low conductivity). For these solutions, use pH paper to determine the pH. Be sure to rinse your probe with deionized water and to wipe with ChemWipes after each measurement. *When using the pH meter, wait at least 20 seconds* for the measurement to stabilize. Use a Büchner funnel with yellow storage solution to store the probe in between measurements. Do not let the pH meter remain in air

for longer than a few seconds and remember that pH meters are fragile (glass bulb) and should be handled carefully. Record the values from your table in Table 20-1.

Part I C: Data Analysis

Compare your results with those of another group and verify that they agree.

1. Compare your pre-lab predictions about the type of substance and type of electrolyte to your conductivity and pH observations for each substance. Did your pre-lab predictions match what you observed? That is, did substances you designated as being strong electrolytes exhibit high conductivity values? Did those described as acids exhibit acidic pHs? If you need to revise your definition of any substance, do so here. Reference the experimental data you reported in Table 20-1 as needed to support your predictions.

2. Draw molecular-level diagrams (similar to Figure 20-5) for each of the four substances in Table 20.1. Each container should contain at least 10 particles. Omit water molecules for clarity.

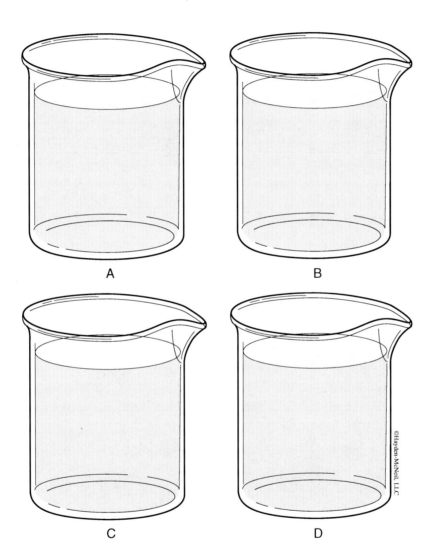

A

B

C

D

3. Is there a relationship between the pH and conductivity values for:

a. different concentrations of the same solution and

b. the same concentration of different solutions?

Describe why or why not.

 WORKSHEET

Check your work with your TA before proceeding to Part II.

Part II. Conductivity and pH of Conjugate Pairs

Eight different solutions containing acetic acid, sodium acetate, ammonia and ammonium chloride, each at two different concentrations, will be studied. Your table will be assigned to work with either acetic acid and sodium acetate, or ammonia and ammonium chloride.

Part II A: Measurements

Measure the conductivity and pH of the four solutions that your table has been assigned and record this information in Table 20-2. Again, work should be divided among students—it is not necessary for each student to make each measurement. Use the criteria you established in Part I of the experiment to determine the type of electrolyte and type of substance for each solution. When you are finished, share your data with others at your table as well as students at a neighboring table to complete Table 20-2.

TABLE 20-2.

Student		Solution	Measurement	Type of Substance	Type of Electrolyte
Table Group I	A	0.1 M CH_3COOH	Conductivity (mS)		
			pH		
	B	0.1 M CH_3COONa	Conductivity (mS)		
			pH		
	C	0.05 M CH_3COOH	Conductivity (mS)		
			pH		
	D	0.05 M CH_3COONa	Conductivity (mS)		
			pH		

Student		Solution	Measurement	Type of Substance	Type of Electrolyte
Table Group II	E	0.1 M NH_3	Conductivity (mS)		
			pH		
	F	0.1 M NH_4Cl	Conductivity (mS)		
			pH		
	G	0.05 M NH_3	Conductivity (mS)		
			pH		
	H	0.05 M NH_4Cl	Conductivity (mS)		
			pH		

Part II B: Data Analysis

1. With your group, write chemical equilibrium equations for the reactions of each member of each conjugate pair with water. Spectator ions should not be included in the equations.

    (A) CH_3COOH $+$ H_2O $\rightleftharpoons$ _____ $+$ _____

    (B)

    (E)

    (F)

2. What, if any, is the relationship between the molarity and the conductivity of the solutions? Explain this on a molecular level.

3. Draw molecular-level diagrams (similar to Figure 20-5) for each of the four solutions measured during Part II (A, B, E, F). Each container should contain at least 10 particles. Omit water molecules for clarity.

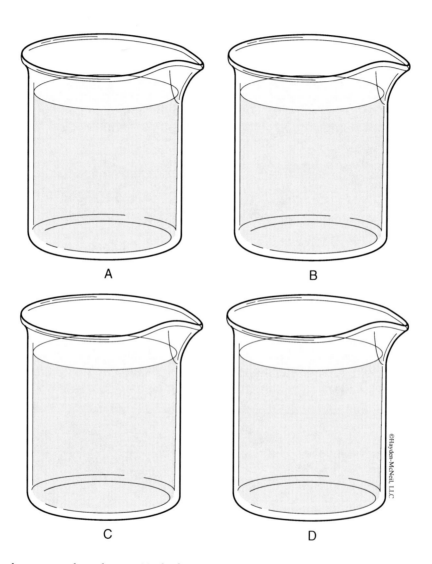

A

B

C

D

Check your work with your TA before proceeding to Part III.

Part III. Conductivity and pH of Solutions Formed by Mixing Conjugate Acid and Base Pairs

In this section, you will mix the conjugate acid–base pairs from Part II in different ratios and test the conductivity and pH of the resultant solutions. If you worked with acetic acid and sodium acetate in Part II, you will prepare acetic acid–sodium acetate mixtures in Part III. If you worked with ammonia and ammonium chloride in Part II, you will prepare ammonia–ammonium chloride mixtures in Part III.

Your table group will need to mix five different combinations of the conjugate acid and base solutions to provide a range of different compositions to be tested. This work should be divided among the members of your table group. Using beakers, obtain a small quantity of your conjugate acid and conjugate base solutions from the stock containers. Mix them in mole ratios of 0.1, 0.5, 1.0, 2.0 and 10.0. This can be done, for example, by mixing 0.1 M sodium acetate with 0.1 M acetic acid in these proportions: 1 mL:10 mL, 5 mL:10 mL, 10 mL:10 mL, 10 mL:5 mL, and 10 mL:1 mL. (See Table 20-3.) Use a graduated pipet to transfer accurate amounts of solutions to small beakers. Once mixed, transfer the resultant solutions to a well plate.

Measure the conductivity and pH of each of the solutions and enter the data into Table 20-3a or 20-3b. You will need to return to this table after completing your data analysis to enter your experimentally determined pK_a value. When you are finished, share your data with another group who tested the other mixture, and complete Tables 20-3a and 20-3b using their data. Save the solution containing 10 mL of each component for further testing in Part IV.

TABLE 20-3a.

Student		Solution Conc.	Acetic Acid (mL)	Sodium Acetate (mL)	Conductivity (mS)	pH	Literature pKₐ Value	Experimental pKₐ Using Your Measurement
Table Group I	A&B	0.1 M	1	10			4.756	
			5	10				
			10	10				
			10	5				
			10	1				
	C&D	0.05 M	1	10			4.756	
			5	10				
			10	10				
			10	5				
			10	1				

TABLE 20-3b.

Student		Solution Conc.	Ammonia (mL)	Ammonium Chloride (mL)	Conductivity (mS)	pH	Literature pKₐ Value	Experimental pKₐ Using Your Measurement
Table Group II	E&F	0.1 M	1	10			9.245	
			5	10				
			10	10				
			10	5				
			10	1				
	G&H	0.05 M	1	10			9.245	
			5	10				
			10	10				
			10	5				
			10	1				

Part III B: Data Analysis and Graphs

Graph #1. Using the data tables and templates that are set up on the lab computers, prepare a graph for the solution your table group tested. This graph will plot measured pH versus $log \dfrac{[conjugate\ base]}{[conjugate\ acid]}$. (NOTE: The concentration of acid or base used in this equation should be the concentration after mixing and not before. This will be automatically calculated by the Excel program.) Determine the best-fit straight-line equation for the line representing your solution. Print your graph when it is finished. You will use it to determine the pKₐ of the weak acid present in your system at equilibrium, as described on the following page.

Consider the equilibrium between a weak acid and its conjugate base.

$$HA + H_2O \rightleftharpoons H_3O^+ + A^-$$

$$\text{where } K_a = \frac{[H_3O^+][A^-]}{[HA]}$$

A little rearranging of this equation to isolate the H_3O^+ gives us:

$$[H_3O^+] = K_a x \frac{[HA]}{[A^-]}$$

Next, we will take the negative log of both sides: Recall: $\log(a \times b) = \log a + \log b$

$$-\log[H_3O^+] = -\log K_a - \log \frac{[HA]}{[A^-]}$$

Finally, we simplify and flip the ratio of acid to conjugate base to get rid of the negative sign. This gives us the equation that is known as the Henderson-Hasselbalch equation:

$$pH = pK_a + \log \frac{[A^-]}{[HA]}$$

Using this information, your data and your graph, answer the following questions:

1. What is the value of the y-intercept on Graph #1? Use this value and the Henderson-Hasselbalch equation to determine the experimental pK_a value for the acid in the conjugate pair that you tested. Show your work. Compare your experimentally determined pK_a value to the literature value of pK_a. Why might these values be different?

2. Work with your table group and write a balanced chemical equation for the equilibrium reaction that is occurring in the solution that you tested in Part III. Is the equilibrium reaction the same for both the solutions that you tested? Is it the same equation as you wrote for that system during Part II of the experiment?

3. Draw a molecular-level diagram (similar to Figure 20-5) for the Part III solution that contained 10 mL of each component. Your container should contain at least 10 particles. Compare your picture diagram with other members of your group.

    Solution containing acetic acid and sodium acetate or ammonia and ammonium chloride:

©Hayden-McNeil, LLC

4. Using Le Châtelier's principle, explain why the solution 10:10 prepared by students A and B or E and F has a different pH compared to the 10:10 solution prepared by students C and D or G and H. (Hint: Write the chemical equation. Water is a reactant. How will this equilibrium system be affected if the solution is less concentrated?)

5. Describe the trend between the relative amount of each component in the mixtures and their observed pH values.

Check your work with your TA before proceeding to Part IV.

Part IV: pH of Solutions after Strong Acid or Strong Base Is Added

Part IV A: Measurements:

Place 15 mL of the solution containing 1:1 ratios of your conjugate acid–base pair (i.e., acetic acid/acetate or ammonia/ammonium) in a well plate and measure the pH of the solution, recording the value in Table 20-4. Add one drop of 2 M HCl, and measure the resulting pH. Continue adding drops and taking pH measurements until 4 drops have been added.

Repeat this procedure with a fresh sample of solution, testing the effects of adding NaOH dropwise.

Next, place 15 mL of KNO_3 solution in a well plate and measure its pH. Add one drop of 2 M HCl, and measure its pH. Continue adding drops and taking pH measurements until 4 drops have been added. Repeat this procedure with a fresh sample of KNO_3, testing the effects of adding NaOH dropwise. Record all measurements in Table 20-4.

Individual students do not need to do all the tests. Instead, divide the work amongst your tablemates.

TABLE 20-4.

	Solution	HCl Drops	NaOH Drops	pH
A&B *or* E&F	0.1 M solution containing 10 mL acetic acid & 10 mL sodium acetate OR 10 mL ammonia & 10 mL ammonium chloride	0		
		1		
		2		
		3		
		4		
			0	
			1	
			2	
			3	
			4	
C&D *or* G&H	0.05 M solution containing 10 mL acetic acid & 10 mL sodium acetate OR 10 mL ammonia & 10 mL ammonium chloride	0		
		1		
		2		
		3		
		4		
			0	
			1	
			2	
			3	
			4	
	$KNO_3(aq)$	0		
		1		
		2		
		3		
		4		
			0	
			1	
			2	
			3	
			4	

Part IV B: Data Analysis and Graphs

Graph #2. Using the graph that follows, plot a line of pH versus 4 drops of HCl added, no drops added, and 4 drops of sodium hydroxide added for the conjugate pair solution that you personally tested in Part IV. Plot another line of the same thing for the KNO_3 solution you tested.

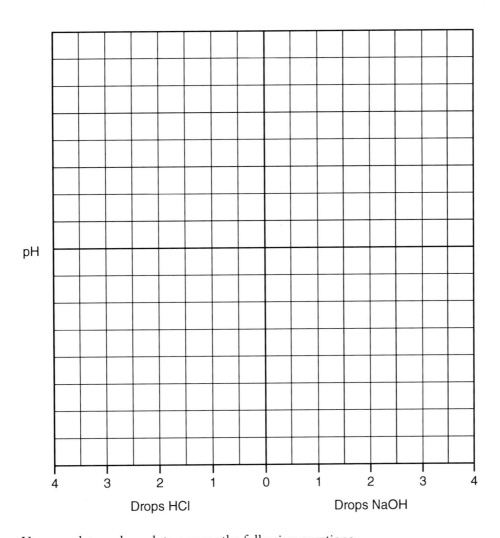

Use your data and graph to answer the following questions:

1. Compare and contrast the effect of adding HCl or NaOH to solutions containing the mixture of a conjugate acid and base pair and the solution containing KNO_3.

2. Compare and discuss your results with a table group that tested the other conjugate acid–base pair. Describe how their system responded to the addition of HCl and NaOH.

3. Write net ionic chemical reaction equations showing what happens to the added HCl and NaOH when added to the solution that your table tested. (Hint: This is an acid–base neutralization reaction.) Spectator ions should not be included in the equation.

$$H_3O^+ \quad + \quad \underline{\hspace{2cm}} \quad \rightleftharpoons$$

$$OH^- \quad + \quad \underline{\hspace{2cm}} \quad \rightleftharpoons$$

Part IV C : Connecting Data and Results to Concepts

Solutions that resist a change in pH when modest amounts of acid or base are added are called *buffer solutions*. Based on your observations and results from Parts I, II, III and IV, provide evidence-based responses to questions (a–e).

a. Is the mixture that you tested during Part IV a buffer solution? What evidence do you have to support your claim?

b. What species must be present in a buffer solution? For your mixture, explicitly identify the acid, the base, the conjugate acid, and conjugate base.

c. How does a buffer solution resist the change in pH when a small amount of acid or base is added?

d. Does the concentration of the buffer impact how the buffer solution responds to the addition of acid and base?

e. Are the solutions in you worked with in Parts I and II buffer solutions? Explain why or why not.

Part V: TA Demonstration

Record the demonstration procedure and observations.

5. REPORT

When completed, tear out these worksheet pages from your lab manual and submit to your TA. If you require additional time to complete the worksheet, you can submit it when you attend lab next week. There is no other report required for this experiment.

exp21

Synthesis of Aspirin and Oil of Wintergreen

History of Aspirin

As long as 3500 years ago, physicians recommended that extracts made from certain plants, such as myrtle, poplar, and willow, be used to relieve pain and fever. All of these plants contain salicylic acid. The modern day history of aspirin began in 1763 when an English clergyman, the Reverend Edward Stone, presented a paper entitled "An Account of the Success of the Bark of the Willow in the Cure of Agues" before the Royal Society of London. (By ague, Stone was referring to what we now call malaria.) Work continued on the extracts of willow and related plants and, in 1830, a 23-year-old Italian chemist by the name of Piria first isolated colorless crystals of salicylic acid.

In the years that followed, salicylic acid became an important analgesic (pain reliever), antipyretic (fever reducer), and anti-inflammatory (swelling supressor) drug. Salicylic acid, however, because of its acid properties, causes severe irritation of the mucous membranes lining the mouth, gullet, and stomach. For patients, such as arthritis

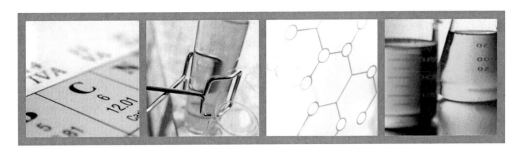

NOTES

▼

sufferers, who had to take salicylic acid over long periods of time, the cure could be worse than the ailment. The search commenced for a derivative of salicylic acid that retained its beneficial properties but which did not have any of its deleterious side effects.

The mid-1800s saw the birth and rapid growth of the coal-tar based textile dye industry in Europe. Finding the textile dye business increasingly competitive and less profitable, one of the leading German dye manufacturers decided to expand its product line to include pharmaceuticals. The name of the company was Farbenfabriken vormals Friedrich Bayer & Co. (literally, color factories formerly known as Friedrich Bayer Co.). In 1897, a Farbenfabriken scientist developed a process for modifying salicylic acid to produce acetylsalicylic acid, to which the company assigned the trade name, Aspirin.

Astonishingly, what would eventually become one of the most popular drugs of modern life languished on the shelf for over a year. The company directors chose not to produce Aspirin at first for two reasons. It was thought that acetylsalicylic acid would produce the same side effects as salicylic acid. Also, the company wanted to focus on production of a second drug that they had introduced that year and which was showing signs of being a tremendous success. While it was being tested, some users of this second drug reported that it made them feel "heroic"—hence its name: heroin.

Eventually, of course, Farbenfabriken Bayer did manufacture and sell Aspirin. The history of Aspirin includes various interesting twists and turns. For instance, during World War I, the US confiscated both the Bayer factory located in NY state and their trademark on the name "Aspirin," so that for much of this century, there were two completely separate companies manufacturing and selling exactly the same drug under exactly the same trademarked name. More recently, in addition to its other benefits, aspirin has been shown to be effective in reducing the occurrence of heart attacks. With Americans buying nearly $3 billion of analgesics each year (the world market is larger still) aspirin could arguably be called one of the most successful drugs ever developed.

Esters and Esterification

Organic acids are compounds that contain the −COOH functional group. Esters are a related group of compounds in which the H of the acid functional group has been replaced by a more complex structure. The following structures should make this relationship clear (R, by convention, indicates an arbitrary organic substructure).

$$R-\overset{\overset{\displaystyle O}{\|}}{C}-OH \qquad R-\overset{\overset{\displaystyle O}{\|}}{C}-O-R'$$

Carboxylic Acid   **Ester**

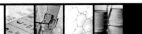
Esters commonly have a fruity or flowery odor. They are widely distributed in nature, and contribute significantly to the flavors and fragrances of foods. A small selection of esters is illustrated here, along with the odor of each. Can you identify the ester functional group in each compound?

ethyl butyrate
pineapple

methyl anthranilate
grape

methyl salicylate
wintergreen

Since esters and carboxylic acids are so closely related in structure, it should come as no surprise that esters can easily be synthesized from carboxylic acids. The process is called esterification. When a carboxylic acid and an alcohol are reacted in the presence of a catalytic amount of mineral acid, an ester is produced. Here are two examples.

acetic acid   **methanol**   **methyl acetate**

(1)

salicylic acid   **acetic acid**   **acetylsalicylic acid**   (2)

Although acetylsalicylic acid can be synthesized using acetic acid as shown above, the reaction is rather slow. Instead, you will use acetic anhydride as shown in the following reaction.

salicylic acid   **acetic anhydride**   **acetylsalicylic acid**   (3)

NOTES

Phenols

Phenols are organic compounds in which the −OH group is attached to an aromatic ring. Here are some examples. Note that salicylic acid is a bifunctional compound. That is, it includes both the −COOH functional group, making it an organic acid, and a hydroxyl group, making it a phenol.

phenol   2-bromobenzenol   salicylic acid

Most phenols form a highly-colored complex with iron(III) chloride. A dilute solution of $FeCl_3$ can therefore be used to test for the presence of phenols. Since salicylic acid is a phenol, it will yield a positive result when tested with $FeCl_3$. Note, however, that aspirin is not a phenol and when mixed with $FeCl_3$ should not produce any color. The iron(III) chloride test can thus be used to determine whether your synthesized aspirin is contaminated by any unreacted salicylic acid.

Purifying a Solid through Recrystallization

If a chemical reaction run in solution produces a material that is not soluble in the solvent (or produces more material than the amount of solvent present can dissolve), the material precipitates out of solution as a solid. Precipitation occurs quickly—so quickly that impurities can be incorporated into the solid structure. The resulting solid can be quite impure. In contrast, when recrystallization of a solid from solution is carried out slowly and in a controlled manner, very pure solid product can be obtained. The primary differences between precipitation and recrystallization are that the former is fast and unselective while the latter is slow and selective.

To purify a solid through recrystallization, the solid is first dissolved in an appropriate solvent near the solvent's boiling point. The solvent should be selected so that the solid is readily soluble at high temperature but only sparingly soluble at low temperature. The quantity of solvent used should be the minimum required to ensure that all of the solid can be dissolved at the higher temperature. Once all of the solid has dissolved, the solution is slowly cooled. As the solution cools, the solid begins to recrystallize as the solvent becomes less and less able to hold the material in solution. The crystals formed in this manner are very pure.

NOTES
▼

In this laboratory experiment, you will synthesize two derivatives of salicylic acid, an organic acid, by a process called esterification. The first compound you will prepare is 2(acetyloxy)benzoic acid (systematic name), also known as acetylsalicylic acid, but probably best known by its trade name, aspirin. The second compound is methyl salicylate, an important component of oil of wintergreen. You will also learn how to purify a solid by recrystallization.

CHEMISTRY IN A SUSTAINABLE WORLD

The development of pharmaceuticals such as aspirin has led to undeniable benefits for humanity. However, these benefits come at a price in terms of the raw materials consumed and waste that is produced. Chemists, following green chemistry principles, are actively engaged in finding new synthesis methods to mitigate the problems associated with the large-scale production of pharmaceuticals. An important assessment of the quantity of waste produced is determination of the atom economy of the reaction. The greater the atom economy, the more efficient the reaction in converting reactant atoms to the desired product, as opposed to waste byproducts. The percent atom economy is calculated by dividing the molecular mass of the desired product by the molecular mass of all products:

$$\% \text{ atom economy} = \frac{\text{molecular mass of desired product}}{\text{molecular mass of all products}} \times 100$$

In addition to the waste that is produced, the consumption of finite resources as raw materials is also a concern. For example, the potent anti-cancer drug Taxol was first isolated from the bark of the Pacific Yew tree. The production of Taxol required the stripping of bark from old-growth trees in the Pacific Northwest, killing the trees in the process. Production of the drug required 11 chemical transformations and 7 isolation steps that used 13 solvents and 13 organic reagents and materials. In 2004, the Bristol-Myers Squibb Co. received the Alternative Synthetic Pathways Green Chemistry Challenge Award from the Environmental Protection Agency for development of a method to grow cell lines from yew trees in large fermentation tanks using only water, sugars, vitamins and trace elements. This process was predicted to eliminate 32 metric tons of hazardous chemicals and other materials within five years of implementation.

PROCEDURE

NOTE
Avoid the impulse to shorten the heating and cooling times in the following procedure. Unfortunately, synthesis and crystallization processes can't be rushed and efforts to do so usually result in failure.

NOTES

▼

> **CAUTION!**
>
> Neither the aspirin nor the methyl salicylate produced as part of this lab is fit for human consumption. Do not attempt to taste or ingest either material. Doing so may result in serious injury. Volumes of methyl salicylate as small as 30 mL, when ingested, can be lethal.

Synthesis of Aspirin

1. When told to begin by your TA, put on gloves and use the following procedure to transfer your pre-weighed ~2 g sample of salicylic acid to a Teflon tube microwave reaction vessel (this looks like a semi-transparent test tube): Using a 125-mL Erlenmeyer flask to hold the tube upright, gently place the top of the tube over the top of the sample vial so that both components are in a vertical position with the open ends facing. Do not force the vial to fit into the tube. Invert the assembly to an upside-down vertical position and use gentle tapping to ensure the transfer into the tube. Some residue will remain in the vial. Do not rinse or add water; just put the cap back on the used vial and place it in the bin on the window bench labeled for empty vials.

2. Proceed to the hood station and slowly add 7 mL of acetic anhydride with the pump dispenser while holding the tube at an angle and rotating it so as to wash all powder from the vessel wall. Then add 5 drops of concentrated H_2SO_4. Your TA will check your vessel and add a small stir bar.

3. Gently mix by holding the tube over your workstation stir plate (cold!). NOTES: Do not attempt to stir the microwave reaction tube on a *hot* stir plate. Do not write or put tape on the tube. The salicylic acid should dissolve in 1–2 minutes. Do not mistake the stir bar for undissolved salicylic acid. When dissolved, return to the microwave area and your TA will place the tube into a pressure container and load it into the carousel. You will be given a position number; you will need this number to retrieve your sample after the microwave heating cycle is complete in about 25 minutes.

4. Next prepare a water bath for later steps by adding 350 mL of tap water to a 600-mL beaker. Put this on your hot plate and heat initially on a high setting. Watch the temperature rise and adjust to a lower setting to reach and maintain a 70°C temperature.

5. Put about 35 mL of DI water in your 100-mL graduated cylinder. Remove the plastic base and heat this to ~70°C in your water bath. The temperature can be recorded by putting the thermometer stem into the DI water in the graduated cylinder. While waiting for the water to reach ~70°C, proceed to the next step.

6. Also prepare an ice bath for the upcoming crystallization step and begin cooling your DI water bottle.

7. You can begin the *Synthesis of Methyl Salicylate* procedure in the manual if you have wait time available. *However, all steps related to the aspirin synthesis are on the critical path to completing this lab in the allotted time and must be done in preference to those of wintergreen.*

8. When the microwave heating cycle is complete and the tubes have cooled to about 65°C, your TA will unload the vessels, release the pressure, and call out the tube position numbers. Go to the hood with your 125-mL Erlenmeyer flask; your TA will give you your reaction tube. Return to your workstation and immediately pour the reaction tube contents, including the stir bar, into the flask. Without delay, begin adding your 35 mL of ~70°C water a few mL at a time with swirling to mix. You should complete the warm water addition within one minute. Proceed to steps 9 and 10.

9. Let the mixture cool to room temperature on the benchtop, waiting (approx. 10 min) for several fluffy crystals to form. (While waiting, place the empty microwave reaction vessel in the collection container on the window wall bench; you do not need to wash it.) Swirl occasionally. If crystals fail to form, try vigorous scratching of the inside surface of the flask with a glass stirring rod which has not been fire polished. The motion of the rod should be vertical and should be vigorous enough to produce an audible scratching. Chill in the ice bath to complete the crystallization. If you see "oil droplets" appear, ask your TA for assistance. This is not uncommon, but will require more effort on your part to effect product crystallization. With vigorous swirling, the "oil" droplets can be kept small and dispersed; this will promote crystal formation.

10. Collect the product on a Büchner funnel: place filter paper on the funnel, make sure the vent valve on the trap flask is closed, wet paper with deionized water and SLOWLY pour the reaction mixture onto the center of the filter paper to prevent crystals from seeping under the edges of the paper. To ensure a complete transfer, rinse the flask with ice-cold distilled water and pour this rinse water onto the filter paper. Once all of the crystals have been collected on the filter paper, use small portions of ice-cold deionized water to rinse the crystals clean. NOTE: If you have trouble with the vacuum filtering operation, check with your TA.

11. Let dry under vacuum for approximately 1 min. Turn off the vacuum at the wall valve. Transfer to a piece of weighed weighing paper, then weigh and record the mass of the crude product.

NOTES
▼

Purification of Aspirin

1. Your crude product from the previous section may be contaminated with unreacted salicylic acid. Let's test this hypothesis. Add 5 mL of distilled water to each of two test tubes. In one test tube, dissolve a few crystals of salicylic acid. In the second test tube, dissolve a few crystals of your aspirin. Add a drop of 1% $FeCl_3$ solution to each test tube. Record what you see. Does your aspirin contain any unreacted salicylic acid?

2. Place your crude product in a clean 125-mL Erlenmeyer flask, reserving a few crystals for seeding later. Add just enough ethanol to dissolve the crystals while heating in the water bath (start with 1.5 mL ethanol/1 g crude aspirin). Your goal is to use as little ethanol as possible. Swirl until dissolved.

3. Cool to room temperature. Add deionized water until the solution maintains its cloudiness at room temperature for one minute of swirling. (Initially, cloudiness will appear and then disappear when swirled.) This will require about 8 mL deionized water per gram crude aspirin. Warm the mixture in the water bath until clarified. Remove from the water bath, seed with reserved crude product, and let cool on the benchtop to room temperature. Stir, then place on ice until the majority of the product has precipitated out (approx. 15–20 min.).

4. Collect the recrystallized product by filtration on the Büchner funnel.

5. Transfer filter paper/crystals to a watch glass and dry in the oven (approx. 10 min).

6. Weigh and record the mass of your recrystallized product.

7. Following the procedure from step one of this section, use the $FeCl_3$ solution to test for the presence of phenol contamination. Record your observations and compare them with the observations made in step one. Did your attempt to purify the aspirin through recrystallization succeed?

8. If instructed to do so, save your synthesized aspirin for analysis during the next laboratory period.

Synthesis of Methyl Salicylate

(This procedure can be performed during one of the waiting periods during the synthesis of aspirin.)

1. Place about 1 g of salicylic acid and 5 mL of methanol in a large test tube.

2. Add 3 drops of concentrated H_2SO_4 to the test tube and swirl the test tube gently to mix the reagents.

3. Place the test tube in a hot water bath heated to 78°C to 82°C and allow the reaction to proceed for 15 minutes. Record any observations, including odor. Measure the temperatures with the probe in the water bath and not the test tube.

4. Add one drop of $FeCl_3$ solution to the test tube and record your observations.

5. Discard contents of the test tube into the appropriate waste container.

CALCULATIONS

1. Calculate the theoretical and experimental yield for your aspirin synthesis. Use the amount of recrystallized product, not the crude product, in your calculations. Theoretical yield is the quantity of material that could, in theory, be produced based on the quantities of starting reactants used. Experimental yield is the quantity of product that was actually produced.

    To calculate theoretical yield

    a. Write down the equation for the chemical reaction being run.

    b. Find the amounts of starting reactants used.

    c. Identify the limiting reagent.

    d. Based on the quantity of limiting reagent used, calculate the amount of product that could, in theory, be produced (i.e., the theoretical yield).

    Test yourself: If 6.1 g of Na is reacted with 10.3 g of Cl to produce solid NaCl, what is the theoretical yield of the reaction in grams? (Answer: 15.5 g NaCl)

    Experimental yield is generally expressed as a percentage, also called percent yield. It is the ratio of product actually produced to the theoretical yield, times 100%.

    $$\text{percent yield} = \frac{\text{actual amount of product}}{\text{theoretical yield}} \times 100\%$$

2. Calculate the percent atom economy for the synthesis of aspirin from salicylic acid and acetic anhydride (rxn. 3) and also for the synthesis from salicylic acid and acetic acid (rxn. 2).

3. According to The Aspirin Foundation (http://www.aspirin-foundation.com/history-of-aspirin/the-chemistry-of-aspirin/, accessed 7/2017), 35,000 metric tonnes of aspirin are produced every year. Given that a metric tonne is equal to 1000 kg, calculate how many kg of acetic acid waste are produced every year in the production of aspirin, assuming that the production is based on reaction (3).

NOTES

▼

DISCUSSION/CONCLUSION

Your report should include a discussion of your theoretical yield versus your experimental yield. If there is a difference between the two, how do you account for the difference? Compare your calculated atom economies and include a discussion of why both the percent yield and atom economy are important when assessing the efficiency of a synthesis reaction. In terms of atom economy and waste production, why is the synthesis from acetic acid (rxn. 2) a more desirable process?

REFERENCES

Mann, C.C., Plummer, M.L. (1991). *The aspirin wars.* Knopf, NY.

Vane, J.R., Botting, R.M, Eds. (1992). *Aspirin and other salicylates.* Chapman & Hall, NY.

exp22

Acid–Base Properties of Indicators and Aqueous Salt Solutions[1]

INTRODUCTION

When there is an acid spill in the lab, baking soda, $NaHCO_3$, is used to neutralize the acid. Have you ever wondered why? The formula of baking soda does not contain OH^- and yet it is a base, just as aluminum chloride, $AlCl_3$, is an acid even though it does not contain the H^+ ion. To understand these acid–base properties of salts, we must first consider the nature of salts and their behavior in aqueous solutions.

Salts are ionic compounds formed as a result of the neutralization reaction between an acid and a base. For example, common table salt is formed by the reaction between sodium hydroxide and hydrochloric acid:

$$HCl(aq) + NaOH(aq) \rightarrow H_2O(l) + NaCl(aq) \qquad (1)$$

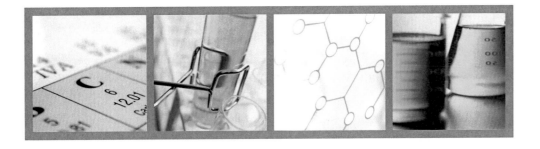

1 Adapted from Nelson, J.H.; Kemp, K.C. Chemistry: The Central Science, 7/e, Prentice-Hall, Inc., 1991; p. 251–262.

NOTES

and washing soda, Na_2CO_3, is formed by the reaction between sodium hydroxide and carbonic acid:

$$H_2CO_3(aq) + 2NaOH(aq) \rightarrow 2H_2O(l) + Na_2CO_3(aq) \tag{2}$$

The salt in solid form can be obtained by evaporating the water. This definition of a salt may seem somewhat confusing since we are generally more accustomed to using salts in their solid form, whether the salt is common table salt from the grocery store or one of the less familiar salts that you use in the lab. You may find it easier to think in terms of the alternate definition of salts, whatever their source, as ionic compounds that contain the cation and anion from a base and an acid. Looking at it this way, we can see that the salt Na_2CO_3 formed in reaction (2) contains the sodium cation from the base sodium hydroxide and the carbonate anion from carbonic acid.

If soluble, salts are completely ionized, or dissociated, when dissolved in water. Thus, the NaCl(aq) formed in reaction (1) exists as $Na^+(aq)$ and $Cl^-(aq)$ ions and the $Na_2CO_3(aq)$ formed in reaction (2) exists as $Na^+(aq)$ and $CO_3^-(aq)$ ions. These ions may then react with water in hydrolysis reactions to produce either the conjugate acid and hydroxide ion, or the conjugate base and hydronium ion. It is these hydrolysis reactions that give salts their acid–base properties.

Neutral Ions

Cations and anions from strong bases and acids *will not* participate in hydrolysis reactions and are considered to be neutral. Their presence in a solution will have no influence on the pH. These ions are listed in Table 22-1.

Ions as Acids

All cations that are not listed in Table 22-1 are the conjugate acids of weak bases and will act as acids in aqueous solution. For example, the ammonium ion, NH_4^+ is the conjugate acid of the weak base ammonia, NH_3. It reacts with water and forms an acidic solution:

$$NH_4^+(aq) + H_2O(l) \rightleftarrows H_3O^+(aq) + NH_3(aq) \tag{3}$$

When dissolved in water, small, highly charged metal cations such as Fe^{3+}, Fe^{2+}, Al^{3+}, Cu^{2+}, and Cr^{3+} are covalently bonded to six water molecules, forming hexaaqua complex ions, $[M(H_2O)_6]^{n+}$. It is these hydrated metal ions that react to make the solutions acidic. The pH of these metal ion solutions vary from one metal to another but the underlying chemistry is the same. Consider the case of the Al^{3+} ion:

$$Al(H_2O)_6^{3+}(aq) + H_2O(l) \rightleftarrows Al(OH)(H_2O)_5^{2+}(aq) + H_3O^+(aq) \tag{4}$$

For the sake of simplicity, the coordinated water molecules are often omitted from such equations and equation (4) can be rewritten as

$$Al^{3+}(aq) + H_2O(l) \rightleftarrows Al(OH)^{2+}(aq) + H^+(aq) \qquad (5)$$

When writing these equations you may be tempted to add two additional water molecules to form neutral molecules as products, rather than ions. Resist this temptation. When metal salts are dissolved in water, a series of equilibria reactions occur. These are complex and a mixture of species is formed. However, most of the acidic character is due to the hydrolysis of one water molecule and can be represented as shown in (4) and (5).

TABLE 22-1. Neutral Ions and Their Parent Acids and Bases

Ion	Parent Base	Ion	Parent Acid
Li^+	LiOH	Cl^-	HCl
Na^+	NaOH	Br^-	HBr
K^+	KOH	I^-	HI
Rb^+	RbOH	HSO_4^-	H_2SO_4
Cs^+	CsOH	NO_3^-	HNO_3
Ca^{2+}	$Ca(OH)_2$	ClO_4^-	$HClO_4$
Sr^{2+}	$Sr(OH)_2$		
Ba^{2+}	$Ba(OH)_2$		

Ions as Bases

All anions that are not listed in Table 22-1 are the conjugate bases of weak acids and will act as proton acceptors to produce basic solutions when dissolved in water. For example, the fluoride ion, F^-, is the conjugate base of the weak acid, hydrofluoric acid, HF.

$$F^-(aq) + H_2O(l) \rightleftarrows HF(aq) + OH^-(aq) \qquad (6)$$

Acid–Base Indicators

As you may be aware, acid–base indicators are weak acids themselves.

$$HIn + H_2O \rightleftarrows H_3O^+ + In^- \qquad (7)$$
$$\text{(Color A)} \qquad \text{(Color B)}$$

where HIn is the acid form of the indicator having color A and In⁻ is the base form of the indicator having color B. Consideration of Le Châtelier's principle tells us that in a strongly acidic environment the acid form, HIn, will dominate and in a

NOTES

▼

highly basic environment the base form, In^- will dominate. The relative amounts of the acid and base forms of the indicator, and thus the color, will be determined by the pH of the solution and the value of the equilibrium constant, K_{In}, for the indicator.

Consider the expression for K_{In} as shown in equation (8).

$$K_{In} = \frac{[H_3O^+][In^-]}{[HIn]} \tag{8}$$

We can determine the value of K_{In} from the pH range of the indicator color change, or conversely, see how the value of K_{In} determines the pH range of the indicator. The color change occurs at the point when half of the indicator is in the acid form and half is in the base form. At this point, when $[HIn] = [In^-]$, it can be seen from equation (8) that $[H_3O^+] = K_{In}$. In other words, the pH of the indicator at the point of the color transition is equal to the pK_{In}. For most indicators, the transition from the pure acid color to the pure base color occurs over a range of about 2 pH units. Given that K_{In} values for different indicators cover a broad range, it is possible to find an indicator for just about any desired pH.

Some indicators have three different colored forms. This is because these indicators are diprotic acids.

$$H_2In \rightleftarrows H_3O^+ + HIn^- \rightleftarrows H_3O^+ + In^{2-} \tag{9}$$
$$\text{(Color A)} \qquad \text{(Color B)} \qquad \text{(Color C)}$$

In this experiment you will determine the pH of several different aqueous salt solutions through the use of acid–base indicators and from that, determine the value of the acid or base dissociation constant for the ions. Because the indicators are acids, it is important to use very small quantities to avoid changing the pH of the solution being tested.

CHEMISTRY IN A SUSTAINABLE WORLD

The salt solutions used in this experiment are non-toxic in the quantities that are used and could theoretically be safely disposed of by pouring down the drain. However, due to the acidic properties of some of the ions, the total waste generated in this experiment is too acidic to be dumped directly and must be collected for processing before disposal.

PROCEDURE

Part A—Determination of Indicator Transition Range

Before you can use indicators to determine the pH of your salt solutions, you and your lab group must determine the color transition pH for the indicators that you

will be using. To do this, place a well plate on the corresponding paper template. Carefully fill the wells in each row about 2/3 full with the corresponding pH buffer and then add 1–2 drops of the designated indicator in each column. If you make a mistake, remove the contents of the problem well(s) with a poly pipet and refill. Record your observations in Table 22-2 and work together to determine the color transition range and value of K_a for each indicator. If you have any uncertainty, you may want to take a photo of this "indicator key" for future reference. Are any of the indicators diprotic? If so, estimate K_{a1} and K_{a2}. When finished, rinse into the large poly beaker at your workstation. Each person should complete and submit a copy of Table 22-2.

Part B—Determination of the pH of Salt Solutions

You will now work independently to determine the pH of several salt solutions using the information that you have learned about the pH transition range of the various indicators. Observations can be recorded directly into Table 22-3 rather than in your lab notebook. You will begin with a TA demonstration of the acid–base properties of carbonated water using Universal Indicator, an acid–base indicator that undergoes multiple color changes. Record your observations of this demonstration and determine the pH of carbonated water to the nearest pH unit before and after boiling.

To test the pH of the salt solutions, begin by filling 6 wells of a plastic well plate about half full with one of the 0.1 M salt solutions indicated in Table 22-3. Add one drop of a different indicator to each well and record the color in Table 22-3. After recording your observations, rinse into the large poly beaker at your workstation and repeat with each of the other salt solutions, being sure to rinse between tests. Solutions may be tested in any order. For $Fe(NO_3)_3$ and $AlCl_3$ only, use methyl violet indicator in addition to the others.

When finished, discard the contents of your rinse beaker into the waste bucket in the hood.

CALCULATIONS

For each solution:

- Calculate the $[H_3O^+]$ and $[OH^-]$ values using the pH values that you have determined and record them in Table 22-4.

- If a hydrolysis reaction occurred, determine which ion underwent the reaction and write the reaction in Table 22-4. Indicate the spectator ion. Note: The hydrolysis reaction is the reaction that occurs when an ion reacts with water, such as the examples in equations (3), (4), (5), and (6). The hydrolysis reaction is not the dissociation process that occurs when a salt is added to water.

NOTES

- If a hydrolysis reaction occurred, use the reaction to record the acid or base dissociation constant expression in Table 22-5. You may be wondering how you know whether it will be K_a or K_b? Start by considering the pH. Was the solution acidic or basic? This should correlate with the products of the hydrolysis reaction that you wrote. If you formed an acid, you will write an expression for K_a. If you formed a base, you will write an expression for K_b. For example, consider reaction (3). In this case, H_3O^+ is a product, the solution is acidic and the acid dissociation constant expression is given by

$$K_a = \frac{[H_3O^+][NH_3]}{[NH_4^+]}$$

In the reaction given by equation (6), hydroxide ions are formed, the solution is basic and the base dissociation constant is given by

$$K_b = \frac{[HF][OH^-]}{[F^-]}$$

Remember that for metal cations with a +2 or +3 charge, the hydrolysis reaction should be written for the reaction with only one water molecule. (See equations (4) and (5).)

- Finally, calculate the value of K_a or K_b for each of the ions that underwent hydrolysis and record this value in Table 22-5. Each of the solutions was originally 0.10 M and because they are weak acids and bases, you can assume that the amount of dissociation was very small compared to this value. Include one complete sample calculation.

DISCUSSION/CONCLUSION

Include and reference all completed tables. Discuss acids, bases, and salts in the context of this experiment: What are Brønsted-Lowry acids and bases? Why do some salts have acidic or basic properties when added to water? What does the magnitude of K_a or K_b tell you about the primary species that are present in the aqueous salt solutions at equilibrium? What is the primary source of error in this experiment? How could you minimize this source of error? Why is it important to only use a few drops of indicator when testing solutions?

TABLE 22-2. Colors and pH Transitions of Common Indicators

pH	Methyl Violet	Methyl Orange	Methyl Red	Bromothymol Blue	Phenol Red	Phenol-phthalein	Alizarin Yellow
1							
2							
3							
4							
5							
6							
7							
8							
9							
10							
11							
12							
Transition Range:							
K_{In}:							

TABLE 22-3. Colors of Salt Solutions with Different Indicators

Solution	Methyl Violet	Methyl Orange	Methyl Red	Bromo-thymol Blue	Phenol Red	Phenol-phtha-lein	Alizarin Yellow	pH	$[H_3O^+]$	$[OH^-]$
					Indicator Color					
NaCl	—									
$NaC_2H_3O_2$	—									
$Fe(NO_3)_3$										
NH_4Cl	—									
$KHCO_3$	—									
$AlCl_3$										
Na_2CO_3	—									

	Color before Boiling	pH before Boiling	Color after Boiling	pH after Boiling
carb. water				

NOTES

TABLE 22-4. Hydrolysis Reactions

Solution	Hydrolysis Reaction (if any)	Spectator Ion(s) (If any)
0.1 M NaCl		
0.1 M NaC₂H₃O₂		
0.1 M Fe(NO₃)₃		
0.1 M NH₄Cl		
0.1 M KHCO₃		
0.1 M AlCl₃		
0.1 M Na₂CO₃		

TABLE 22-5. Acid and Base Dissociation Constants

Solution	Dissociation Constant Expression	Value of K_a or K_b
0.1 M NaCl		
0.1 M NaC$_2$H$_3$O$_2$		
0.1 M Fe(NO$_3$)$_3$		
0.1 M NH$_4$Cl		
0.1 M KHCO$_3$		
0.1 M AlCl$_3$		
0.1 M Na$_2$CO$_3$		

Sample Calculation:

NOTES

exp23

Acid–Base Titrations

Read *Volumetric Analysis: Titration* (page xl).

Acid–base reactions in aqueous solutions represent one of the most important categories of chemical reaction and are commonly investigated by means of acid–base titrations. In this weeks experiment you will use titrimetric analysis to determine the concentration of a weak acid solution to a high level of precision and will also determine the acid dissociation constant of the acid from the titration data. By pooling results with your classmates you will be able to make predictions about the relationship between K_a values and the shapes of titration curves.

Acid–base reactions are particularly suitable for titration methods because of the very rapid rate of the proton transfer process and the speed at which equilibrium is reached at each point in the titration. The titration of a weak acid with a strong base may be represented by equation (1):

$$HA + OH^- \rightarrow A^- + H_2O \tag{1}$$

The equilibrium constant for this reaction is sufficiently large that we can state that the reaction goes to completion. The point at which the number of moles of OH^- is exactly

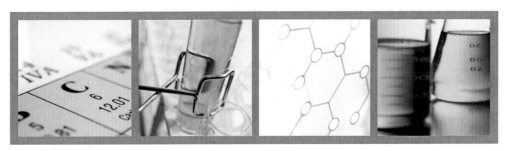

209

NOTES
▼

equal or equivalent to the number of moles of HA is referred to as the *equivalence point* of the titration. Prior to the equivalence point, there will be excess unreacted acid present. This acid undergoes a proton transfer reaction with water:

$$HA + H_2O \rightleftarrows H_3O^+ + A^- \qquad (2)$$

Using H^+ to represent H_3O^+ and omitting water from the expression, a simpler representation of the acid ionization is given by:

$$HA \rightleftarrows H^+ + A^- \qquad (3)$$

The extent of the acid ionization is represented by the acid ionization constant, K_a:

$$K_a = \frac{[H^+][A^-]}{[HA]} \qquad (4)$$

During a titration, the state of the system can be monitored by measuring the concentration of H^+ (or H_3O^+) ions that are present. For convenience the concentration of H^+ ions is frequently expressed as the pH of the solution, where

$$pH = -\log[H^+] \qquad (5)$$

Consider equation (1) again. At the point in the titration when enough base has been added to neutralize exactly half the quantity of acid present, the concentration of unreacted acid, HA, is equal to the concentration of the A^- ion that has been produced. This point is referred to as the half-equivalence point.

$$[HA] = [A^-] \quad \text{at the half-equivalence point} \qquad (6)$$

The half-equivalence point is significant because the pH at this point is directly related to the value of the acid dissociation constant. We can see this by incorporation of the relationship expressed in equation (6) into equation (4):

$$K_a = \frac{[H^+]\cancel{[A^-]}}{\cancel{[HA]}} = [H^+]$$

or, taking the negative log of both sides,

$$pK_a = pH \quad \text{at the half-equivalence point}$$

Therefore, to determine the acid dissociation constant from a pH titration curve, it is first necessary to determine the volume of base necessary to reach the equivalence point. Half of this volume is the half-equivalence point. The pH at this point, read from the titration curve, is equal to pK_a for the weak acid.

NOTES

Experimentally, pH is monitored in two ways during the titration. One method, which you may already be familiar with, is to use an indicator. Acid–base indicators exist in two different pH-dependent colored forms. The acid form is one color, which by loss of a proton, is converted into a differently colored base form. The equilibrium reaction for the indicator is

$$HIn_A \leftrightarrows H^+ + In_B^-$$
$$\text{(Color A)} \qquad \text{(Color A)}$$

where HIn_A is the acid form of the indicator having color A and In_B^- is the base form of the indicator having color B. As an acid is added to a solution containing an indicator, Le Châtelier's principle tells us that the equilibrium in the solution will have color A. Likewise, if a base is added, the indicator will be present in the form of In_B^- and the solution will have color B. There are many different indicators available, each of which has a different pH-transition range.

The point where the color change occurs is referred to as the *endpoint* of the titration. Because there are many different indicators available that change colors over a variety of pH ranges, it is possible to select an indicator which undergoes a color change at or near the equivalence point of the titration. (The equivalence point will occur at different pH values for different acid–base systems.)

The second method involves direct measurement of pH using a pH meter. A pH meter works over a broad range of hydrogen ion concentrations and, when properly calibrated, provides much more precise information than does an indicator. However, use of an indicator is frequently much more rapid than a pH meter. The choice of whether to use an indicator or a pH meter depends largely upon the results that are desired.

Before performing the titration to determine the unknown acid concentration you must first accurately determine the concentration of the titrant, sodium hydroxide, by titrating it against a very pure sample of potassium hydrogen phthalate (KHP) of known weight. This is a process known as standardization and KHP is referred to as a primary standard. Primary standards are substances which are 1) available in pure form, 2) stable, 3) have high molecular weights, and 4) are readily available and inexpensive. KHP meets all these criteria. You may be wondering why it is necessary to standardize sodium hydroxide, rather than preparing a solution of known concentration by weighing a sample on the analytical balance and carefully diluting it. Unfortunately, solid sodium hydroxide is somewhat unstable and unavailable in primary standard purity. Solutions can only be prepared to approximate concentrations and must be standardized to accurately determine their concentrations. The indicator phenolphthalein will be used to signal the endpoint for the standardization titrations.

The standardized sodium hydroxide solution will be used for the titration of a weak acid. For this titration, rather than using an indicator to determine the endpoint, changes will be monitored with a pH meter. The pH changes will be used to

determine the concentration of the acid and the acid dissociation constant, K_a, of the acid. While it is not necessary to add an indicator if a pH meter is used, you will again add phenolphthalein to the reaction mixture. The purpose of this is to provide you with an opportunity to experimentally determine the pH range of the color change of this indicator. You will also be able to assess whether phenolphthalein is a good indicator choice for this acid–base system. That is, does the endpoint agree with the equivalence point of the reaction?

PROCEDURE

Part A—Standardization of Sodium Hydroxide (~0.2 M)

Obtain approximately 120 mL of ~0.2 M sodium hydroxide (NaOH) from the side bench.

Weigh out three samples of potassium hydrogen phthalate (KHP), between 0.80 g and 0.90 g each, and record the masses to the nearest 0.0001 g. Place the samples in 3 clean and marked Erlenmeyer flasks (125 mL or 250 mL). Add about 40 mL of deionized water and two drops of phenolphthalein solution to each flask.

Prepare your buret for use. (See *Volumetric Analysis: Titration*, page xl.) Fill the buret with the sodium hydroxide solution. Make sure there are no air bubbles, especially in the tip. Record the initial volume.

Position one of the flasks under the buret and slowly add the sodium hydroxide solution, swirling after each addition. As the sodium hydroxide solution is added, a pink color appears that rapidly dissipates and disappears with swirling. Check to see that all KHP is now dissolved. Then carefully add small volumes of sodium hydroxide while swirling.

> Any titrant that hangs on the tip of the buret or is splashed onto the flask above the liquid *will not* react with acid in the flask but *will* be read as volume delivered from the buret. That's why you should take care to deliver all of the NaOH solution to the liquid in the flask. Rinsing with a small amount of deionized water will bring any drops of sodium hydroxide solution down into the liquid in the flask but will not affect the acid–base reaction.

As the equivalence point is approached, the pink color disappears more slowly with swirling. When this occurs, rinse the sides of the flask with deionized water from your wash bottle and carefully continue small volume additions. When one drop of sodium hydroxide solution turns the solution in the flask from colorless to pale pink (which does not fade on standing for 30 seconds), the equivalence point is reached. Record the final buret reading.

Repeat this procedure with the other samples of KHP. It is not necessary to empty the buret; simply refill it with additional sodium hydroxide solution and record the new initial buret reading.

Before concluding this part of the experiment, calculate the molarity of the sodium hydroxide solution (4 significant figures). If the relative average deviation[1] of the three determinations is greater than 1.0%, repeat the standardization with additional samples of accurately weighed KHP. (Check with your instructor before performing more than 5 trials.)

$$relative\ average\ deviation = \frac{\bar{d}}{\bar{x}} \times 100 = \frac{\sum |x_i - \bar{x}|/n}{\bar{x}} \times 100$$

Where x_i is the value of an individual measurement, $\bar{x}$ is the average value and n is the total number of measurements. After completion of the standardization titrations, the solutions in the flasks should be discarded as directed. Save the rest of your (now standardized) sodium hydroxide solution for use in Part B of the procedure.

Part B—Titration of a Weak Acid

Work with a partner for Part B. Different pairs of students will be working with different weak acids. The acids that will be used are shown in Table 23-1.

TABLE 23-1. Weak Acids

Name	Formula	Structure
acetic acid	CH_3COOH	
formic acid	$HCOOH$	
lactic acid	$CH_3CH(OH)COOH$	
mandelic acid	$C_6H_5CH(OH)COOH$	

These are all monoprotic carboxylic acids (one acidic H^+). Carboxylic acids are compounds that contain the carboxyl (–COOH) group. They are acidic because of

---

1 *The average deviation ($\bar{d}$) is a measure of the variability in your data. It is calculated by finding the differences between the individual results and the mean, regardless of sign, summing the deviation and dividing by the number of results. The relative average deviation is expressed as a percentage, relative to the magnitude of the measured quantity.*

NOTES

▼

the hydrogen in the carboxyl group. In water, a hydrogen ion is transferred from the –COOH group to a water molecule. The other hydrogen atoms in these molecules are not acidic.

In this section of the experiment you will be using Vernier LabPro™ digital pH probes and Logger *Pro*™ software. You will also be using acids and bases which aren't compatible with keyboards. Please use care with your solutions.

Pre-Calibration Setup

1. Obtain 25 mL of pH 4 and pH 10 buffer solution in two 50-mL beakers.

2. Start Logger *Pro* 3.4.6 by clicking the Logger *Pro* 3.4.6 icon on the computer desktop. A "new" file will open, the probe will be detected and a pH value will appear on the data column side of the screen. If this does not appear, inform your TA.

3. Select the Data Collect icon from the Logger *Pro* tool bar to open the dialog box. From "Mode," select "Events with Entry" from the pull-down menu. Pull down the Experiment menu and select Data Collection.

4. The "Number of Columns" should be set to 1; use pull-down menu to change if necessary. In the "Name" box, enter Sodium Hydroxide. In the "Short Name" box enter NaOH. Click the highlighted "Done" box when finished.

Calibration

1. From the Menu bar, select Calibrate and then select the single highlighted option (LabQuest Mini: port#: pH) which appears.

2. From the open Sensor Calibration box, select the gray "Calibrate Now" button.

3. Reading 1 box becomes active. Remove the pH probe from the storage solution, rinse it with DI water, gently remove excecess water with a Kimwipe, place the probe in one of your pH buffers and swirl gently. When the Volt reading is stable (this should be just a few seconds), you can enter your known pH value in the highlighted box. **Note: This will be either a 4.00 or 10.00 value, it will NOT be the Volt number.** Now press the Keep buttom for Reading 1 which has now become active.

4. The Reading 2 box now becomes active. Rinse the probe and repeat the process using your second buffer. When this is complete, select OK to close the Sensor Calibration box.

Experiment

1. Fill the buret to the 0.00 mL mark with the sodium hydroxide solution.

2. Place approximately 50 mL deionized water into a clean 150-mL beaker. Clean a 10-mL volumetric pipet and rinse with deionized water followed by your

weak acid solution. Pipet 10.00 mL of the acid solution into the 150-mL beaker containing the deionized water. Add 2 drops of phenolphthalein indicator solution. Place a magnetic stirring bar into the beaker.

3. Carefully lower the combination electrode of the pH meter into the solution. Adjust the height of the electrode so that it will not come in contact with the magnetic stir bar when the stirrer is turned on. Clamp the electrode into place. Turn on and adjust the stirrer so that the magnet is spinning in the solution at a slow to moderate rate. Make sure the magnet does not touch the electrode!

4. Position the buret containing the sodium hydroxide solution so that the tip of the buret is inside the beaker but not touching the walls of the beaker.

5. Prepare the program to collect data:

   - Change the x-axis to a maximum value of 25 mL by using the cursor to highlight the largest value, then type in 25, and then Enter to save this value.

   - Click Collect.

   - Identify the current pH reading located at bottom of graph. This is a continuous reading of the pH in the beaker.

   - Click Keep and enter the value of the initial buret reading.

6. While watching the pH meter, add NaOH from the buret until a pH change of approximately 0.2 has been produced. Stop adding NaOH and select Keep. When asked to Enter a Number, enter the new buret reading. Continue titrating in this manner, recording the pH and volume every time a 0.2 pH change is observed. While doing the titration, record observations in your lab notebook and note the pH where the phenolphthalein color change occurs. Be careful— as you approach the equivalence point, very small additions of base cause large changes in the pH. Once you are able to clearly see the equivalence point, stop the titration. Do not exceed pH 12 as it will damage the pH electrode.

7. Once you have the desired titration curve and are ready to quit, click on Stop. If you need to edit an entry, click on the value and make the correction at this time.

Vernier Analysis

The Logger *Pro*™ software allows you to determine the equivalence point volume.

- To determine the equivalence point volume, pull down the Analyze menu and select Tangent.

- Move the cursor along the curve and notice how the tangent line changes. The box at the top right of the screen indicates the slope of the tangent line and corresponding NaOH volume. The point on the curve with the steepest slope is the equivalence point of the titration. The corresponding NaOH volume is the equivalence point volume. Record this value.

- Helpful hints: You can enlarge the print size in the Analyze-Tangent box by double clicking on it. An options box opens and you can enlarge the font size. To print the graph without moving the cursor from the tangent point of maximum slope, use the keyboard to select ⌘p to open a print dialog box. Now you can move the mouse again to add a title and enter control other print functions.

- Print the graph and data table by selecting Print Screen under the File menu.

Cleanup

1. Remove electrode, rinse thoroughly, and return to storage solution.

2. When finished with the buret, rinse thoroughly to remove all sodium hydroxide solution and invert in the buret clamp. (Dried sodium hydroxide will clog the buret.)

ANALYSIS, GRAPHING AND CALCULATIONS

Part A: KHP ($KHC_8H_4O_4$, molar mass = 204.2 g/mol) is a monoprotic acid. Therefore, in the titration of NaOH against KHP, the number of moles of base added at the equivalence point is equal to the number of moles acid originally present. The concentration of sodium hydroxide is calculated from the known mass of KHP and the volume of sodium hydroxide required to neutralize the acid.

Calculate the average concentration and standard deviation of your three trials. Enter your results into the class database.

Part B: Indicate the equivalence and half-equivalence points on the titration curve. Indicate the color change region for phenolphthalein on your graph.

Calculate the molarity of the acid solution, based upon the molarity of NaOH determined in Part A and the volume required to reach the equivalence point.

From the pH value at the half-equivalence point, determine the pK_a and K_a of the acid.

Calculate the percent dissociation of the weak acid (before titration) from the initial pH and the calculated molarity of the acid.

Write a balanced equation for the reaction of your weak acid with water.

Write a balanced equation for the complete neutralization of your weak acid with sodium hydroxide.

Write a balanced equation to show the interaction of your major anion, the one responsible for influencing the pH, with water at the equivalence point.

Class Data: Enter your values for the initial pH, percent dissociation and K_a into the class data table.

DISCUSSION

Refer to the general guidelines for writing a Discussion section. The bullet points below should further guide your writing. Include the graph you prepared in part B. Class data and graphs do not need to be included.

Part A:

- Report your average concentration and standard deviation of the standardized NaOH solution and also the class values. Did your value fall within one standard deviation of the class value?

- What is the purpose of standardization and why was it necessary to standardize the NaOH?

Part B:

- Report the molarity of the weak acid you analyzed.

- Report the initial pH, half-equivalence point pH and equivalence point pH.

- Report the K_a of your weak acid based on the pH at the half-equivalence point.

- Compare the K_a value you determined for your weak acid to the K_a literature value. Do not report a percent error but comment on this qualitatively. Were your results reasonably accurate (within one order of magnitude)?

Analysis of Class Data:

- Rank the acids from lowest strength to highest strength based on 1) percent dissociation and 2) calculated K_a values. Do the rankings agree?

- What is the relationship between the initial pH, percent dissociation and acid strength?

- Refer to the titration curves generated in the class data spreadsheet. Compare the initial pH and shape of your titration curve to the titration curves of the other weak acids and to the curve of HCl. How does the shape of the curve change as the acid strength decreases?

- Comment on the appropriateness of phenolphthalein as an indicator for weak acid–strong base titrations. Why was an indicator used in part A and a pH meter used in part B?

NOTES

exp24

Antacid Effectiveness

Heartburn. Millions of Americans suffer from this painful and sometimes harmful condition that is caused by an excess of acid in the stomach. Gastric acid, composed primarily of dilute HCl, has a pH of approximately 1–2, making it about a million times more acidic than pure water. When there is an excess of stomach acid, heartburn, or Gastroesophageal Reflux Disease (GERD) results. Many sufferers turn to one of the many over-the-counter antacids such as Tums or Rolaids to neutralize the excess acid and reduce pain. How can a consumer know which antacid to choose? One consideration is certainly the active ingredient in each product and how well it works for a given individual. Another factor is cost, and which antacid will provide the most acid neutralization power for the least amount of money. In this laboratory experiment, you will work with your classmates to determine the acid neutralizing power of several different antacids and establish which is the most cost effective.

The active ingredient in all antacids is one or more basic salts, such as calcium carbonate ($CaCO_3$), that react with and neutralize the acid. In addition, antacids contain an assortment of inactive binders, fillers, flavors and colors. To find the amount of base that is present in a sample, the standard method is to titrate with an acid of known concentration. (If you haven't yet read "Volumetric Analysis: Titration" in this book,

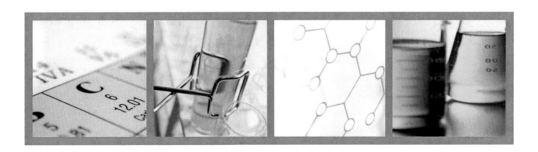

please do so now, before proceeding.) However, a conventional acid/base titration is difficult when dealing with antacids because most are relatively insoluble in water. This problem can be overcome by dissolving the antacid tablets in a measured excess of acid. Some of this acid will be neutralized by reacting with the antacid and some will be left over. This excess acid can be titrated with a standardized sample of base. By calculating the amount of acid that was in excess and knowing the amount of acid that was originally added, the amount of acid neutralized by the base can be determined by simple subtraction. This technique of adding a measured excess and titrating to find the amount remaining is called a **back titration** and it will be used to tell us the acid neutralizing power of the different antacids.

PROCEDURE

1. Your lab instructor will assign you a brand of antacid to work with. Obtain three tablets of this antacid. Avoid touching with your fingers as much as possible. Record the brand name and the identity and quantity (mg) of the active ingredient(s) in the antacid.

2. Working with other students in your section that have been assigned the same antacid, write the balanced equation(s) for the neutralization reaction(s) between the active ingredient(s) and hydrochloric acid. Then, determine the amount of 1.5 M hydrochloric acid that is theoretically necessary to neutralize the antacid based upon the amount of active ingredient(s) in the antacid tablets.

3. Obtain about 60 mL standardized NaOH in a 100-mL beaker and about 80 mL of standardized HCl in a 150-mL beaker. You can get more later if needed.

4. Working individually, prepare two burets for use as described in "Volumetric Analysis: Titration." Fill one buret with standardized M HCl and one with standardized M NaOH. Once the burets have been filled, be sure to record the exact concentrations of the acid and base in your laboratory notebook.

5. Place one antacid tablet into an Erlenmeyer flask.

6. Record the initial volume of HCl in the buret, remembering that the buret volume can be read to ±0.01 mL. Add an excess of HCl from the buret to the flask containing the antacid tablet. Because you will need an excess for the back titration, this quantity should be equal to the volume that you calculated in step 2, plus 10 mL. Record the final volume of HCl. The volume of acid added is the difference between the initial and final readings.

7. Refill the buret with HCl and repeat with your other two antacid tablets, being sure to keep track of which flask is which.

8. Using a hot plate turned on to a medium-low setting, warm gently to dissolve the samples and then boil the solutions for about a minute. This process will drive off any excess CO_2 generated in the neutralization reaction. Some components of the antacid tablets may remain undissolved but these will not cause problems. Do not overheat as this may cause undesirable color changes.

9. Let the flasks cool while sitting on the bench for at least five minutes.

10. While the flasks are cooling, work with your group to determine which indicator will be best to use for the titration. Be sure to select indicators that have an endpoint at or near the equivalence point of your titration. Within your group, you may want to try a few different indicators to determine which will provide the most visible color change at the endpoint.

11. When the solutions have reached room temperature, add 3–4 drops of indicator to each and swirl to mix. Use a wash bottle to wash the walls of the flask with deionized water.

12. Titrate the first sample to the endpoint with standard NaOH, being sure to record starting and finishing volumes.

13. Refill the buret with NaOH and repeat the titration with the remaining dissolved tablets.

14. Dispose of excess reagents and reaction products in the labeled containers in the hood.

15. Rinse the burets as directed and clean the flasks thoroughly to remove all undissolved material from the walls of the flasks.

ANALYSIS AND CALCULATIONS

To be completed before leaving lab:

Calculate the acid neutralizing power, which is the number of mg of acid neutralized by each tablet:

    a. Calculate the number of moles of HCl added to the antacid.

    b. Calculate the number of moles of base used for each titration. This is equivalent to the moles of acid that were in excess, after neutralization by the antacid.

    c. Subtract the number of moles in excess from the amount added to get the number of moles neutralized by your tablets.

    d. Use the molar mass of HCl to calculate the mg of acid neutralized.

Based on your ability to see the endpoint, indicate your confidence in your results as low, medium, or high.

Work with your group to calculate the average number of mg neutralized, along with the standard deviation. If any trials have low confidence due to a poor choice of indicator, do not include them in the calculation.

Record your group's average value in the class data spreadsheet, along with a confidence ranking.

Before leaving lab, record the acid neutralizing power (mg HCl neutralized), cost per package, and number of tablets per package of each of the different antacids that were analyzed.

Calculate the cost per tablet (cents), acid neutralizing power per tablet, and acid neutralizing power per penny for each of the antacids.

CHEMISTRY IN A SUSTAINABLE WORLD

At the end of every experiment we need to consider waste handling and disposal. In addition to reaction products, there are frequently leftover reagents to consider as well. Waste can be handled in essentially two different ways. It can be disposed of directly in a landfill, or it can be treated chemically to transform hazardous waste into a less hazardous substance. These substances are then either released into the environment or land-filled, though in a less-hazardous form.

Prepare a table of all of the waste and leftover reagents from this lab. Assess the risk and quantities produced of each, and propose a chemical treatment plan to handle anything that is of concern. (This can all be included in the same table.) Include the waste list, risk assessment and treatment plan with your lab report.

DISCUSSION/CONCLUSION

Which antacid had the greatest acid-neutralizing power? Which antacid provides the greatest value? What is the basis for your decision? Are there any other factors that would influence your decision to buy a particular antacid?

Comment on why and how titrimetric analysis is used and how a back-titration differs from a regular titration. Why wasn't a direct titration performed for this analysis? Which indicator did you use, and why?

Be sure to include the sources of error in a titration and indicate whether the effect would result in an erroneously high or low value for the neutralization capacity of the antacid. How would the results be impacted if the antacid solution was not boiled to drive off the carbon dioxide?

exp25

Bioavailability of Iron[1]

Iron is the most abundant trace element in the human body. It is found circulating in the blood in hemoglobin and transferrin and also in muscle tissue in myoglobin. It is stored in the liver, spleen, and bone marrow in ferritin and is associated with various enzymes. Iron is available from a variety of food sources and supplements though most of us absorb less than 15% of the 10–15 mg of iron contained in our daily diets.

Iron absorption is limited by a control mechanism in our intestines where the absorption occurs. This control mechanism, which is not well understood, decreases the uptake of iron when the body's needs have been met. When the body's needs have not been met, in a condition called anemia, a normally functioning body will respond by increasing its uptake of iron to 20 or 30% of what is ingested. Increased absorption occurs commonly during pregnancy or when a large number of red blood cells have been lost through bleeding. Conversely, an excess of iron in our systems, a much more rare condition called hemochromatosis, is a toxic condition that is detrimental to liver, heart, and pancreas function.

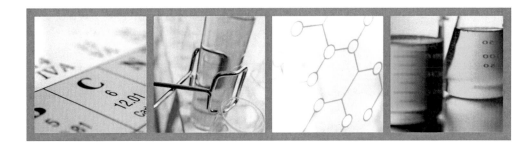

---

1 *Kimbrogh, D.R.; Martinez, N.; Stolfus, S. J. Chem. Ed. 1995, 72, 558.*

The bioavailability of iron is also a function of its chemical form and the presence of food components that either promote or inhibit its absorption. Many foods are enriched by the manufacturer with iron as a nutrient. Most consumers, even chemists, are often surprised to learn that food labels listing "iron" or "reduced iron" mean the foods have actual metallic iron filings added to them. The bioavailability of iron in this form is open to question, depending on the particle size, the food being fortified and the pH.[2]

Iron in the metallic form cannot be absorbed, but presumably it dissolves as it is oxidized by the hydrochloric acid in the pH 2 environment of the stomach. In the lab we will simulate this by dissolving iron filings in a pH 2 hydrochloric acid solution. The reaction of metallic iron with hydrochloric acid is given by

$$Fe(s) + 2HCl(aq) \rightarrow Fe^{2+}(aq) + 2Cl^-(aq) + H_2(g) \tag{1}$$

At this low pH, the formation of iron(II) is favored over iron(III). However, iron absorption does not occur in the stomach but in the small intestine which is strongly buffered to pH 8. An increase in pH is accompanied by the oxidation of iron(II) to iron(III), uptake of iron(III) by mucosal cells or precipitation as iron(III) hydroxide:

$$Fe^{3+}(aq) + 3OH^-(aq) \rightleftarrows Fe(OH)_3(s) \tag{2}$$

The formation of insoluble iron(III) hydroxide dramatically illustrates the biounavailability of iron, for in order to be absorbed the iron must remain in a soluble form. Once a precipitate forms, the iron is no longer available for absorption and instead passes through the digestive tract and is eliminated from the body. Fortunately, there are many substances that complex with, or chelate, iron and keep it soluble, thus enhancing the possibility of absorption. The biological activity of iron depends on the presence of these substances and the formation of soluble complex ions. A complex ion is a metal ion with Lewis bases attached to it through coordinate covalent bonds. (Review these terms in your general chemistry text if necessary.)

There are also several substances commonly present in food digestion that decrease iron absorption, presumably because they hinder iron solubility. In this lab you will investigate the behavior of iron in the presence of several different substances and predict which of these enhance and which inhibit the absorption of iron in the intestines.

CHEMISTRY IN A SUSTAINABLE WORLD

Metal-ion complexes are important not only in physiological systems but in many non-biological applications as well. One example of this can be seen in the

2 *Garcia-Casal, M.N, et. al.* Nutrition Research 2003, *23*, 451–463.

production of gold. Currently about 90% of the gold that is obtained from low-grade ores is extracted using the cyanide process, in which gold is solubilized from the ore through the formation of a gold-cyanide complex ion, $Au(CN)_2^-$. The gold is then recovered and the cyanide is left as waste. Concerns about the environmental risks associated with the cyanide process have prompted many states and countries to ban the process and have incentivized the industry to look for greener alternatives. The iron(III)-oxalate complex that you will be studying in this experiment is currently being investigated by the gold mining industry as they try to move toward more environmentally sustainable methods of extraction. In this process, thiosulfate is used to complex the gold with the iron(III) acting as an oxidizing agent in the process. The oxalate is used to keep iron in solution, just as it does in the human body. The iron(III)-oxalate complex undergoes photocatalytic decomposition to form iron(II) and iron(III) oxides, CO_2 and CO_3^{2-} and can thus be discharged after use to a mine tailings area without causing a serious threat to the environment.[3,4]

PROCEDURE

Part A—Isolation of Metallic Iron from Breakfast Cereal

> **NOTE**
>
> The purpose of this portion of the experiment is to verify the presence of iron filings in cereal. It will not be possible to isolate enough iron in this procedure to use in Part B of this experiment. Your lab instructor will perform this procedure as a demonstration.

Part B—Behavior of Iron in Simulated Physiological Conditions

Obtain about 50 mL of a 5% solution of sodium hydroxide from the side bench.

Place 5–10 mL of the pH 2 solution of iron dissolved in simulated stomach acid into a test tube. Add a 5% solution of sodium hydroxide dropwise to raise the pH to approximately 8, thus simulating the passage from the acidic stomach to the strongly buffered basic small intestine. Monitor the pH with pH indicator paper. This is done most efficiently by stirring the solution in the test tube and then touching the end of the stirring rod to the pH paper. Note any changes that occur as the pH changes. This test tube will serve as your "control" solution to be used for comparison purposes.

You can now test the effect of various substances on the behavior of iron in the human digestive system. To another 5–10 mL sample of the pH 2 iron solution, add

3 Chandra, I.; Jeffrey, M.I. Hydrometallurgy 2005, 77, 191–201.

4 Dudeney, A.W., Tarasova, I.I. Hydrometallurgy 1998, 47, 243–257.

NOTES

approximately 0.2 g of one of the substances in Table 25.1. Stir to dissolve. Check the pH and again increase the pH to 8 by the dropwise addition of the 5% sodium hydroxide solution and note any changes that occur. Be careful not to go past pH 8. Allow the test tube to sit and make further observations. It may take a few minutes for a precipitate to settle out. Repeat with the other substances in the table. When testing the effect of sodium carbonate and sodium phosphate, be sure to check the pH before adding any NaOH. These salts will produce an increase in the pH. (Can you explain why?)

After completing your tests, compare your results with other members of your groups. Did everyone make the same observations? Repeat any tests with ambiguous results. Working together, formulate a list of the substances that should enhance and the substances that should hinder the absorption of iron. The first test tube you observed demonstrated the behavior of iron ions in a basic solution in the absence of any ligands/ions. Compare all subsequent observations to the original sample. If less precipitate was observed in one of the other test tubes, the iron presumably formed a complex ion and remained in solution. The more the iron is solubilized, the better the chances of its absorption.

TABLE 25-1. Substances That Enhance or Inhibit the Absorption of Iron in the Small Intestine

Substance	Dietary Sources
ascorbic acid (vitamin C)	citrus fruits, potatoes, green vegetables
oxalic acid	green leafy vegetables
tannic acid	tea
caffeine	coffee, tea, cola drinks
histidine	eggs, meat, milk (essential amino acid)
lysine hydrochloride	eggs, meat, milk (essential amino acid)
methionine	eggs, meat, milk (essential amino acid)
sodium carbonate (Na_2CO_3)	antacids, calcium supplements
sodium phosphate (Na_3PO_4)	soft drinks
citric acid	soft drinks, citrus fruits
fructose	honey, ripe fruits

DISCUSSION/CONCLUSION

Iron undergoes an interesting journey as it travels through the human digestive tract. Discuss the processes that occur in the stomach and the intestines and the pH dependence of each process. Explain why it is an acceptable process for manufacturers to nutritionally enrich foods with iron filings.

Consider the K_{sp} values (Table 25-2) of iron(II) hydroxide and iron(III) hydroxide and use them to explain your observations of the first test tube. (Both substances may have been present.)

TABLE 25-2.

Substance	K_{sp}
$FeCO_3$	3.13×10^{-11}
$FePO_4$	4.0×10^{-27}
$Fe(OH)_2$	8.0×10^{-16}
$Fe(OH)_3$	6.3×10^{-38}

Of the substances you tested, which best enhanced the bioavailability of iron? Which would hinder the intestinal uptake of iron? Explain the observations you made when sodium phosphate and sodium carbonate were added to the iron/acid solution in terms of K_{sp} values and solubility rules.

Explain, qualitatively, how the solubility of a slightly soluble ionic compound is influenced by the presence of a complexing agent. (You may need to look up this topic in your general chemistry text.)

Consider the substances you tested and the sources for these substances in the American diet. What recommendations can you make which would optimize iron absorption? What conclusions can be reached about the importance of dietary chelating agents for the bioabsorption of iron?

NOTE

When thinking about this experiment, keep in mind that complex ions are formed in steps, with the Lewis bases being added one at a time. Without further information, we can't predict exactly which complex ions are formed in this experiment. You are not expected to write balanced equations or predict the specific reaction products.

Visit a drug or grocery store (or your own kitchen and bathroom) and find at least three different products that include chelating agents that have been added to enhance product performance. In your report, describe the product, the chelating agent and its purpose in the product.

QUESTIONS

1. The tendency to form complex ions is one of the general characteristics of all transition metal ions. Describe this in terms of the Lewis definition of acids and bases. What must the structures of all the chelating agents you tested have in common?

2. The Chemistry in a Sustainable World feature discusses the iron(III) oxalate complex ion. Look up the structure of the oxalate ion in your general chemistry text or on the internet. What is the chemical formula of the iron(III)-oxalate complex ion? Draw the structure of this ion, indicating the coordinate covalent bonds that form.

NOTES
▼

NOTE

Contrary to the conclusions that you may have reached following this lab, experimental data in the literature tells us that oxalic acid actually hinders the intestinal uptake of iron and therefore much of the iron in spinach is biounavailable.[5] There clearly must be other processes at work beyond our simplistic model of the digestive system.

---

5 *Linder, M. C. Nutritional Biochemistry and Metabolism with Chemical Applications; Linder, M. C., Ed., Elsevier, New York, 1985.*

exp26
Electrochemistry

Oxidation–reduction (or *redox*) reactions are one of the most important categories of chemical reactions. These reactions involve the transfer of electrons from one species (oxidation) to another (reduction). When this process occurs spontaneously, forming products that are in a lower energy state than the reactants, the excess energy is released to the surroundings, frequently in the form of heat. Combustion in your car's engine, photosynthesis, "burning" calories in the gym and the rusting of iron all fall into this category. When the oxidation and reduction processes are physically separated in an electrochemical cell, the electrons are transferred through a wire connecting the cells and an electrical current can either be generated or used to drive the reaction. As the name implies, **electrochemistry** is the science that studies this union of chemistry and electricity. Batteries and fuel cells utilize *spontaneous* redox processes to convert chemical energy into electrical energy. On the other hand, electrical energy can be used to drive *non-spontaneous* processes, converting the electrical energy into chemical energy that is stored in the reaction products.

In redox reactions, electrons move from reactants to products because of a difference in potential energy between two substances. This difference in potential energy is known as **voltage** and the SI unit is the **volt (V)**, an intensive property that measures the energy

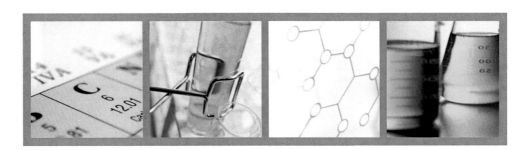

229

per unit charge (Joule/coulomb). The flow of electrons is analogous to water in a stream flowing downhill due to the difference in gravitational potential energy between the top of the hill and the bottom. To carry the analogy a little further, **current** measures the rate at which electrons flow through the wire, which is analogous to the rate at which water flows down the hill. That rate might be measured in gallons per second. Electrical current is measured in units of **amperes (A)**. One ampere is equal to one coulomb per second or 6.241×10^{18} electrons per second.

In this laboratory experiment you will study various electrochemical processes to gain a better understanding of the basics of electricity and the study of electrochemistry. Measurements will be made using a digital multimeter. In addition to voltage and amperage, there is a third basic measurement that can be made in an electrical circuit. This is the resistance, R, which is a measurement of how difficult it is for electrons to flow through a substance. The resistance is measured in Ohms (Ω) and is related to the current in the circuit and voltage across the circuit by Ohm's law.

$$\text{voltage} = \text{current} \bullet \text{resistance, or } V = IR$$

where V is the voltage, I is the current in amps and R is the resistance in Ohms (Ω). Multimeters are capable of measuring the voltage, current or resistance in an electrochemical system. **In Part A of this experiment you will familiarize yourself with the use of a digital multimeter before moving on to the subsequent measurements.**

Electrochemical cells fall into two broad categories. **Voltaic (or galvanic) cells** produce electricity from spontaneous redox processes. Batteries are a common example of this type of cell. Cells that use electricity to drive non-spontaneous reactions are called **electrolytic cells**. Both will be investigated in this laboratory experiment. The basic components of an electrochemical cell are:

1. Two compartments separated by a "salt bridge" through which ions can flow. Oxidation occurs in the anode compartment and reduction occurs in the cathode compartment.

2. Two solid electrodes that are connected by a wire. The electrodes often are involved in the reaction. However, in some reactions the electrodes don't directly participate in the reaction but the electrodes do serve as a site where an oxidation half-reaction or a reduction half-reaction can occur.

3. Two solutions of electrolytes into which the electrodes are immersed. The ions of the electrolytes may participate in the reaction or they may be inert electrolytes that are present to carry charge. Remember, all chemical processes are balanced with respect to charge.

4. In every electrochemical cell, there is an oxidation half-reaction occurring at one electrode and a reduction half-reaction occurring at the other electrode. These two processes occur simultaneously. Redox involves a transfer

of electrons. In the example of a simple Ag–Ag electrolysis cell the two half-reactions are:

$$Ag(s) \rightarrow Ag^+(aq) + 1e^- \qquad \text{and} \qquad Ag^+(aq) + e^- \rightarrow Ag(s)$$

In the example of a Cu–Cu electrolysis cell the two half-reactions are:

$$Cu(s) \rightarrow Cu^{2+}(aq) + 2e^- \qquad \text{and} \qquad Cu^{2+}(aq) + 2e^- \rightarrow Cu(s)$$

Note, it takes one electron to reduce one Ag^+ ion to one Ag atom. It takes two electrons to reduce one Cu^{2+} ion to one Cu atom. Complete the table below and compare the number of Al, Cu, and Ag atoms reduced when 30 electrons, 120 electrons, 1,200 electrons, then one mole of electrons are involved in the reduction half-reaction.

# of electrons	Al Atoms	Cu Atoms	Ag Atoms
12 electrons	4	6	12
30 electrons			
120 electrons			
1,200 electrons			
6.02×10^{23} electrons			

Different metals have different tendencies to undergo oxidation, or lose electrons. Likewise, their cations have different tendencies to undergo reduction. This tendency is measured in terms of the metal cation's reduction potential. The cell potential, E_{cell}, for a given electrochemical cell is the difference between the tendencies of the metal cations in their respective half-cells to undergo reduction. **In a voltaic cell, the substance with the highest (most positive, or least negative) reduction potential will undergo reduction and the metal in the other compartment will be oxidized. For the reaction to be spontaneous, the overall cell potential must be positive.** More information about standard reduction potentials can be found in your General Chemistry textbook.

VOLTAIC CELLS

A typical laboratory set up for a zinc–lead voltaic cell is shown below.

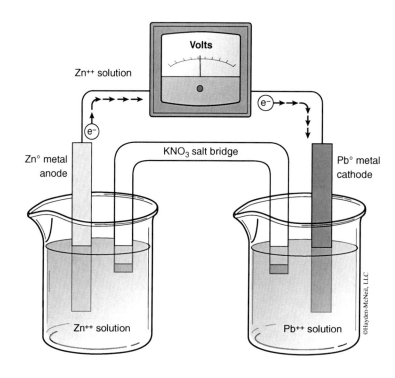

FIGURE 26-1. Zinc–lead voltaic cell

To minimize waste and conserve materials, the cells that we will use in this experiment will be set up using well plates instead of beakers and string saturated with an electrolyte solution will serve as the salt bridge.

In Part B of this experiment you will build voltaic cells and measure the reduction potential of several different metals. Utilizing this information you will be able to order the metals in terms of increasing reduction potential.

In Part C you will build an iron–magnesium voltaic cell and determine the cell potential.

ELECTROLYTIC CELLS

While voltaic cells convert chemical energy into electrical energy, electrolytic cells do just the opposite, converting electrical energy from an outside source into chemical energy and driving non-spontaneous chemical reactions. Electrolytic processes, also known as electrolysis, have many important commercial applications such as the production and purification of metals from ores and electroplating of metals on everything from car bumpers to the inside of "tin" cans. For example,

NOTES

▼

consider the situation when a piece of iron metal is placed in a solution of aqueous chromium(III) nitrate.

$$Fe(s) + Cr(NO_3)_3(aq) \rightarrow \text{no reaction}$$

Because iron has a larger reduction potential than chromium, no reaction spontaneously occurs. However, in an electrolysis cell, this reaction *will* occur, forming $Cr(s)$ and $Fe(NO_3)_3$ as products.

$$\text{electrolysis cell: } \text{energy} + Fe(s) + Cr(NO_3)_3(aq) \rightarrow Cr(s) \text{ and } Fe(NO_3)_3$$

In this way, chromium metal is plated onto steel for wheel rims, bumpers and motorcycle parts. Because an input of energy is always required, electrolysis is costly in terms of both money and resources.

In Part D of this lab you will construct an electrolytic cell and conduct an electroplating experiment.

CHEMISTRY FOR A SUSTAINABLE WORLD

Solar, hydro and wind power are important renewable energy sources that will help us eliminate our dependence on fossil fuels and achieve a sustainable energy supply. However, before they can become widely utilized, two significant challenges must be overcome. The first is the problem of transmitting the power they produce to the areas where it is most needed. The second has to do with how the energy will be stored until it is needed. For example, solar energy can only be produced during daylight hours and wind can only generate energy when the wind blows. By using electrolytic processes to convert the electrical energy produced by these sources into chemical energy, these barriers to their adoption can be removed. One example of this is a process that uses electrical energy to transform atmospheric CO_2 into easily stored liquid synthetic fuels such as methanol (CH_3OH) in an electrolytic cell. When the methanol is subsequently oxidized (burned) as a fuel, CO_2 will be released into the atmosphere in an amount equal to what was consumed in making the methanol. The result is a carbon neutral process with no net increase of CO_2 in the atmosphere.[1] Electrical energy can also be used to split water into hydrogen and oxygen, releasing the oxygen into the atmosphere and storing the hydrogen until needed when it is recombined with atmospheric oxygen to generate electricity in a fuel cell or internal combustion engine.[2]

FUEL CELLS

Fuel cells are devices that harness the energy produced from the reaction of hydrogen and oxygen to form water. The result is clean energy and very little pollution. Hydrogen can be used directly in fuel cells but methanol and other hydrogen-containing fuels can also be oxidized in these cells. Like batteries, fuel cells convert

NOTES
▼

the fuel into an electrochemical current but unlike a battery, they do not re-charging as long as there is a supply of hydrogen.

The diagram below (Figure 26-2) shows how a fuel cell works. This is an example of a Polymer Electrolyte Membrane (PEM) fuel cell, which is the type of fuel cell that you will be using in the laboratory. The two platinum electrodes are separated by the electrolyte, a thin proton-conducting polymer membrane. Hydrogen gas (left side) is supplied to one electrode and oxygen gas (right side) to the other. The anode is a catalyst for the dissociation of hydrogen into protons and electrons. Both protons and electrons now travel to the cathode side (on the right) but, very importantly, on different paths. While the H^+ ions pass through the cell's proton-conducting membrane the electrons move through the closed external circuit and thereby provide the fuel cell's electric power. At the cathode the protons and electrons finally react with the oxygen to form water, the fuel cell's only by-product.[3]

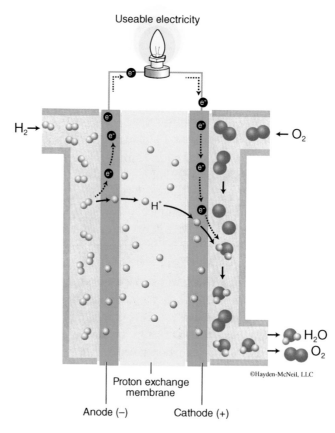

©Hayden-McNeil, LLC

Anode reaction:	$2H_2 \rightarrow 4H^+ + 4e^-$
Cathode reaction:	$4H^+ + 4e^- + O_2 \rightarrow 2H_2O$
Overall reaction:	$2H_2 + O_2 \rightarrow 2H_2O$

FIGURE 26-2. Polymer Electrolyte Membrane fuel cell

NOTES

In a Direct Methanol Fuel Cell (DMFC), the fuel is methanol, not hydrogen. The advantage of this is that methanol can be handled, stored and transported much more easily than hydrogen. The disadvantage is that methanol is a man-made substance and energy and resources must be expended to produce it. Hydrogen is catalytically separated from the methanol at the anode and is reduced to protons and electrons. The remaining carbon and oxygen react with oxygen to form CO_2, the by-product of this reaction.

Anode reaction:	$CH_3OH + H_2O \rightarrow CO_2 + 6H^+ + 6e^-$
Cathode reaction:	$6H^+ + 6e^- + 1.5O_2 \rightarrow 3H_2O$
Overall reaction:	$CH_3OH + 1.5O_2 \rightarrow CO_2 + 2H_2O$

Fuel cells are much more than just laboratory curiosities. Hydrogen fuel cell powered buses are on the streets in many major cities, every major automobile manufacturer has a hydrogen fuel cell car on the roads or in the planning stage, fuel cell power plants are functioning in a variety of locations, and technology is being developed to use fuel cells to power every kind of personal electronic device, from hearing aids to cell phones to laptop computers.

In Part E of this experiment you will run a direct methanol fuel cell and determine the maximum power that can be obtained from the cell.

2. PROCEDURE

For this laboratory experiment you do not need to record data in your laboratory notebook. Instead, record all data and observations in the data table/worksheet pages that follow the procedure.

A. Using the Digital Multimeter

From your supplies kit, examine the AA size alkaline battery to find the positive (+) end and insert this into the correct position of the battery holder. Connect the red and black leads of the battery holder to the like-colored leads of the multimeter with the alligator clips. Referring to the digital multimeter section of the Equipment Instruction card, turn the meter ON to measure DC volts. You should get a reading in excess of +1.5 volts. Examine the output on the various DCV scales. For this experiment, you may want to make most of your measurements in millivolts to utilize the full precision of the meter. Note that 1.5 V equals 1500 mV. Reverse the red and black leads at the connection between the battery holder and the multimeter and record your observations.

SAFETY NOTE
Do not attempt to measure AC line voltage from the outlets!

B. Cell Voltages

i. Design an Experiment

Beginning Question: Which metals are the most likely to be reduced and which are most likely to be oxidized?

ii. Experimental

Collect ten pieces of string and soak in a 50 mL beaker containing about 20 mL of 0.1 M KNO_3 solution. You may have to use your plastic tweezers to get these wetted by submersion. These will be used as salt bridges.

While the strings are wetting, gather two copper electrodes from your supply kit and clean the end to be placed into solution (opposite end from the color ID band) with abrasive paper. Using a poly transfer pipet, fill two adjacent wells on your test plate about 2/3 full with 0.1 M KNO_3 solution. Using your tweezers, place a conditioned string between the cells so that each end is in contact with the solution in the well. Carefully connect the copper electrodes to the leads of the multimeter with the alligator clips near the color banded end and place the freshly cleaned end of the electrodes in each of the wells. See Figure 26-3. Turn on the multimeter to observe any voltage, and record your finding after 60 seconds.

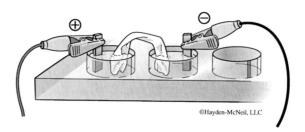

©Hayden-McNeil, LLC

FIGURE 26-3. Experimental voltaic cell setup

PROCEDURAL NOTE

For best results with the following electrochemical cells, use a fresh piece of abrasive for cleaning each electrode to avoid cross-contamination and clean immediately before use.

Next we will repeat this procedure using dissimilar metal couples. Remove the salt bridge (conditioned string) and place it on a dry paper towel for later disposal. Clean and rinse your well plate as before. Fill nine adjacent wells each about 2/3 full with 0.1 M KNO_3 solution. Connect a cleaned stainless electrode to the red multimeter lead, and place it in the center well. Connect a freshly cleaned aluminum electrode to the black lead and place in the second well. Observe the voltage and record at 60 seconds; be sure to note measurement units.

Use a new conditioned string to bridge between the two wells. Again, observe the voltage and record at 60 seconds. Repeat with copper, iron, magnesium, manganese, tin, titanium and zinc electrodes using a new well and bridge string for each trial with the same stainless steel electrode in the center well. Dispose of waste as instructed.

C. Fe–Mg Voltaic Cell

i. Design an Experiment

Beginning Question: What is the cell potential for the Fe–Mg voltaic cell?

ii. Experimental

Starting with a clean well plate, fill one well with 0.1 M $FeSO_4$ solution and an adjacent well with 0.1 M $MgCl_2$ solution. Bridge with a new conditioned string and place a clean Fe wire in the iron(II) sulfate well. Put a cleaned Mg piece in the magnesium chloride well. Connect the multimeter, adjusting the red/black leads as needed to get a positive (+) reading, and record the voltage at 60 seconds. All solutions may be dumped into the sink for clean-up. The paper towel with the used string salt bridges is safe to discard in the regular trash.

D. Electrolysis

i. Design an Experiment

Beginning Question: How does the amount of current, the time of applied current, and the type of metal cation influence the amount of mass of material plated (mass gained) on an electrode in an electrolytic cell?

ii. Experimental

Cell Preparation

1. At each bench, one pair of students will work with zinc and the other pair with copper.

2. Clean two electrode strips (either copper or zinc) with abrasive paper, rinse with water, and dry. Be careful not to get skin oil on the cleaned surface.

3. Weigh each using the analytical balance; record values in the worksheet data table.

4. Connect one to the red terminal clamp; this will be the anode. Connect the other to the black terminal clamp; this will be the cathode. The electrodes should be vertical and spaced 2–3 cm apart from each other. (They must not touch!) See Figure 26-4.

NOTES
▼

FIGURE 26-4. Cu/Cu/CuSO$_4$ cell shown ready to connect to DC power supply; the Zn/Zn/ZnSO$_4$ cell arrangement is analogous

5. Collect ~200 mLs of electrolyte (CuSO$_4$ for the copper cell or ZnSO$_4$ for the zinc cell) and record. Pour the electrolyte into the cell.

6. Now connect the cell to the power supply according to the following instructions.

MPJA Variable Output DC Power Supply Operating Instructions for Powering Faraday's Law Electrochemical Cell

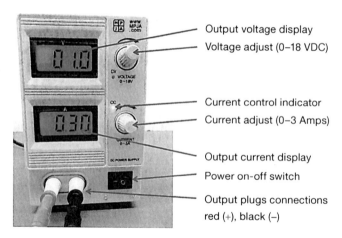

Output voltage display
Voltage adjust (0–18 VDC)

Current control indicator
Current adjust (0–3 Amps)

Output current display
Power on-off switch
Output plugs connections red (+), black (–)

FIGURE 26-5.

1. With the power supply in the "O" or OFF position, connect the loaded EW cell to the power supply with the banana plug cords, red-to-red and black-to-black. See Figure 26-5.

2. Refer to the worksheet to determine the time and amp setting that should be used at your bench.

3. Set the voltage adjustment to about 75% (this exact setting is not critical as you will control power output by amperage). Now turn the current adjustment knob all the way to the left (counterclockwise) which sets it at zero.

4. When ready, start by putting the power switch in the ON position and then turning the current control knob slowly to the right (clockwise) to reach your desired ampere setting. Remember to start the timer. The power supply will hold the current to within +/− 0.01A. You should verify this during the run time while you are working on other tasks.

5. Turn OFF when you reach your desired run time duration.

6. Continue with the EW Cell Unloading steps that follow.

Cell Unloading

1. Carefully unclamp the electrodes and rinse with DI water over the large poly waste beaker. Be sure to keep track of which is the anode and cathode.

2. When dry, weigh and record each.

3. Empty the electrolyte from the cell into your waste beaker, rinse, and then wash it with water at the sink. Empty your waste beaker into the collection bucket in the hood.

4. Analyze your data and work with your classmates to complete the worksheet data table.

E. Alcohol–Air Fuel Cell

i. Design an Experiment

Beginning Question: What is the maximum power output of an alcohol–air fuel cell under normal laboratory conditions?

ii. Experimental

Referring to the Equipment Instruction card, locate the fuel and air ports of the fuel cell. At the front bench fueling station, empty the cell by turning it sideways and blowing air into the upper fuel port with a poly pipet so that the liquid drains into the catch beaker. Turn the cell upright and fill with the alcohol fuel using a poly pipet. Remember to record the fuel type and concentration. The cell should stabilize in about 10 minutes and be ready for voltage measurements at different power loads (which are achieved by putting a resistive load in series with the cell's output terminals).

While you are waiting, organize the test resistors in your supplies kit and measure the actual resistance of each. See Figure 26-6 for the appropriate connections. Be sure to record your findings.

EXP 26: Electrochemistry

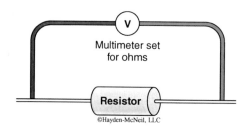

FIGURE 26-6. Wiring schematic for resistor measurements

First measure the "no-load" output voltage of the fuel cell by connecting the red and black leads to the corresponding ones of the multimeter using the DC millivolt scale. It will be necessary to use the mini-banana plug adapters in the supplies kit to make the connections to the fuel cell. See Figure 26-7 for the appropriate connections. Record this voltage.

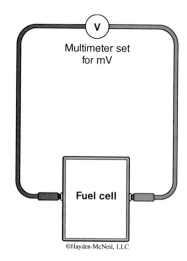

FIGURE 26-7. Wiring schematic for "no-load" measurement

Connect the fuel cell and multimeter according to Figure 26-8, and record the output voltage in mV with each of the nine resistors. A power output curve can be generated from this data.

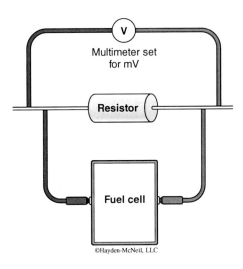

FIGURE 26-8. Wiring schematic for fuel cell measurements

Next investigate the effect of air on fuel cell performance. Return the resistors to the supplies kit, and connect the multimeter directly to the fuel cell. Carefully place the fuel cell in a plastic bag so that the leads remain connected and you will be able to close off most of the bag's opening. Deflate the bag as much as possible, squeezing out the air.

SAFETY NOTE

Use gloves when handling dry ice. Do not allow dry ice to contact skin tissue; the temperature is about –56°C and can cause frostbite.

Prepare a CO_2 generator by putting about 50 mL of warm tap water into a 125-mL Erlenmeyer flask. Then carefully add about 4 g of dry ice chips (solid CO_2). CO_2 in gas form will evolve immediately. Fit the stopper-tubing assembly to the flask and insert the end of the tube into the bag so that the end of the hose is close to the air vent side of the fuel cell. Be sure to keep the cell upright. Monitor the fuel cell's output as the air in the bag is replaced with carbon dioxide. Record your observations. Does the voltage recover when the cell is repositioned to the open room air?

Empty the fuel cell's liquid into the catch beaker at the fuel station using a poly pipet and refill the chamber with DI water.

NOTES

ENDNOTES

1   "New Electrolytic Cells to Play a Role in Tomorrow's Local Energy Supply" *Science Daily*, 4/27/2010. http://www.sciencedaily.com/releases/2010/04/100427071232.htm, accessed 6/2019.

2   "Wind to Hydrogen Project" Hydrogen and Fuel Cells Research, https://www.nrel.gov/hydrogen/wind-to-hydrogen.html, accessed 6/2019.

3   *Fuel Cell Technology for Classroom Instruction*, Voigt, C., Hoeller, S., Kueter, U.; Wasserstoff-Energie-Systeme GmbH, Hydrogen Energy Systems, Luebeck, Germany, 2005.

26

ELECTROCHEMISTRY

Name

TA

Lab Section

PART A: USING THE DIGITAL MULTIMETER

Voltage of the AA battery:	
Voltage with leads reversed:	
Observations	

Questions

1. Which of the DCV scales that you examined provides the maximum precision of the meter?

2. AA, AAA, C, and D cells all deliver the same voltage (1.5 V) when the batteries are fully charged. However, as the size of the battery increases, the amount of current that can be delivered by the battery also increases. What is different inside these batteries that accounts for the increase in current with size? Explain. (Hint: Think about where the chemical reactions occur in the cell.)

3. The overall reaction for an alkaline battery is given by

$$Zn(s) + MnO_2(s) + H_2O(l) \rightarrow ZnO(s) + Mn(OH)_2(s)$$

Does metallic zinc function as the anode or the cathode in this system?

PART B: MEASUREMENT OF CELL VOLTAGES OF SEVERAL ELECTROCHEMICAL CELLS

Cell	Voltage	Observations
Cu–Cu		
SS–Al w/out salt bridge		
SS–Al		
SS–Cu		
SS–Fe		
SS–Mg		
SS–Mn		
SS–Sn		
SS–Ti		
SS–Zn		

Note: "SS" = stainless steel

Questions

1. Was there a measurable voltage for the cell built with two copper electrodes? Why or why not?

2. You have learned that a salt bridge is necessary for a voltaic cell to function. Do your observations support this? Why or why not?

3. Using the table of standard reduction potentials found in Appendix D of your general chemistry text (Silberberg), arrange the eight metals (Al, Cu, Fe, Mg, Mn, Sn, Ti, and Zn) in order of decreasing reduction potentials of the metal ions. Compare this list to your experimental results. Is the order the same? (Note: E° for Ti^{2+} is -1.6 V.)

4. Based on your measurements, which of the metals is the easiest to oxidize?

PART C: FE–MG VOLTAIC CELL

Cell	Voltage	Observations
Mg–Fe		

Questions

1. Write the oxidation half-reaction, the reduction half-reaction, and the balanced overall reaction for this cell.

    Oxidation:

    Reduction:

    Overall:

2. Using the list of standard reduction potentials available in your general chemistry text-book, calculate the cell potential for this electrochemical system. Do your experimental results agree with the value you calculated?

PART D: ELECTROLYSIS

Data

metal (Zn or Cu):

initial mass		final mass	
at black electrode	at red electrode	at black electrode	at red electrode

Work with your classmates to complete this table:

	Settings		Results		
Lab bench	Time (min)	Amp setting	Charge (C)	Mass gain (g)	Mass loss (g)
1 (copper)	20	0.3			
1 (zinc)	20	0.3			
2 (copper)	15	0.5			
2 (zinc)	15	0.5			
3 (copper)	20	0.6			
3 (zinc)	20	0.6			
4 (copper)	25	0.8			
4 (zinc)	25	0.8			

OBSERVATIONS

Sketch a diagram of your electrolysis experiment (zinc–zinc or copper–copper electrochemical cell). Label the main components of the cell, including:

- cathode (indicate identity of the metal)
- anode (indicate identity of the metal)
- connections to the power supply
- electrolyte solution (include identity)
- direction of electron flow
- direction of ion flow
- half-reactions occurring at each electrode

Questions

1. What is the purpose of the direct current power supply in these experiments?

2. What relationship is observed between the applied current and the mass gained when the time and voltage are held constant?

3. What relationship is observed between the time and the mass gained when the applied current and voltage are held constant?

4. Were these relationships the same for both metals?

5. a. For the metal you used, calculate the moles of electrons transferred using amps and time.

    b. Using the moles of electrons transferred, calculate the theoretical moles and mass of metal that should be deposited on the cathode.

c. How closely does this agree with the mass that was experimentally determined? Is this reasonable given your experimental technique?

6. What is the relationship between mass lost and mass gained? Is this consistent with what you would predict? Explain.

PART E: ALCOHOL–AIR FUEL CELL

Fuel type and concentration

Resistance measurements		Voltage measurements	
expected (Ω)	measured (Ω)	load (measured) (Ω)	voltage (V)
1.1		"no-load"	
2			
5.1			
10			
20			
51			
100			
270			
470			

Quenching

Observations

Questions

What is the maximum power output of the fuel cell under the laboratory operating conditions? To answer this question, you will need to prepare a power output curve using Excel. Begin by setting up an Excel spreadsheet:

Spreadsheet

column A:	measured resistance (Ω)
column B:	measured voltage (V)
column C:	calculated current in milliamps (mA), using the relationship $$current = \frac{voltage}{resistance}$$ To get mA, multiply the value by 1000.
column D:	calculated power in milliwatts (mW), using the relationship power (watts) = voltage • current. Because you will be using the calculated current in mA, your calculated power will have the units of mW.

The power output curve is a graph of voltage vs. power (column B vs. column D).

When setting up the graph, the chart type is *XY scatter*. The chart sub-type is *scatter with data points connected by smooth lines.*

From the graph, determine the maximum power of the fuel cell. Submit this graph with your worksheet.

exp27

Explorations in Nuclear Chemistry

NUCLEAR CHEMISTRY IN A SUSTAINABLE WORLD

While studying the properties of fluorescent minerals in 1896, the French physicist Henri Becquerel serendipitously discovered natural radioactivity being emitted from samples of uranium ore. Though his discovery was to have a deep impact on the future of humankind, it was relatively ignored by most in the lay and scientific community. Two years later, the element radium was discovered by Marie Curie and interest in nuclear radiation became widespread. These early discoveries triggered a chain of events that culminated with the detonation of the "Little Boy" and "Fat Man" nuclear bombs over the Japanese cities of Hiroshima and Nagasaki during World War II.

Since that time, the world has been struggling with how to deal with both the threats and opportunities associated with harnessing the energy of the nucleus. The explosive power and destructive aftermath of nuclear weapons threatens all of humanity while at the same time, benefits from the "friendly atom" abound. Nuclear medicine specialists utilize safe and painless techniques to image the body and treat disease, food irradiation is used in over 40 countries to ensure a healthy and reliable food supply, and nuclear

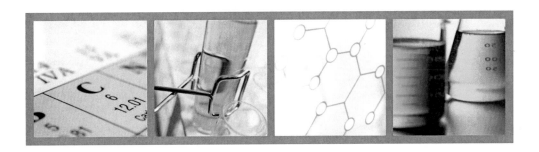

NOTES

power plants offer the promise of an unlimited supply of energy without the global warming concerns associated with fossil fuels.

The U.S. Congress has passed legislation to decrease our nation's dependence on oil. To achieve this goal as well as to decrease carbon dioxide emissions, it will be necessary to use a variety of non carbon-based fuel sources. Along with such renewable energy sources as photovoltaic electricity, solar thermal energy, and wind power, nuclear energy is believed by many to have the potential to be a sustainable energy option for the future. Before committing to nuclear energy, however, serious questions must be addressed regarding the supply of nuclear fuel, long-term economics, the environment and waste management. Only when these complex and controversial questions are answered will nuclear energy become an acceptable option for inclusion on our sustainable energy source-list.

INTRODUCTION

All atoms of a particular element contain the same number of protons in their nucleus. However, not all atoms of an element have the same number of neutrons, leading to the existence of isotopes, atoms with the same number of protons but different numbers of neutrons. Isotopes of an element generally have the same physical and chemical properties but have differing nuclear stabilities. For unstable radioisotopes, the nucleus undergoes a spontaneous decay process. This radioactive decay is accompanied by the release of radioactive particles. Energy for nuclear bombs and power plants is the result of nuclear fission, the process of splitting an atom into two or more lighter atoms. This process is almost always the result of the bombardment of a heavy nucleus by free neutrons and results in the production of unstable isotopes that undergo subsequent radioactive decay.

No matter which radioisotope is undergoing nuclear disintegration, the radiation that is produced is the same. The three most common forms are alpha and beta particles and gamma rays. These high energy forms of radiation produce ions in the material they strike and are therefore referred to as ionizing radiation.

Alpha particles are dense, positively charged particles that are identical to helium nuclei. They are symbolized by α or $_2^4\text{He}^{2+}$.

Beta particles are negatively charged particles identified as high-speed electrons. They are symbolized as β, β^-, or $_{-1}^0\beta$.

Gamma rays are very high-energy photons. They are symbolized by γ and travel at the speed of light.

Whatever the source of radiation, there will be biological effects when it strikes living tissue. If the dose is low and the cellular damage is limited, cellular repair mechanisms can repair the damage without any long term effects to the organism. However, large doses of ionizing radiation can cause damage to living tissue. The degree of damage caused by radiation depends on many factors including dose,

dose rate, type of radiation, the part of the body exposed, age, and health. In addition to shielding from the radiation source, exposure to ionizing radiation can be limited by minimizing the time spent near the source of radiation and increasing the distance from the source. In this laboratory experiment you will investigate the effects of both shielding and distance on minimizing radiation.

Radioisotopes have differing stabilities and undergo decay at different rates. The half-life ($t_{1/2}$) is the time that it takes for half of the nuclei in a given sample to disintegrate. The half-life, which may range from microseconds to billions of years, is different for every radioisotope. Radioactive decay follows first-order kinetics and the number of remaining nuclei is halved after each half-life. A general rule of thumb is that ten half-lives must elapse before the emissions from a radioactive sample have dropped to a safe level. Thus, strontium-90, which is produced in nuclear fission reactions and has a half-life of 28.9 years, must be stored for 289 years before it is no longer considered to be a threat.

The half-life of a radioisotope can be determined using standard kinetic methods. Because radioactive decay is a first order process, a plot of ln (counts per minute) vs time will yield a straight line plot with the slope = –k. Once the rate constant has been determined, you will be able to determine the half-life of a radioisotope from the relationship

$$t_{1/2} = \frac{\ln 2}{k} \tag{1}$$

(For a complete derivation of this relationship, see your General Chemistry text.)

In your daily life you are constantly being exposed to low level radiation from natural sources. This background radiation comes from rocks and soil, radon gas escaping from the earth, cosmic rays from outer space and consumer products. This radiation will vary depending on your location, but no place is nuclear radiation free. In order to measure the radioactivity of our samples in lab, you will first need to determine the level of background radiation in the lab.

Nuclear radiation can not be seen, smelled nor tasted. Therefore, specialized instruments and detection devices must be used to measure and monitor radiation. For example you may have noticed certain medical personnel wearing film badges that measure the worker's cumulative exposure to radiation. Other devices function by using the ionizing power of radiation to reveal its presence. For this laboratory experiment, you will use one such device, the Vernier™ Digital Radiation Monitor. This monitor incorporates a Geiger-Mueller tube to detect the radiation.

SAFE HANDLING OF RADIOACTIVE MATERIALS

The radioactive sources that will be used in parts A and B of this experiment are small samples of Po-210 (alpha), Sr-90 (beta and gamma) and Co-60 (gamma), embedded in plastic disks. All of the radioactive samples and materials used in this experiment are low-level radioactive emitters and are considered to be safe to handle and inspect. Disposable gloves should be worn when handling the Ba/Cs-137 planchet for the half-life determination. In the event of a spill, notify your instructor and do not attempt to clean it up on your own. (A planchet is a small shallow metal container in which a radioactive substance is deposited for measurement of its activity.) If you are pregnant and have any concerns about performing this experiment, please consult with your instructor.

PROCEDURE

Part A—Shielding Studies and Determination of the Type of Radiation from a Source

In this section of the experiment you will determine the effect of shielding on different sources of radiation and use this information to identify the type of radiation being emitted by an unknown source.

1. Prepare the computer for data collection.

   a. Open Vernier Logger *Pro*™ by clicking the ▨ icon in the computer dock.

   b. Click on the data collection icon. (This is the icon that looks like a clock inserted into a graph.) Select Collection > Time Based.

   c. Check the box for continuous data collection. Set length = 1 minute, sampling rate = 1 sample/minute. Click Done.

   d. Enlarge the data table by clicking, holding and dragging the lower right corner of the table. (You will not be using the graphing function.)

2. Background radiation:

   a. Move all sources away from the monitor. Click ▭ Collect to begin collecting data. (You may see the words "Waiting for Data" while data is being collected.) It will take 60 seconds before any values are recorded in the data table. Allow data to be collected for three minutes.

   b. After the number of counts for three 1-minute samplings appears, click ▭ Stop. Calculate the average number of counts per minute and record this information in worksheet Table 27-1. This is the average background radiation. Also record this value in the first row of Table 27-2.

3. Alpha, beta, and gamma radiation:

   a. Place an alpha, beta or gamma source in the top shelf of holder, approximately 1 cm from the DRM. The disk should be positioned with the backing toward the plastic brace and the uncovered side toward the DRM.

   b. Measure the number of counts for one minute only, following the procedure in step 2. Record the number of counts per minute in Table 27-2.

   c. Place a single sheet of paper between the source and the DRM. Measure the number of counts for one minute and record in Table 27-2. Select the option to Store Latest Run when asked.

   d. Repeat two more times, using a sheet of aluminum and a sheet of lead as absorbers.

   e. Repeat steps 3a–3d using the other two sources, recording all data in Table 27-2.

   f. What are you able to conclude about the penetrating power of alpha, beta, and gamma radiation?

4. Obtain a blue unknown source disk. Record the source identification in your laboratory notebook. Use shielding measurements to propose the type of radiation that is being emitted by the unknown source.

Part B—Distance Studies

What is the relationship between the amount of radiation and the distance from a radioactive source? In this section of the experiment you will measure this relationship and graphically determine the relationship.

Obtain either a Sr-90 or Co-60 source disk. Position the source in the top shelf of the holder. Measure the counts per minute and record in the worksheet data Table 27-3. Move the source to the second shelf and measure the number of counts per minute. Continue measuring the activity with the source on the third shelf and then every other shelf after that, for a total of six measurements. Copy and paste the data into a Microsoft Excel spreadsheet.

Analysis

Prepare a graph of the corrected counts per minute vs distance. Inspect the graph. How does the intensity of radiation vary with distance from the source? Is it proportional, or would you say that it is inversely proportional? Does the fall-off in radiation follow the Inverse Square Law given in equation (2)?

$$\text{Intensity} \propto \frac{1}{d^2} \qquad\qquad (2)$$

NOTES
▼

This tells us that the intensity of radiation is inversely proportional to the square of the distance (d) from the radiation source. You will need to change your graph to answer this question. Replot your data but for this graph, the x-axis values should be $1/\text{distance}^2$. Does this provide a linear relationship and do your data agree with the equation (2)? To answer this question, add a trendline to your data. To do this, click once on a data point. On the toolbar, go to Chart >Add Trendline. Select Options and check "Display Equation on Chart" and "Display R-squared on Chart." The closer the value of R^2 is to one, the better the fit of the line to the data. What do your readings tell you about how far people must be from radiation sources to reach a normal background level?

Print your graph with the best fit line and equation.

Part C—Determination of the Half-Life of a Radioactive Isotope

Prepare to collect data using the Vernier Logger Pro™ software. Click on the "Data Collection" icon and set the time for 20 min. Uncheck the "Continuous Data Collection" box.

Remove the clear plastic planchet/disk tray from the DRM holder.

Take the white foam height adjustment block with the planchet fastened to it to your TA for filling with a Ba-Cs137 solution. Immediately return to your work area, place the white foam holder into the top slot of the DRM holder in the direction of the arrow, as shown in Figure 27-1. Begin data collection without delay.

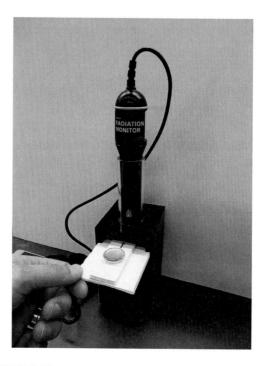

FIGURE 27-1. Placement of planchet in DRM holder

NOTES
▼

Set the DRM aside and dispose of the barium solution and planchet as directed by your instructor.

Copy and paste the data into a Microsoft Excel spreadsheet.

Analysis

Using Microsoft Excel, subtract the average background radiation from each of your radiation counts. Next, calculate the natural log of the corrected counts per minute and prepare a graph of this value vs. elapsed time. Perform a linear regression analysis to find the line of best fit to the data. Use equation (1) and the slope of the best fit line to determine the half-life of Ba-137m. Print your graph.

Part D—Testing for Radiation in Common Products and Substances

Radioactive isotopes are found in many consumer products and naturally occurring substances. For example, Morton Salt Substitute, which is primarily potassium chloride, contains approximately 0.0012% potassium-40, and "antique" ceramic pottery with a deep red-orange color was produced using uranium oxide in the glaze. There are several of these products as well as samples of uranium ore on the dispensing bench. Select at least 3 of these and determine what type of radiation is being emitted. Record your observations in worksheet data Table 27-4. Note that some are only weakly radioactive and it may be necessary to place them as close as 0.5 cm from the detector. In addition to emitting radiation, glassware that contains uranium will fluoresce in ultraviolet light.

REPORT

There is no lab report required for this experiment. Complete the worksheet pages and submit at the end of your laboratory period.

NOTES

EXPLORATIONS IN NUCLEAR CHEMISTRY

Name _____

TA _____

Lab Section _____

This completed worksheet (along with relevant graphs) should be submitted instead of a lab report.

PART A: SHIELDING STUDIES AND DETERMINATION OF THE TYPE OF RADIATION FROM A SOURCE

TABLE 27-1. Background Radiation Determination

Individual background radiation readings	Average	Standard Deviation

TABLE 27-2. Radiation Sources

Source	Radiation type	Counts Per Minute (CPM)			
None	Background	No shielding (Average)	Paper	Aluminum	Lead
Po-210			—	—	—
Sr-90					
Co-60					
Unknown # _____					

1. Compare your background radiation reading with your classmates. Are your readings similar?

2. What are some major sources of background radiation?

3. Briefly explain how you determined the kind of radiation your unknown source was emitting.

PART B: DISTANCE STUDIES

TABLE 27-3. Data for Distance Studies

Data point	Distance (cm)	Distance^2 (cm)^2	CPM	Data point	Distance (cm)	Distance^2 (cm)^2	CPM
1.				5.			
2.				6.			
3.							
4.							

Source used: _____

1. Calculate the *corrected* counts per minute (cpm) from your source by subtracting the average background from your readings. Create a graph of cpm vs. distance. Inspect the graph. How does the intensity of radiation vary with distance from the source? Is it proportional, or would you say that it is inversely proportional?

2. Change your graph, with the values for the x-axis being $1/\text{distance}^2$. Add a trendline to the graph as instructed previously. The Inverse Square Law says that as the distance from a radiation source is doubled, the radiation exposure decreases by a factor of four (eqn. 2). Do your data agree with this law? Provide data-based reasoning to support your answer. Print and attach your graph.

3. Based on your data, would handling a radioactive source with foot-long tweezers instead of your hand make a significant difference in your radiation exposure? Explain.

4. Based on your observations in parts A and B, what are the best ways to minimize exposure to radiation? Explain.

PART C: DETERMINATION OF HALF-LIFE

1. Create a graph of the natural log of the corrected cpm of Ba-137m vs. time with a linear trendline. Print and attach the graph.

2. What is the half-life of Ba-137m? Show your calculation.

3. How long will it take before the radiation emitted by Ba-137m has dropped to a level that is regarded as safe? Explain your answer.

PART D: RADIATION IN COMMON SUBSTANCES

1. List *at least 3 items* that you observed and indicate the type of radiation that is being emitted. Provide valid evidence for identification of radiation type.

TABLE 27-4.

	Item	Radiation Type	Evidence/ Basis for Identification
1.			
2.			
3.			
4.			
5.			
6.			
7.			
8.			
9.			

2. Polonium-210 is an alpha emitter that was used to murder Russian spy Alexander Litvinenko in 2006. Given that alpha radiation can be stopped by a piece of paper, why is this radioisotope, and other alpha emitters, so dangerous to human health?

CLAIMS & EVIDENCE

Provide claims for two of your beginning questions. If you can't answer your original beginning questions, provide new beginning questions you may have thought of and the claims and evidence for those questions. Reference your data tables and observations.

Claims:

"Evidence":

exp28

Thermodynamics of the Vaporization of Water[1]

Background reading: Review the section in your General Chemistry text that deals with the topics of vapor pressure and phase changes.

Suppose we have a pure liquid such as water in equilibrium with its vapor at temperature T:

$$H_2O(l) \rightleftarrows H_2O(g)$$

Molecules in the gas phase exert a pressure known as the *vapor pressure* of the liquid. This pressure is characteristic of the substance and depends only on the temperature. The higher the temperature, the higher the vapor pressure due to the larger fraction of molecules possessing sufficient energy to "escape" into the gas phase. A plot of vapor pressures against absolute temperatures, known as a vapor pressure curve, is non-linear, becoming ever steeper as the temperature is increased. This non-linearity makes it difficult to use the curve to estimate or predict vapor pressures at other temperatures.

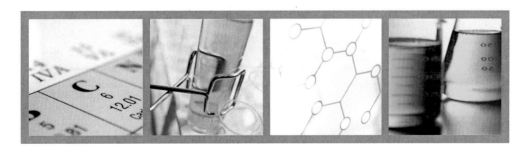

---

1 Levinson, G. S. *A Simple Experiment for Determining Vapor Pressure and Enthalpy of Vaporization of Water,* Journal of Chemical Education 1982 *59,* 337–338.

NOTES
▼

As is often the case, however, a linear equation can be obtained by manipulation of the variables. In this situation, a linear relationship is obtained when the natural logarithm of the vapor pressure is plotted against the inverse of the absolute temperature. Recalling that a linear graph is characteristic of mathematical equations of the form y = mx + b, we can express this relationship as:

$$\ln P = m\left(\frac{1}{T}\right) + b \qquad (1)$$

When we substitute appropriate expressions for the slope and y-intercept, obtained from the field of thermodynamics, we obtain what is known as the Clausius-Clapeyron equation:

$$\ln P = \frac{-\Delta H_{vap}}{R}\left(\frac{1}{T}\right) + \frac{\Delta S_{vap}}{R} \qquad (2)$$

where ΔH_{vap} is the enthalpy of vaporization, ΔS_{vap} is the entropy of vaporization, T is the absolute (Kelvin) temperature, and R is the ideal gas constant. (Derivation of the Clausius-Clapeyron equation is beyond the scope of this course and will not be gone into here.)

The Clausius-Clapeyron equation makes it possible to determine the enthalpy and entropy of vaporization of a liquid by measuring its vapor pressure at several temperatures and then plotting the results to obtain the slope and intercept of the line. Alternatively, once these thermodynamic quantities are known, the vapor pressure of the liquid at any other temperature can be calculated. In this laboratory procedure, we will measure the vapor pressure of water at several temperatures to determine the enthalpy and entropy of vaporization of water.

> ## AN INTERESTING SIDE NOTE...
>
> The enthalpy of vaporization of water is the amount of energy required to convert one mole of liquid water at 100°C to one mole of gaseous water at 100°C. The importance and magnitude of this energy can be better understood by looking at Earth's weather patterns, specifically the phenomenon known as hurricanes. Heat builds up in the tropics during long hot summers and hurricanes are one means of exporting this excess tropical heat to the mid-latitudes. As the sun heats the tropical oceans, water undergoes a phase change from a liquid state to a gaseous state and possesses what is known as latent heat. (The latent heat is also referred to as the latent heat of vaporization.) Latent heat can be thought of as "stored heat." The same energy provided by the sun to evaporate the water will later be released into the air as the water vapor cools and returns to a liquid state. The condensation heat energy released by a hurricane in one day can be the equivalent of the energy released by exploding four hundred, 20-megaton hydrogen bombs. One day's released energy, converted to electricity, could supply the United States' electrical needs for about six months! Hurricanes are thus an example of unharnessed solar energy.

PROCEDURE

Overview

In this procedure, a sample of air will be trapped over water. The water will then be heated to about 80°C and the trapped air will rapidly become saturated with water vapor. The temperature of the water and the volume of the gas will be recorded as the bath is cooled to below 5°C. As the system is cooled, the amount of trapped air remains constant. However, the number of moles of water in the gas phase changes with temperature. At temperatures near 0°C, the amount of water in the gas phase is less than 1% of the total and may be ignored. Therefore, the number of moles of trapped air can be found from measurements of volume and pressure at this temperature. The ideal gas law allows us to determine the pressure of the trapped air at higher temperatures. The vapor pressure of water at the same temperature can then be determined through use of Dalton's law of partial pressures.

There is a small, constant, determinate error in this procedure resulting from the use of an inverted graduated cylinder because the meniscus at the gas-water interface is reversed. It has been estimated, by introducing known volumes of air into a completely filled, inverted cylinder, that the error involved with such a use of the cylinder is 0.2 mL. This value will be subtracted from each volume reading to correct for the determinate error.

1. Fill a 500-mL flask to within one or two millimeters of the top with deionized water and place the flask on a plastic tray to catch spilled water. Fill a 10-mL graduated cylinder about two-thirds full with deionized water. Cover the top

NOTES

▼

with a finger and quickly invert and lower the cylinder into the water in the flask. Keeping the mouth of the flask submerged, pour out a little water from the flask into the sink and then continue lowering the cylinder in the flask until it is completely covered with water. An air sample of four to five milliliters should be trapped within the cylinder.

2. Add more water, if necessary, to the flask to ensure that the trapped air is surrounded by water. Then heat the flask over a Bunsen burner to approximately 80°C, but watch the volume of trapped air as you do. When it expands beyond the scale of the cylinder, stop heating the water.

3. As the water cools, stir the water in the flask frequently to avoid thermal gradients and watch the volume of trapped air. When it contracts so that the volume can be read (at the bottom of the meniscus), read and record the volume to the nearest tenth of a milliliter and the temperature.

4. Carefully move the flask and cylinder to the plastic tray on the bench top. As the water cools down, make additional measurements at approximately five-degree intervals down to 50°C. Ice may be needed to speed cooling; any overflow from the bath will be trapped in the tray below the flask.

5. After the temperature has reached 50°C, cool the water to less than 5°C by adding ice. Record the gas volume and the water temperature.

6. Record the barometric pressure.

CALCULATIONS

NOTE

It is strongly recommended that you use a spreadsheet program (*Excel*, *Lotus*, etc.) for the calculations associated with this laboratory.

Set up a table to record your data and calculated values. A sample table is shown below. Show one sample calculation for each calculation.

Correct all volume readings by subtracting 0.2 mL to compensate for the inverted meniscus.

Using the measured values for volume and temperature from step 5 and the atmospheric pressure, calculate the number of moles of trapped air. This calculation assumes that the vapor pressure of water is negligible compared to atmospheric pressure at these low temperatures.

For each temperature, calculate the partial pressure of air in the gas mixture using the ideal gas law and number of moles of trapped air calculated in the previous step.

$$P_{air} = n_{air}RT/V \qquad\qquad (3)$$

NOTES
▼

Calculate the vapor pressure of water at each temperature using Dalton's law of partial pressures:

$$P_{water} = P_{atm} - P_{air} \qquad (4)$$

Calculate $\ln P_{water}$ and $1/T$ (Kelvin)

Plot $\ln P_{water}$ vs. $1/T$ (Kelvin) and perform a linear regression analysis to determine the line of best fit to the data. Use the Clausius-Clapeyron equation (equation 2) to determine the enthalpy and entropy of vaporization.

Use these values and the Clausius-Clapeyron equation to determine the vapor pressure of water at 65°C and also at the temperature which you recorded in step 5 of the procedure.

NOTES

Sample data table:

T, °C	T, K	$1/T$, K^{-1}	Vol, mL	(Vol – 2)/1000, L	P_{air}, atm	P_{water}, atm	ln P
79.5	352.7	2.836E–03	10.00	9.80E–03	0.5929	0.4034	–0.9079
75.0	348.2	2.872E–03	9.20	9.00E–03	0.6374	0.3589	–1.0247
70.0	343.2	2.914E–03	8.28	8.08E–03	0.6998	0.2965	–1.2156
65.0	338.2	2.957E–03	7.60	7.40E–03	0.7530	0.2433	–1.4133
60.0	333.2	3.002E–03	6.92	6.72E–03	0.8169	0.1794	–1.7181
55.0	328.2	3.047E–03	6.58	6.38E–03	0.8475	0.1488	–1.9052
50.0	323.2	3.095E–03	6.26	6.06E–03	0.8787	0.1176	–2.1401
45.0	318.2	3.143E–03	5.90	5.70E–03	0.9197	0.0766	–2.5692
3.8	277.0	3.611E–03	4.78	4.58E–03	—	—	—

NOTES
▼

DISCUSSION/CONCLUSION

Report the values for the entropy (in units of J/molK) and enthalpy of vaporization (in units of J/mol) of water which you obtained. Depending on the units of R used in your calculations, you may need to convert from L atm to J. The conversion is 1 L atm = 101.325 J.

The literature value for ΔH_{vap} between 50 and 80°C is 42.7 kJ/mol and for ΔS_{vap} the literature value is 108.9 J/molK. Compare your calculated values to these values and discuss deviations in terms of the error and uncertainty present in the procedure.

Do your calculations indicate that the assumption made in step 5 that the vapor pressure of water at low temperatures is negligible was justified?

The literature value for the vapor pressure of water at 65°C is 187.5 mmHg. Compare your calculated value to this value.

Different liquids have widely differing vapor pressures at the same temperature. Discuss the reasons for this range of vapor pressures in terms of entropy and enthalpy, recalling that entropy changes are changes in order (or disorder), while enthalpy changes result principally from changes in intermolecular forces.

Given that water is the only reagent, this experiment may seem like the perfect application of green chemistry. However, green chemistry is about more than just the chemicals that are used and the waste that is generated. Review the Twelve Principles of Green Chemistry (page vi) and comment on why this experiment is still not the "ultimate" in green chemistry.

NOTES

appA
Density of Air-Free Water

T (°C)	d (g/mL)	T (°C)	d (g/mL)
0.0	0.99987	28.0	0.99626
5.0	0.99999	28.5	0.99612
10.0	0.99973	29.0	0.99597
15.0	0.99913	29.5	0.99583
20.0	0.99823	30.0	0.99568
20.5	0.99813	35.0	0.99406
21.0	0.99802	40.0	0.99225
21.5	0.99791	45.0	0.99024
22.0	0.99780	50.0	0.98807
22.5	0.99768	55.0	0.98573
23.0	0.99757	60.0	0.98324
23.5	0.99745	65.0	0.98059
24.0	0.99733	70.0	0.97781
24.5	0.99720	75.0	0.97489
25.0	0.99707	80.0	0.97183
25.5	0.99694	85.0	0.96865
26.0	0.99681	90.0	0.96534
26.5	0.99668	95.0	0.96192
27.0	0.99654	100.0	0.95838
27.5	0.99640		

Source: International Critical Tables of Numerical Data, Physics, Chemistry, and Technology, *Volume III, W. W. Washburn, Editor, McGraw-Hill Book Company, New York, 1928.*

NOTES

appB

Vapor Pressure of Water at Various Temperatures

Temperature (°C)	Pressure (mmHg)	Temperature (°C)	Pressure (mmHg)
0	4.6	26	25.2
1	4.9	27	26.7
2	5.3	28	28.3
3	5.7	29	30.0
4	6.1	30	31.8
5	6.5	31	33.7
6	7.0	32	35.7
7	7.5	33	37.7
8	8.0	34	39.9
9	8.6	35	42.2
10	9.2	40	55.3
11	9.8	45	71.9
12	10.5	50	92.5
13	11.2	55	118.0
14	12.0	60	149.4
15	12.8	65	187.5
16	13.6	70	233.7
17	14.5	75	289.1
18	15.5	80	355.1
19	16.5	85	433.6
20	17.5	90	525.8
21	18.7	95	633.9
22	19.8	97	682.1
23	21.1	99	733.2
24	22.4	100	760.0
25	23.8	101	787.6

NOTES

appC

Using MS Excel for Mac 2016

A Summary of Basic Spreadsheet Operations

STARTING EXCEL

To create a new spreadsheet:

To begin with a new spreadsheet, double click the Microsoft Excel icon on the desktop. Excel will start up, and a new spreadsheet labeled "Book1" will appear.

To open a previously created spreadsheet:

To open a previously prepared spreadsheet, double-click on the icon in the folder that stores the spreadsheet.

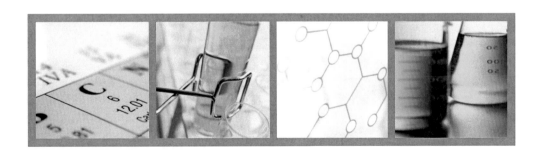

CELLS AND CELL NUMBERS

A spreadsheet consists of a group of boxes called **cells**, laid out in rows and columns. The columns are labeled by letters across the top of the spreadsheet: A, B, C, D.... The rows are indicated by numbers down the left side. Each cell can be identified by a letter–number combination; for example cell **C5** is found in **Column C, Row 5**.

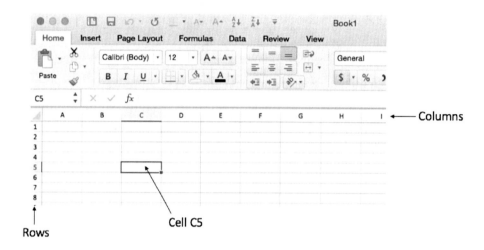

FIGURE C-1.

CELL CONTENTS

Cells can contain either numbers or text. Those containing text are used to label columns or rows, or to provide other information about the spreadsheet. Since the primary use of a spreadsheet is for numerical calculations, the cells containing numbers are by far the more important. The number that appears within a cell may be a number that you have directly typed into that cell, or it may be a number that is the result of a calculation based on a formula which you entered into that cell.

DIRECT ENTRY OF NUMBERS OR TEXT

To **select** a cell for entry, use the mouse to put the cross-shaped cursor over the cell, and click the mouse. The cell will become surrounded by a thick dark line. In the upper left corner of the window, there is a box that displays the number of the selected cell.

After selecting a cell, a number (or some text) may be entered into it by typing on the keyboard. Notice that what you type appears in the cell itself and also is displayed near the top of the window along the row to the right of the cell number. This display area (the second row below the menu bar) is referred to as the **formula bar**. To finalize the entry, click on the check mark in the formula bar or press Enter on the keyboard.

NOTES

▼

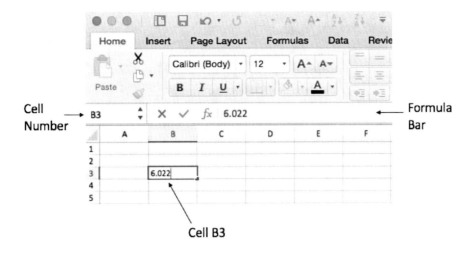

FIGURE C-2.

EXPONENTIAL NUMBERS

An exponential number appears in a cell in conventional computer format; i.e., the number 6.55×10^{-12} is displayed in the cell as 6.55E-12. Use this format when entering an exponential number into a cell. (Note that in the *formula bar*, the number may convert to decimal form when you click the check mark; e.g., 0.00000000000655.)

CHANGING THE CONTENTS OF A CELL

Select the cell with the mouse. Move the cursor to the formula bar. It changes to an I-beam shape when it is placed in the formula bar. The cell entry may be changed by editing the display in the formula bar in the way usually done in a word processor. After any change, finalize the change by clicking the check mark or press Enter on the keyboard.

The contents of a cell may be deleted by selecting the cell and pressing the **Delete** key on the keyboard.

ENTRY OF FORMULAS

The virtue of a spreadsheet lies in its ability to take numbers from various cells, perform an instant calculation with them, and display the result in a different cell. This is done by entering a formula for the calculation into the cell in which you want the result to appear.

To enter a formula, type an equal sign (=) as the first character, followed by the formula.

To denote addition and subtraction, + and − are used in the usual way. For multiplication and division, the symbols * and / are used. The symbol ^ is used for exponents.

Addition	+
Subtraction	− (hyphen)
Multiplication	*
Division	/
Exponent	^ (shift 6)

Example 1

If you would like to multiply the contents of cell A1 by the contents of cell B1, and then divide by the contents of cell C1 and have this value displayed in cell D1, you would begin by placing the thick white cross cursor over cell D1 and clicking. The cell should now be surrounded by a thick dark line. In the formula bar you would type

$$= A1*B1/C1$$

The answer for the calculation will appear in cell D1 as soon as you click the check mark or press Enter. The formula will continue to be displayed in the formula bar. To increase or decrease the number of decimal places displayed, click in the appropriate decimal place box. Note that this only changes the display. Excel still carries all the decimal places in its memory.

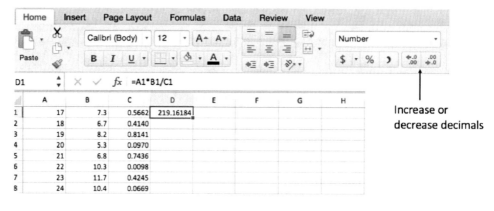

FIGURE C-3.

Helpful hint: As you are typing a formula, you can enter a cell number simply by clicking on that cell. To enter the formula in Example 1, you would type = and then

click on cell **A1**, then type a * sign, click on cell **B1**, then type a / sign and click on cell **C1**.

Example 2

It is important to note that when the computer does a calculation, the order in which operations in a formula are carried out is as follows: exponentiation is done first, then multiplication and division, and then addition and subtraction. If you want an addition to be done before a multiplication, you must put the addition in parentheses. Therefore, for the formula $\frac{A+B}{C}$, where A is in cell D10, B is in cell E10, and C is in F10, enter

$$= (D10+E10)/F10$$

Note the parentheses. Without the parentheses in the last expression, the value of **A+(B/C)** would be returned instead of the value of **(A+B)/C**.

Once a formula has been entered into a given cell, that cell will display the result of the calculation based on the current contents of the other cells whose numbers are part of the formula. If any of these other cell contents are changed, the result displayed in the formula cell will also instantaneously change.

FILLING DOWN

The power of a spreadsheet rests primarily on its ability to rapidly perform the same calculations repeatedly on a large array of data. We can apply the same formula to different sets of data from different groups of cells. For example, we could apply the formula in Example 1 not only to the contents of cells **A1**, **B1** and **C1**, but also to the contents of **A2**, **B2** and **C2**, and to **A3**, **B3** and **C3**, etc.

This may be done in the following way: the sets of data are entered in separate rows in the spreadsheet, such that all the related values in the formula are in the same column. For example, column A might contain a series of length measurements, column B might contain a series of width measurements, etc. The results of the desired calculation would appear in a separate column. In the latter column, each cell contains the formula for the calculation. The formula for each row uses the cell references appropriate for that row. For example, we've seen that for row 1, the formula would be =**A1*B1/C1**; for row 2, the formula would be **A2*B2/C2**; and so on.

To avoid the tedious process of having to enter a formula into each cell of the answer column individually, we can use what is called a **fill down** operation.

NOTES
▼

Procedure

Method 1

1. Click on the top cell in the column where you want to add new formulas. Enter the formula as described previously in Example 1.

2. Select all the cells in the column, including the one that contains the formula entered in step 1. To select the cells in a given column, put the cursor into the top cell so the cell is surrounded by a thick dark line. Hold the mouse button down, and drag the cursor down the column through all the cells that you wish to select. Release the mouse button. All the selected cells will be surrounded by a wide dark line and the cells will be highlighted.

3. From the **Edit** menu, hover over **Fill** then select **Down**. This will enter the formula into each selected cell of the column, each with the cell numbers appropriate to its row.

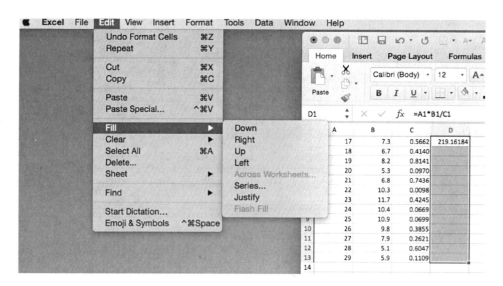

FIGURE C-4.

Method 2

1. Click on the top cell in the column where you want to add new formulas. Enter the formula as described previously.

2. While the cell containing the cursor is active (or highlighted), move the cursor to the lower right-hand corner of the cell. The cursor will change from a thick white cross to a thin dark cross.

3. When the thin dark cross appears, hold the mouse button down, and drag the cursor down the column through all the cells that you wish to select. Release the mouse button. This will enter the formula into each selected cell of the column, each with the cell numbers appropriate to its row.

The Fill Down operation can be carried out on several columns simultaneously by selecting all of the columns as a group. To select several adjacent columns, start with the cursor in the top cell of the leftmost column and drag down and to the right, ending up at the bottom cell of the rightmost column. Then, when you do a Fill Down, each column will filled with the particular formula which had been entered in the top cell of that column.

RELATIVE AND ABSOLUTE CELL REFERENCES

As you have seen above, the result of a fill down operation is a set of similar formulas in which the cell references change relative to the row they are in. But suppose you wanted to include a cell reference which wouldn't change during the fill operation and would remain the same in every formula in the column. To do this, when you enter the formula in the top cell, you need to use an absolute cell reference for the cell number that you want to remain the same in all the formulas. Absolute cell references have dollar signs in front of the column letter and row number, e.g., **B5**. The dollar sign confines Excel to either the column (when it is placed in front of the letter) or the row (when it is in front of the number) when using that reference in formulas. For example, consider a situation where you want to convert a series of measurements in cm into inches. You would type the conversion factor in a specific cell. In this example, the cell **H3** contains the value of 0.3937008 in/cm. The formula for converting the length appears in cell **E3**. When this formula is filled down, **B3** will change to **B4**, **B5**, etc, but **H3** will not change in the calculations.

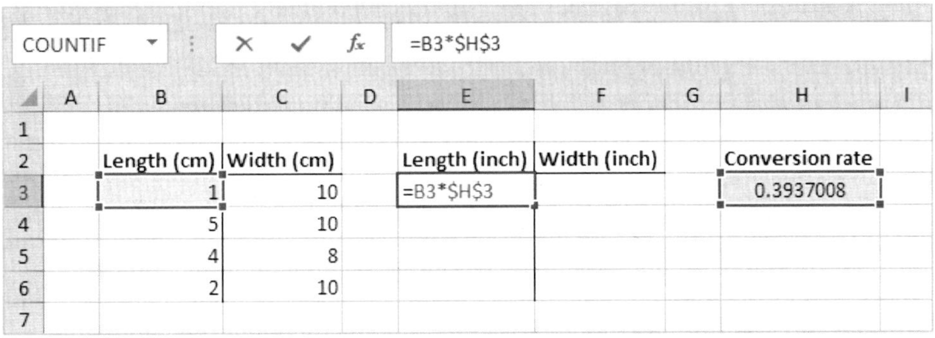

COUNTIF	▼	⁝	×	✓	*fx*	=B3*H3			
◢	A	B	C	D	E	F	G	H	I
1									
2		Length (cm)	Width (cm)		Length (inch)	Width (inch)		Conversion rate	
3		1	10		=B3*H3			0.3937008	
4		5	10						
5		4	8						
6		2	10						
7									

FIGURE C-5.

ADDING NEW ROWS OR COLUMNS

If it becomes necessary to make more room in the spreadsheet, additional rows or columns may be added.

To *insert a new row*, select one of the cells in the row just below the place where you want to insert the new row. From the **Insert** menu, select **Rows**.

NOTES
▼

To *insert a new column*, select one of the cells in the column just to the right of the place where you want to insert a new column. From the **Insert** menu, select **Columns**.

Several rows may be added at once by selecting a group of cells in more than one row before doing the insert operation. The number of rows inserted will be equal to the number of rows covered by the initial selection. In a similar way, several columns may be added simultaneously.

Columns or rows may be deleted by selecting them and then selecting **Delete**... from the Edit menu. In the dialog box that appears, select the **Entire Row** option then click **OK** to delete an entire row. Likewise for an entire column.

SAVING YOUR SPREADSHEET DOCUMENT

Select **Save** from the Excel **File** menu, then type a name for the document into the name box of the dialog window that appears. Be sure that you save it into the right folder. If working on a chemistry laboratory computer, save your file in the desktop folder labeled **Temp.StudentFiles**. Click on the **Save** button. After the document has been saved once, selecting Save will not open a dialog window. The document will be saved in the location that was chosen in the first save operation. As with any computer document, ***you should save it frequently while working on it***.

PRINTING YOUR SPREADSHEET DOCUMENT

Select **Print**... from the Excel **File** menu. Verify that the correct printer has been selected. Click on the **Print** button.

QUITTING EXCEL

When you are finished working on your spreadsheet, select **Quit** from the file menu.

appD
Graphing with MS Excel

For Mac 2016

CREATING THE GRAPH

Open Microsoft Excel by double-clicking the Excel icon on the laboratory computer desktop. Excel will start up, and a new spreadsheet labeled "Book1" will appear.

Enter x-axis data in Column A and y-axis data in Column B. If you want a printed data table, you may opt to print at this time.

Highlight all of the data you wish to graph.

Click on Insert > Chart > xy (scatter) in the tool bar at the top of the screen. (Graphs are referred to as Charts in Excel.)

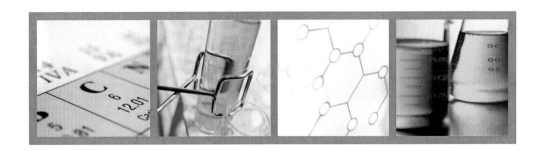

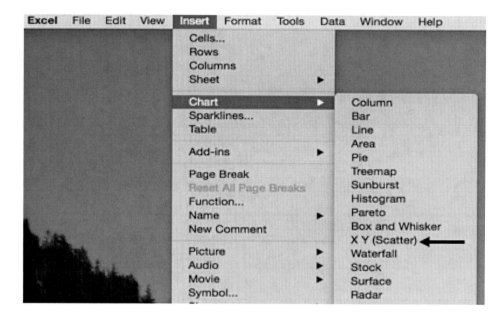

FIGURE D-1.

You can also access this by clicking on Insert within your spreadsheet and selecting the xy (*scatter*) icon:

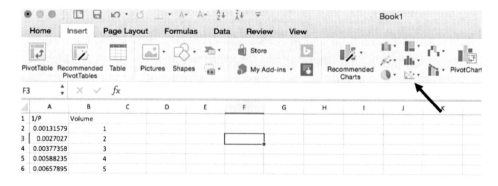

FIGURE D-2.

For the graph sub-type, select the option that does not "connect the dots."

A graph will appear in your Excel worksheet. Click on the graph. In the formula bar at the top of your workbook you will see **Chart Design** and **Format**. Click on **Chart Design**.

In the top left corner of your worksheet, click on **Add Chart Element**. From here you can add a chart title, gridlines, axis labels, etc. You can customize your graph using **Quick Layout**, **Change Colors** and the various graph templates located under **Chart Design**.

To change components of the graph, such as data points, background and gridlines, double-click on these items on the graph.

To rescale an axis, double-click the axis. From the toolbar at the top of the screen, click **Format** > **Format Selection** and then use the options at the right of the workbook.

You will generally want to display the graph alone on a page. To do so, under **Chart Design** at the right side of the worksheet, select **Move Chart** > **New Sheet** > **OK**.

Before finishing, refer to the Graphing Guidelines on pages xxxi–xxxiii to be sure you have included all the components of a good graph.

INSERTING A TRENDLINE

To insert the best-fit line for your data, under **Chart Design**, select **Add Chart Element** > **Trendline** and select the type of fit you want to perform. In General Chemistry, this is usually **Linear**, but not always.

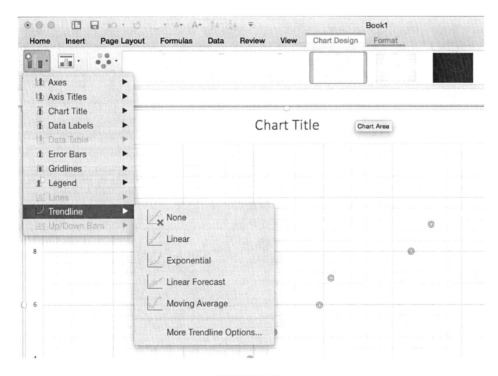

FIGURE D-3.

To display the equation for the line fit or the R2 on the graph, click on the trendline. Under Format Trendline, click the Trendline Options icon.

Select the options you wish to display. You can also change the type of line fit from this pane.

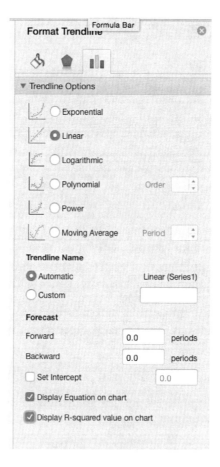

FIGURE D-4.

CHANGING THE NUMBER OF DECIMAL PLACES THAT ARE DISPLAYED WITH THE LINE EQUATION

After displaying the equation on the graph, click on the equation to highlight it.

Click the **Trendline Options** icon. Under **Category**, select **Number** and indicate the number of desired decimal places to be displayed.

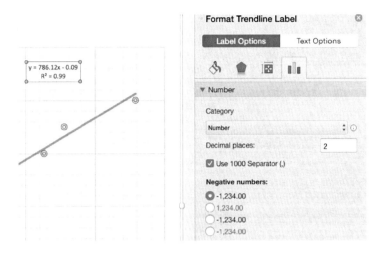

FIGURE D-5.

DISPLAYING MULTIPLE CURVES ON ONE CHART

To add a second curve to your chart, first enter your data in the same spreadsheet you are using for the first curve. Under **Chart Design**, select **Select Data** at the top right of the screen. You will see a pop-up window that looks like this:

FIGURE D-6.

The information that is shown is for your first curve, Series 1. In the name box, title your first data series. (For example, 5 mL initial volume.)

Click the (+) sign to add another series.

NOTES

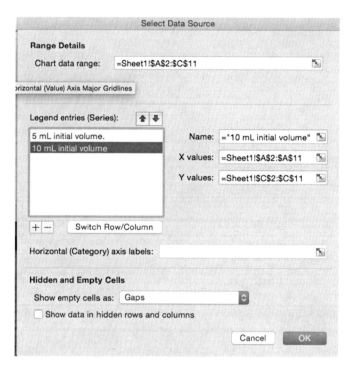

FIGURE D-7.

Provide an appropriate name for the data series.

Click in the X values box. Highlight the data in your spreadsheet you want to use for the x-axis.

Click in the Y values box. If it has been pre-populated with any information, delete that information and then highlight the values you want to use for the y-axis.

Notice that in this example the same values are used for the x-axis and different values are used for the y-axis but this is not necessary.

After selecting your data ranges, click OK and the new curve should appear on your graph. You can now insert a trendline following the previous instructions. Repeat this process to add another data series to your graph.

appE
Spectrophotometry

Changes in the energies of atoms and molecules which result in changes in their electronic configurations produce spectra in the visible and ultraviolet region of the electromagnetic spectrum. Decreases in energy, with emissions of photons of light of the same energy, give rise to **emission spectra** of those atoms and molecules. The study of light **emission** provides us with a powerful technique for the study of the electronic structure of atoms and molecules.

Another technique that is used extensively is the study of light **absorption** by a chemical system. Increases in energy, with absorptions of photons of light of the same energy, give rise to **absorption spectra**. For example, consider white light falling on a solution of red food dye. The solution looks red because only red light is being **transmitted** by the solution. All the other colors have been **absorbed** by the molecules of red food dye dissolved in the solution. (The color of the light absorbed by a molecule largely depends on the electronic energy levels of the molecule.)

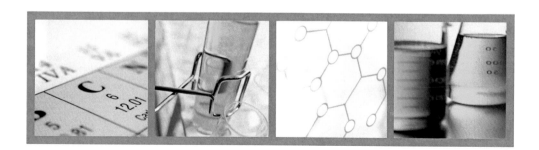

NOTES

▼

Analysis of the *energy* of the light absorbed and transmitted by a molecule can be used to provide information about the *chemical structure* of the molecule. A careful measurement of the *amount* of light absorbed light is determined by measurement of the wavelength (or frequency) and measurement of the amount absorbed involves determination of the reduction in power suffered by a beam of light of a particular wavelength as a consequence of passing through the colored solution. Or, in simpler terms, determination of how much light has been transmitted through the solution.

If we give the symbol P_0 to the power of the incident beam and symbol P to the power remaining unabsorbed after passage through the sample, we can express absorption of light as the **transmittance**, T:

$$T = P / P_0$$

Light absorbance by a solution follows a general law known as the Beer-Lambert law (or more commonly, as Beer's law). This law states that the transmittance of light is an exponential function of the concentration of the absorbing species and can be expressed mathematically as

$$T = 10^{-\varepsilon bc}$$

where

T is the transmittance,

ε is a constant dependent on the wavelength and the absorbing species (molar/absorptivity constant),

b is the length of the light path through the solution (in cm), and

c is the concentration of the absorbing species.

Generally, the units of absorptivity are $cm^{-1}M^{-1}$ and the concentration is expressed in terms of molarity (M).

This law is more often expressed in linear form as

$$A = \varepsilon bc$$

where A, the absorbance is defined as

$$A = -\log T$$

It can be seen that a plot of absorbance vs. concentration will yield a straight line with a slope of εb and y-intercept of zero. However, Beer's law has limitations and

can be expected to fail (that is, show non-linear behavior) when the concentration of the absorbing species is greater than about 0.1 M.

In instruments known as spectrophotometers, the amount of light absorbed or transmitted is accurately and quantitatively detected and measured by solid state electronic devices. Such instruments vary in complexity, performance, ease of operation, and cost, but have the following components in common.

- The radiation source: a lamp that emits light consisting of a range of wavelengths needed for an experiment. A tungsten lamp is most often used for photometric measurements in the visible region of the spectrum.

- A dispersing device: filters, prisms, or gratings may be used to separate light into its constituent colors (wavelengths). These devices allow certain small wavelength-regions to be selected.

- A sample chamber: a compartment within the instrument into which the solution kept in a cuvet is placed in such a manner that the light of selected wavelength passes through a defined thickness of the solution.

- A cuvette: test tubes or special cells with two optical surfaces (that are never to be touched), a uniform wall thickness, and exactly defined inner diameter (path length) are used to hold the solution. A path length of 1.00 cm is frequently used. High quality cuvettes are made from quartz and are available in matched pairs.

- A radiation detector: radiation detectors (such as photomultiplier tubes) produce an electric current that is proportional to the amount of radiation reaching them per unit time.

NOTES

▼

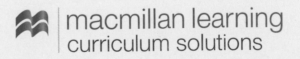